THE MEMOIRS
OF JACQUES CASANOVA
DE SEINGALT

THE RARE UNABRIDGED LONDON EDITION OF
1894 TRANSLATED BY ARTHUR MACHEN TO
WHICH HAS BEEN ADDED THE CHAPTERS DIS-
COVERED BY ARTHUR SYMONS A SUPPLEMENT
AND BIBLIOGRAPHY.

VOLUME FOUR

The Memoirs of
JACQUES
CASANOVA
DE SEINGALT

—◂❦▸—

ADVENTURES
IN THE SOUTH

—◂❦▸—

*Volume Four of the first complete and
unabridged English translation*

BY

ARTHUR MACHEN

Illustrated with Old Engravings

G. P. PUTNAM'S SONS, NEW YORK
ELEK BOOKS, LONDON

Published in England by
ELEK BOOKS LIMITED
14 Great James Street
London, W.C.1

Published in the United States of America by
G. P. PUTNAM'S SONS
210 Madison Avenue
New York City 16
New York

Published in Canada by
LONGMANS, GREEN AND COMPANY
Toronto

W

Printed in the United States of America

CONTENTS

vi   *CONTENTS*

CONTENTS

The Memoirs of
JACQUES CASANOVA

CHAPTER I

The Door-Keeper's Daughters—The Horoscopes— Mdlle. Roman

THE idea of the sorry plight in which I had left the Marquis de Prié, his mistress, and perhaps all the company, who had undoubtedly coveted the contents of my cash-box, amused me till I reached Chambéri, where I only stopped to change horses. When I reached Grenoble, where I intended to stay a week, I did not find my lodging to my liking, and went in my carriage to the post-office, where I found several letters, amongst others, one from Madame d'Urfé, enclosing a letter of introduction to an officer named Valenglard, who, she told me, was a learned man, and would present me at all the best houses in the town.

I called on this officer and received a cordial welcome. After reading Madame d'Urfé's letter he said he was ready to be useful to me in anything I pleased.

He was an amiable, middle aged man, and fifteen years before had been Madame d'Urfé's friend, and in a much more intimate degree the friend of her daughter, the

1

Princess de Toudeville. I told him that I was uncomfortable at the inn, and that the first service I would ask of him would be to procure me a comfortable lodging. He rubbed his head, and said,——

"I think I can get you rooms in a beautiful house, but it is outside the town walls. The door-keeper is an excellent cook, and for the sake of doing your cooking I am sure he will lodge you for nothing."

"I don't wish that," said I.

"Don't be afraid," said the baron, "he will make it up by means of his dishes; and besides, the house is for sale and costs him nothing. Come and see it."

I took a suite of three rooms and ordered supper for two, warning the man that I was dainty, liked good things, and did not care for the cost. I also begged M. de Valenglard to sup with me. The door-keeper said that if I was not pleased with his cooking I had only to say so, and in that case I should have nothing to pay. I sent for my carriage, and felt that I had established myself in my new abode. On the ground floor I saw three charming girls and the door-keeper's wife, who all bowed profoundly. M. de Valenglard took me to a concert with the idea of introducing me to everybody, but I begged him not to do so, as I wished to see the ladies before deciding which of them I should like to know.

The company was a numerous one, especially where women were concerned, but the only one to attract my attention was a pretty and modest-looking brunette, whose fine figure was dressed with great simplicity. Her charming eyes, after having thrown one glance in my direction, obstinately refused to look at me again. My vanity made me conclude at once that she behaved thus only to increase my desire of knowing her, and to give me plenty of time to examine her side-face and her figure, the proportions of which were not concealed by her simple attire. Success begets assurance, and the wish is father to the thought. I cast a hungry gaze on this young lady without more ado, just as if all the women in Europe were only a seraglio kept for my pleasures. I told the baron I should like to know her.

"She is a good girl," said he, "who sees no company, and is quite poor."

"Those are three reasons which make me the more anxious to know her."

"You will really find nothing to do in that quarter."

"Very good."

"There is her aunt, I will introduce you to her as we leave the concert-room."

After doing me this service, he came to sup with me. The door-keeper and cook struck me as being very like Lebel. He made his two pretty daughters wait on me, and I saw that Valenglard was delighted at having lodged me to my satisfaction, but he grumbled when he saw fifteen dishes.

"He is making a fool of you and me," he said.

"On the contrary, he has guessed my tastes. Don't you think everything was very good?"

"I don't deny it, but . . . "

"Don't be afraid; I love spending my money."

"I beg your pardon, I only want you to be pleased."

We had exquisite wines, and at dessert some ratafia superior to the Turkish *visnat* I had tasted seventeen years before at Yussuf Ali's. When my landlord came up at the end of supper, I told him that he ought to be Louis XV.'s head cook.

"Go on as you have begun, and do better if you can; but let me have your bill every morning."

"You are quite right; with such an arrangement one
can tell how one is getting on."

"I should like you always to give me ices, and you
must let me have two more lights. But, unless I am
mistaken, those are candles that I see. I am a Venetian,
and accustomed to wax lights."

"That is your servant's fault, sir."

"How is that?"

"Because, after eating a good supper, he went to bed,
saying he was ill. Thus I heard nothing as to how you
liked things done."

"Very good, you shall learn from my own lips."

"He asked my wife to make chocolate for you to-
morrow morning; he gave her the chocolate, I will make
it myself."

When he had left the room M. de Valenglard said, in a
manner that was at the same time pleased and surprised,
that Madame d'Urfé had been apparently joking in telling him to spare me all expense.

"It's her goodness of heart. I am obliged to her all
the same. She is an excellent woman."

We stayed at table till eleven o'clock, discussing innumerable pleasant topics, and animating our talk with
that choice liqueur made at Grenoble, of which we drank
a bottle. It is composed of the juice of cherries, brandy,
sugar, and cinnamon, and cannot be surpassed, I am
sure, by the nectar of Olympus.

I sent home the baron in my carriage, after thanking
him for his services, and begging him to be my companion early and late while I stayed at Grenoble—a request which he granted excepting for those days on which
he was on duty. At supper I had given him my bill of
exchange on Zappata, which I endorsed with the name
de Seingalt, which Madame d'Urfé had given me. He

discounted it for me next day. A banker brought me four hundred louis and I had thirteen hundred in my cash-box. I always had a dread of penuriousness, and I delighted myself at the thought that M. de Valenglard would write and tell Madame d'Urfé, who was always preaching economy to me, what he had seen.

I escorted my guest to the carriage, and I was agree-ably surprised when I got back to find the doorkeeper's two charming daughters.

Le Duc had not waited for me to tell him to find some pretext for not serving me. He knew my tastes, and that when there were pretty girls in a house, the less I saw of him the better I was pleased.

The frank eagerness of the two girls to wait on me, their utter freedom from suspicion or coquetry, made me determine that I would shew myself deserving of their trust. They took off my shoes and stockings, did my hair and put on my night-gown with perfect propriety on both sides. When I was in bed I wished them a good-night, and told them to shut the door and bring me my chocolate at eight o'clock next morning.

I could not help confessing that I was perfectly happy as I reflected over my present condition. I enjoyed per-fect health, I was in the prime of life, I had no calls on me, I was thoroughly independent, I had a rich store of experience, plenty of money, plenty of luck, and I was a favourite with women. The pains and troubles I had gone through had been followed by so many days of happiness that I felt disposed to bless my destiny. Full of these agreeable thoughts I fell asleep, and all the night my dreams were of happiness and of the pretty brunette who had played with me at the concert.

I woke with thoughts of her, and feeling sure that we

should become acquainted I felt curious to know what success I should have with her. She was discreet and poor; and as I was discreet in my own way she ought not to despise my friendship.

At eight o'clock, one of the door-keeper's daughters brought me my chocolate, and told me that Le Duc had got the fever.

"You must take care of the poor fellow."

"My cousin has just taken him some broth."

"What is your name?"

"My name is Rose, and my sister is Manon."

Just then Manon came in with my shirt, on which she had put fresh lace. I thanked her, and she said with a blush that she did her father's hair very well.

"I am delighted to hear it, and I shall be very pleased if you will be kind enough to do the same offices for me till my servant recovers."

"With pleasure, sir."

"And I," said Rose, laughing, "will shave you."

"I should like to see how you do it; get the water."

I rose hastily, while Manon was preparing to do my hair. Rose returned and shaved me admirably. As soon as she had washed off the lather, I said,——

"You must give me a kiss," presenting my cheek to her. She pretended not to understand.

"I shall be vexed," said I, gravely but pleasantly, "if you refuse to kiss me,"

She begged to be excused, saying with a little smile, that it was not customary to do so at Grenoble.

"Well, if you won't kiss me, you shan't shave me."

The father came in at that point, bringing his bill.

"Your daughter has just shaved me admirably," said I, "and she refuses to kiss me, because it is not the custom at Grenoble."

"You little silly," said he, "it is the custom in Paris. You kiss me fast enough after you have shaved me, why should you be less polite to this gentleman?"

She then kissed me with an air of submission to the paternal decree which made Manon laugh.

"Ah!" said the father, "your turn will come when you have finished doing the gentleman's hair."

He was a cunning fellow, who knew the best way to prevent me cheapening him, but there was no need, as I thought his charges reasonable, and as I paid him in full he went off in great glee.

Manon did my hair as well as my dear Dubois, and kissed me when she had done without making as many difficulties as Rose. I thought I should get on well with both of them. They went downstairs when the banker was announced.

He was quite a young man, and after he had counted me out four hundred louis, he observed that I must be very comfortable.

"Certainly," said I, "the two sisters are delightful."

"Their cousin is better. They are too discreet."

"I suppose they are well off."

"The father has two thousand francs a year. They will be able to marry well-to-do tradesmen."

I was curious to see the cousin who was said to be prettier than the sisters, and as soon as the banker had gone I went downstairs to satisfy my curiosity. I met the father and asked him which was Le Duc's room, and thereon I went to see my fine fellow. I found him sitting up in a comfortable bed with a rubicund face which did not look as if he were dangerously ill.

"What is the matter with you?

"Nothing, sir. I am having a fine time of it. Yesterday I thought I would be ill."

"What made you think that?"

"The sight of the three Graces here, who are made of better stuff than your handsome housekeeper, who would not let me kiss her. They are making me wait too long for my broth, however. I shall have to speak severely about it."

"Le Duc, you are a rascal."

"Do you want me to get well?"

"I want you to put a stop to this farce, as I don't like it."

Just then the door opened, and the cousin came in with the broth. I thought her ravishing, and I noticed that in waiting on Le Duc she had an imperious little air which well became her.

"I shall dine in bed," said my Spaniard.

"You shall be attended to," said the pretty girl, and she went out.

"She puts on big airs," said Le Duc, "but that does not impose on me. Don't you think she is very pretty?"

"I think you are very impudent. You ape your betters, and I don't approve of it. Get up. You must wait on me at table, and afterwards you will eat your dinner by yourself, and try to get yourself respected as an honest man always is, whatever his condition, so long as he does not forget himself. You must not stay any longer in this room, the doorkeeper will give you another."

I went out, and on meeting the fair cousin I told her that I was jealous of the honour which she had done my man, and that I begged her to wait on him no longer.

"Oh, I am very glad!"

The door-keeper came up, and I gave him my orders, and went back to my room to write.

Before dinner the baron came and told me that he had

just come from the lady to whom he had introduced me. She was the wife of a barrister named Morin, and aunt to the young lady who had so interested me.

"I have been talking of you," said the baron, "and of the impression her niece made on you. She promised to send for her, and to keep her at the house all day."

After a dinner as good as the supper of the night before, though different from it in its details, and appetising enough to awaken the dead, we went to see Madame Morin, who received us with the easy grace of a Parisian lady. She introduced me to seven children, of whom she was the mother. Her eldest daughter, an ordinary-looking girl, was twelve years old, but I should have taken her to be fourteen, and said so. To convince me of her age the mother brought a book in which the year, the month, the day, the hour, and even the minute of her birth were entered. I was astonished at such minute accuracy, and asked if she had had a horoscope drawn.

"No," said she, "I have never found anybody to do it."

"It is never too late," I replied, "and without doubt God has willed that this pleasure should be reserved for me."

At this moment M. Morin came in, his wife introduced me, and after the customary compliments had passed, she returned to the subject of the horoscope. The barrister sensibly observed that if judicial astrology was not wholly false, it was, nevertheless, a suspected science; that he had been so foolish as once to devote a considerable portion of his time to it, but that on recognizing the inability of man to deal with the future he had abandoned astrology, contenting himself with the veritable truths of astronomy. I saw with pleasure that I had to deal with a man of sense and education, but Valenglard, who was a believer in astrology, began an

argument with him on the subject. During their discussion I quietly copied out on my tablets the date of
Mdlle. Morin's birth. But M. Morin saw what I was
about, and shook his head at me, with a smile. I understood what he meant, but I did not allow that to
disconcert me, as I had made up my mind fully five
minutes ago that I would play the astrologer on this
occasion.

At last the fair niece arrived. Her aunt introduced
me to her as Mdlle. Roman Coupier, her sister's daughter;
and then, turning to her, she informed her how ardently
I had been longing to know her since I had seen her at
the concert.

She was then seventeen. Her satin skin by its dazzling whiteness displayed to greater advantage her magnificent black hair. Her features were perfectly regular,
and her complexion had a slight tinge of red; her fine
eyes were at once sweet and sparkling, her eyebrows
were well arched, her mouth small, her teeth regular and
as white as pearls, and her lips, of an exquisite rosy hue,
afforded a seat to the deities of grace and modesty.

After some moments' conversation, M. Morin was
obliged to go out on business, and a game of quadrille
was proposed, at which I was greatly pitied for having
lost a louis. I thought Mdlle. Roman discreet, judicious,
pleasant without being brilliant, and, still better, without
any pretensions. She was high-spirited, even-tempered,
and had a natural art which did not allow her to seem
to understand too flattering a compliment, or a joke
which passed in any way the bounds of propriety. She
was neatly dressed, but had no ornaments, and nothing
which shewed wealth; neither ear-rings, rings, nor a
watch. One might have said that her beauty was her
only adornment, the only ornament she wore being a

small gold cross hanging from her necklace of black ribbon. Her breast was well shaped and not too large. Fashion and custom made her shew half of it as innocently as she shewed her plump white hand, or her cheeks, whereon the lily and the rose were wedded. I looked at her features to see if I might hope at all; but I was completely puzzled, and could come to no conclusion. She gave no sign which made me hope, but on the other hand she did nothing to make me despair. She was so natural and so reserved that my sagacity was completely at fault. Nevertheless, a liberty which I took at supper gave me a gleam of hope. Her napkin fell down, and in returning it to her I pressed her thigh amorously, and could not detect the slightest displeasure on her features. Content with so much I begged everybody to come to dinner with me next day, telling Madame Morin that I should not be going out, and that I was therefore delighted to put my carriage at her service.

When I had taken Valenglard home, I went to my lodging building castles in Spain as to the conquest of Mdlle. Roman.

I warned my landlord that we should be six at dinner and supper the following day, and then I went to bed. As Le Duc was undressing me he said,——

"Sir, you are punishing me, but what makes me sorry you are punishing yourself in depriving yourself of the services of those pretty girls."

"You are a rogue."

"I know it, but I serve you with all my heart, and I love your pleasure as well as my own."

"You plead well for yourself; I am afraid I have spoilt you."

"Shall I do your hair to-morrow?"

"No; you may go out every day till dinner-time."

"I shall be certain to catch it."

"Then I shall send you to the hospital."

"That is a fine prospect, *por Dios.*"

He was impudent, sly, profligate, and a rascally fellow; but also obedient, devoted, discreet, and faithful, and his good qualities made me overlook his defects.

Next morning, when Rose brought my chocolate, she told me with a laugh that my man had sent for a carriage, and after dressing himself in the height of fashion he had gone off with his sword at his side, to pay calls, as he said.

"We laughed at him."

"You were quite right, my dear Rose."

As I spoke, Manon came in under some pretext or other. I saw that the two sisters had an understanding never to be alone with me; I was displeased, but pretended not to notice anything. I got up, and I had scarcely put on my dressing-gown when the cousin came in with a packet under her arm.

"I am delighted to see you, and above all to look at your smiling face, for I thought you much too serious yesterday."

"That's because M. le Duc is a greater gentleman than you are; I should not have presumed to laugh in his presence; but I had my reward in seeing him start off this morning in his gilded coach."

"Did he see you laughing at him?"

"Yes, unless he is blind."

"He will be vexed."

"All the better."

"You are really very charming. What have you got in that parcel?"

"Some goods of our own manufacture. Look; they are embroidered gloves."

"They are beautiful; the embroidery is exquisitely done. How much for the lot?"

"Are you a good hand at a bargain."

"Certainly."

"Then we must take that into account."

After some whisperings together the cousin took a pen, put down the numbers of gloves, added up and said,——

"The lot will cost you two hundred and ten francs."

"There are nine louis; give me six francs change."

"But you told us you would make a bargain."

"You were wrong to believe it."

She blushed and gave me the six francs. Rose and Manon shaved me and did my hair, giving me a kiss with the best grace imaginable; and when I offered my cheek to the cousin she kissed me on the mouth in a manner that told me she would be wholly mine on the first opportunity.

"Shall we have the pleasure of waiting on you at the table?" said Rose.

"I wish you would."

"But we should like to know who is coming to dinner first; as if it is officers from the garrison we dare not come; they make so free."

"My guests are Madame Morin, her husband, and her niece."

"Very good."

The cousin said,——

"Mdlle. Roman is the prettiest and the best girl in Grenoble; but she will find some difficulty in marrying, as she has no money."

"She may meet some rich man who will think her goodness and her beauty worth a million of money."

"There are not many men of that kind."

"No; but there are a few."

Manon and the cousin went out, and I was left alone with Rose, who stayed to dress me. I attacked her, but she defended herself so resolutely that I desisted, and promised it should not occur again. When she had finished I gave her a louis, thanked her, and sent her away.

As soon as I was alone I locked the door, and proceeded to concoct the horoscope I had promised to Madame Morin. I found it an easy task to fill eight pages with learned folly; and I confined myself chiefly to declaring the events which had already happened to the native. I had deftly extracted some items of information in the course of conversation, and filling up the rest according to the laws of probability and dressing up the whole in astrological diction, I was pronounced to be a seer, and no doubts were cast on my skill. I did not indeed run much risk, for everything hung from an *if,* and in the judicious employment of *ifs* lies the secret of all astrology.

I carefully re-read the document, and thought it admirable. I felt in the vein, and the use of the cabala had made me an expert in this sort of thing.

Just after noon all my guests arrived, and at one we sat down to table. I have never seen a more sumptuous or more delicate repast. I saw that the cook was an artist more in need of restraint than encouragement. Madame Morin was very polite to the three girls, whom she knew well, and Le Duc stood behind her chair all the time, looking after her wants, and dressed as richly as the king's chamberlain. When we had nearly finished dinner Mdlle. Roman passed a compliment on my three fair waiting-maids, and this giving me occasion to speak of their talents I got up and brought the gloves I had purchased from them. Mdlle. Roman praised the quality of the material and the work. I took the opportunity, and begged leave of the aunt to give her and her niece a dozen pair apiece. I obtained this favour, and I then gave Madame Morin the horoscope. Her husband read it, and though an unbeliever he was forced to admire, as all the deductions were taken naturally from the position of the heavenly bodies at the instant of his daughter's birth. We spent a couple of hours in talking about astrology, and the same time in playing at quadrille, and then we took a walk in the garden, where I was politely left to enjoy the society of the fair Roman.

Our dialogue, or rather my monologue, turned solely on the profound impression she had made on me, on the passion she had inspired, on her beauty, her goodness, the purity of my intentions, and on my need of love, lest I should go down to the grave the most hapless of men.

"Sir," said she, at last, "if my destiny points to marriage I do not deny that I should be happy to find a husband like you."

I was emboldened by this frank declaration, and seizing her hand I covered it with fiery kisses, saying passionately that I hoped she would not let me languish long. She turned her head to look for her aunt. It was getting dark, and she seemed to be afraid of something happening to her. She drew me gently with her, and on rejoining the other guests we returned to the dining-room, where I made a small bank at faro for their amusement. Madame Morin gave her daughter and niece, whose pockets were empty, some money, and Valenglard directed their play so well that when we left off to go to supper I had the pleasure of seeing that each of the three ladies had won two or three louis.

We sat at table till midnight. A cold wind from the

Alps stopped my plan of proposing a short turn in the garden. Madame Morin overwhelmed me with thanks for my entertainment, and I gave each of my lady-visitors a respectful kiss.

I heard singing in the kitchen, and on going in I found Le Duc in a high state of excitement and very drunk. As soon as he saw me he tried to rise, but he lost his centre of gravity, and fell right under the kitchen table. He was carried away to bed.

I thought this accident favourable to my desire of amusing myself, and I might have succeeded if the three Graces had not all been there. Love only laughs when two are present, and thus it is that the ancient mythology tells no story of the loves of the Graces, who were always together. I had not yet found an opportunity of getting my three maids one after the other, and I dared not risk a general attack, which might have lost me the confidence of each one. Rose, I saw, was openly jealous of her cousin, as she kept a keen look-out after her movements. I was not sorry, for jealousy leads to anger, and anger goes a long way. When I was in bed I sent them away with a modest good night.

Next morning, Rose came in by herself to ask me for a cake of chocolate, for, as she said, Le Duc was now ill in real earnest. She brought me the box, and I gave her the chocolate, and in doing so I took her hand and shewed her how well I loved her. She was offended, drew back her hand sharply, and left the room. A moment after Manon came in under the pretext of shewing me a piece of lace I had torn away in my attempts of the day before, and of asking me if she should mend it. I took her hand to kiss it, but she did not give me time, presenting her lips, burning with desire. I took her hand again, and it was just on the spot when the cousin came in. Manon held the piece of lace, and seemed to be waiting for my answer. I told her absently that I should be obliged if she would mend it when she had time, and with this she went out.

I was troubled by this succession of disasters, and thought that the cousin would not play me false from the earnest of her affection which she had given me the day before in that ardent kiss of hers. I begged her to give me my handkerchief, and gently drew her hand towards me. Her mouth fastened to mine, and her hand, which she left to my pleasure with all the gentleness of a lamb, was already in motion when Rose came in with my chocolate. We regained our composure in a moment, but I was furious at heart. I scowled at Rose, and I had a right to do so after the manner in which she had repulsed me a quarter of an hour before. Though the chocolate was excellent, I pronounced it badly made. I chid her for her awkwardness in waiting on me, and repulsed her at every step. When I got up I would not let her shave me; I shaved myself, which seemed to humiliate her, and then Manon did my hair. Rose and the cousin then went out, as if to make common cause together, but it was easy to see that Rose was less angry with her sister than her cousin.

As Manon was finishing my toilette, M. de Valenglard came in. As soon as we were alone, the officer, who was a man of honour and of much sense, in spite of his belief in astrology and the occult sciences, said that he thought me looking rather melancholy, and that if my sadness had any connection with the fair Roman, he warned me to think no more of her, unless I had resolved to ask her hand in marriage. I replied that to put an end to all difficulties I had decided on leaving Grenoble in a few days. We dined together and we then called on Madame Morin, with whom we found her fair niece.

Madame Morin gave me a flattering welcome, and Mdlle. Roman received me so graciously that I was emboldened to kiss her and place her on my knee. The aunt laughed, the niece blushed, and then slipping into my hand a little piece of paper made her escape. I read on the paper the year, day, hour, and minute of her birth, and guessed what she meant. She meant, I thought, that I could do nothing with her before I had drawn up her horoscope. My resolve was soon taken to profit by this circumstance, and I told her that I would tell her whether I could oblige her or not next day, if she would come to a ball I was giving. She looked at her aunt and my invitation was accepted.

Just then the servant announced *"The Russian Gentleman."* I saw a well-made man of about my own age, slightly marked with the small-pox, and dressed as a traveller. He accosted Madame Morin with easy grace, was welcomed heartily by her, spoke well, scarcely gave me a glance, and did not say a word to the nieces. In the evening M. Morin came in, and the Russian gave him a small phial full of a white liquid, and then made as if he would go, but he was kept to supper.

At table the conversation ran on this marvellous liquid of his. M. Morin told me that he had cured a young man of a bruise from a billiard ball in five minutes, by only rubbing it with the liquid. He said modestly that it was a trifling thing of his own invention, and he talked a good deal about chemistry to Valenglard. As my attention was taken up by the fair Mdlle. Roman I could not take part in their conversation; my hope of succeeding with her on the following day absorbed all my thoughts. As I was going away with Valenglard he told me that nobody knew who the Russian was, and that he was nevertheless received everywhere.

"Has he a carriage and servants?"

"He has nothing, no servants and no money."

"Where did he come from?"

"From the skies."

"A fair abode, certainly; how long has he been here?"

"For the last fortnight. He visits, but asks for nothing."

"How does he live?"

"On credit at the inn; he is supposed to be waiting for his carriage and servants."

"He is probably a vagabond."

"He does not look like one, as you saw for yourself, and his diamonds contradict that hypothesis."

"Yes, if they are not imitation stones, for it seems to me that if they were real he would sell them."

When I got home Rose came by herself to attend on me, but she continued to sulk. I tried to rouse her up, but as I had no success I ordered her to go and tell her father that I was going to give a ball next day in the room by the garden, and that supper was to be laid for twenty.

When the door-keeper came to take my orders the following morning, I told him that I should like his girls to dance if he didn't mind. At this Rose condescended to smile, and I thought it a good omen. Just as she went out with her father, Manon came in under the pretext of asking me what lace I would wear for the day. I found her as gentle as a lamb and as loving as a dove. The affair was happily consummated, but we had a narrow escape of being caught by Rose, who came in with Le Duc and begged me to let him dance, promising that he would behave himself properly. I was glad that everybody should enjoy themselves and consented, telling him to thank Rose, who had got him this favour.

I had a note from Madame Morin, asking me if she might bring with her to the ball two ladies of her acquaintance and their daughters. I replied that I should be delighted for her to invite not only as many ladies but as many gentlemen as she pleased, as I had ordered supper for twenty people. She came to dinner with her niece and Valenglard, her daughter being busy dressing and her husband being engaged till the evening. She assured me that I should have plenty of guests.

The fair Mdlle. Roman wore the same dress, but her beauty unadorned was dazzling. Standing by me she asked if I had thought about her horoscope. I took her hand, made her sit on my knee, and promised that she should have it on the morrow. I held her thus, pressing her charming breasts with my left hand, and imprinting fiery kisses on her lips, which she only opened to beg me to calm myself. She was more astonished than afraid to see me trembling, and though she defended herself successfully she did not lose countenance for a moment, and in spite of my ardent gaze she did not turn her face away. I calmed myself with an effort, and her eyes expressed the satisfaction of one who has vanquished a generous enemy by the force of reason. By my silence I praised the virtue of this celestial being, in whose destiny I only had a part by one of those caprices of chance which philosophy seeks to explain in vain.

Madame Morin came up to me, and asked me to explain some points in her daughter's horoscope. She then told me that if I wanted to have four beauties at my ball she had only to write a couple of notes. "I shall only see one beauty," said I, looking at her niece. "God alone knows," said Valenglard, "what people will say in Grenoble!" "They will say it is your wedding ball," said Madame Morin to her niece.

"Yes, and they will doubtless talk of my magnificent dress, my lace, and my diamonds," said the niece, pleasantly.

"They will talk of your beauty, your wit, and your goodness," I replied, passionately, "goodness which will make your husband a happy man."

There was a silence, because they all thought I was alluding to myself. I was doing nothing of the sort. I should have been glad to give five hundred louis for her, but I did not see how the contract was to be drawn up, and I was not going to throw my money away.

We went to my bedroom, and while Mdlle. Roman was amusing herself with looking at the jewellry on my toilette-table, her aunt and Valenglard examined the books on the table by my bedside. I saw Madame Morin going to the window and looking closely at something she held in her hand. I remembered I had left out the portrait of the fair nun. I ran to her and begged her to give me the indecent picture I had so foolishly left about.

"I don't mind the indecency of it," she said, "but what strikes me is the exact likeness."

I understood everything, and I shuddered at the carelessness of which I had been guilty.

"Madam," I said, "that is the portrait of a Venetian lady, of whom I was very found."

"I daresay, but it's very curious. These two M's, these cast-off robes sacrificed to love, everything makes my surprise greater."

"She is a nun and named M—— M——."

"And a Welsh niece of mine at Cambéri is also named

M—— M——, and belongs to the same order. Nay, more, she has been at Aix, whence you have come, to get cured of an illness."

"And this portrait is like her?"

"As one drop of water is like another."

"If you go to Chambéri call on her and say you come from me; you will be welcome and you will be as much surprised as I am."

"I will do so, after I have been in Italy. However, I will not shew her this portrait, which would scandalize her; I will put it away carefully."

"I beg you not to shew it to anyone."

"You may rely on me."

I was in an ecstasy at having put her off so effectually.

At eight o'clock all my guests arrived, and I saw before me all the fairest ladies and the noblest gentlemen of Grenoble. The only thing which vexed me was the compliments they lavished on me, as is customary in the provinces.

I opened the ball with the lady pointed out to me by M. Valenglard, and then I danced with all the ladies in succession; but my partner in all the square dances was the fair Mdlle. Roman, who shone from her simplicity— at least, in my eyes.

After a quadrille, in which I had exerted myself a good deal, I felt hot and went up to my room to put on a lighter suit, and as I was doing so, in came the fair cousin, who asked me if I required anything.

"Yes, you, dearest," I replied, going up to her and taking her in my arms. "Did anyone see you coming in here?"

"No, I came from upstairs, and my cousins are in the dancing-room."

"That is capital. You are fair as Love himself, and

this is an excellent opportunity for shewing you how much I love you."

"Good heavens! What are you doing? Let me go, somebody might come in. Well, put out the light."

I put it out, shut the door, and, my head full of Mdlle. Roman, the cousin found me as ardent as I should have been with that delightful person. I confess, too, that the door-keeper's niece was well worthy of being loved on her own merits. I found her perfect, perhaps better than Mdlle. Roman, a novice, would have been. In spite of my ardour her passion was soon appeased, and she begged me to let her go, and I did so; but it was quite time. I wanted to begin over again, but she was afraid that our absence would be noticed by her two Argus-eyed cousins, so she kissed me and left the room.

I went back to the ball-room, and we danced on till the king of door-keepers came to tell us supper was ready.

A collation composed of the luxuries which the season and the country afforded covered the table; but what pleased the ladies most was the number and artistic arrangement of the wax lights.

I sat down at a small table with a few of my guests, and I received the most pressing invitations to spend the autumn in their town. I am sure that if I had accepted I should have been treated like a prince, for the nobility of Grenoble bear the highest character for hospitality. I told them that if it had been possible I should have had the greatest pleasure in accepting their invitation, and in that case I should have been delighted to have made the acquaintance of the family of an illustrious gentleman, a friend of my father's.

"What name is it?" they asked me, altogether.

"Bouchenu de Valbonnais."

"He was my uncle. Ah! sir, you must come and stay with us. You danced with my daughter. What was your father's name?

This story, which I invented, and uttered as I was wont, on the spur of the moment, turned me into a sort of wonder in the eyes of the worthy people.

After we had laughed, jested, drank, and eaten, we rose from the table and began to dance anew.

Seeing Madame Morin, her niece, and Valenglard going into the garden, I followed them, and as we walked in the moonlight I led the fair Mdlle. Roman through a covered alley; but all my fine speeches were in vain; I could do nothing. I held her between my arms, I covered her with burning kisses, but not one did she return to me, and her hands offered a successful resistance to my hardy attempts. By a sudden effort, however, I at last attained the porch of the temple of of love, and held her in such a way that further resistance would have been of no avail; but she stopped me short by saying in a voice which no man of feeling could have resisted,——

"Be my friend, sir, and not my enemy and the cause of my ruin."

I knelt before her, and taking her hand begged her pardon, swearing not to renew my attempts. I then rose and asked her to kiss me as a pledge of her forgiveness. We rejoined her aunt, and returned to the ball-room, but with all my endeavours I could not regain my calm.

I sat down in a corner of the room, and I asked Rose, who passed by me, to get me a glass of lemonade. When she brought it she gently chid me for not having danced with her, her sister, or her cousin.

"It will give people but a poor opinion of our merits."

"I am tired," said I, "but if you will promise to be kind I will dance a minuet with you."

"What do want me to do?" said she.

"Go into my bedroom and wait for me there in the dark when you see your sister and your cousin busy dancing."

"And you will only dance with me."

"I swear."

"Then you will find me in your room."

I found her passionate, and I had full satisfaction. To keep my word with her I waited for the closing minuet, for having danced with Rose I felt obliged in common decency to dance with the other two, especially as I owed them the same debt.

At day-break the ladies began to vanish, and as I put the Morins into my carriage I told them that I could not have the pleasure of seeing them again that day, but that if they would come and spend the whole of the day after with me I would have the horoscope ready.

I went to the kitchen to thank the worthy door-keeper for having made me cut such a gallant figure, and I found the three nymphs there, filling their pockets with sweetmeats. He told them, laughing, that as the master was there they might rob him with a clear conscience, and I bade them take as much as they would. I informed the door-keeper that I should not dine till six, and I then went to bed.

I awoke at noon, and feeling myself well rested I set to work at the horoscope, and I resolved to tell the fair Mdlle. Roman that fortune awaited her at Paris, where she would become her master's mistress, but that the monarch must see her before she had attained her eighteenth year, as at that time her destiny would take a different turn. To give my prophecy authority, I told her

some curious circumstances which had hitherto happened
to her, and which I had learnt now and again from herself or Madame Morin without pretending to heed what
they said.

With an Ephemeris and another astrological book, I
made out and copied in six hours Mdlle. Roman's horoscope, and I had so well arranged it that it struck Valenglard and even M. Morin with astonishment, and made
the two ladies quite enthusiastic.

I hoped I should be asked to take the diamond to
Paris myself, and I felt inclined to grant the request. I
flattered myself that they could not do without me, and
that I should get what I wanted, if not for love at any
rate through gratitude; indeed, who knew what might
become of the plan? The monarch would be sure to be
caught directly. I had no doubts on that subject, for
where is the man in love who does not think that his
beloved object will win the hearts of all others? For the
moment I felt quite jealous of the king, but, from my
thorough knowledge of my own inconstancy, I felt sure
that my jealousy would cease when my love had been
rewarded, and I was aware that Louis XV. did not altogether hold the opinions of a Turk in such concerns.
What gave an almost divine character to the horoscope
was the prediction of a son to be born, who would make
the happiness of France, and could only come from the
royal blood and from a singular vessel of election.

A curious fancy increased my delight, namely, the
thought of becoming a famous astrologer in an age when
reason and science had so justly demolished astrology. I
enjoyed the thought of seeing myself sought out by
crowned heads, which are always the more accessible to
superstitious notions. I determined I would be particular to whom I gave my advice. Who has not made his

castles in Spain? If Mdlle. Roman gave birth to a daughter instead of a son I should be amused, and all would not be lost, for a son might come afterwards.

My horoscope must only be known to the young lady and her family, who would no doubt keep the secret well. After I had put the finishing touches to it, read it, and read it again, I felt certain that I had made a masterpiece, and I then dined in bed with my three nymphs. I was polite and affectionate to them all, and we were all happy together, but I was the happiest. M. de Valenglard came to see me early the next day, and informed me that nobody suspected me of being in love with Mdlle. Roman, but that I was thought to be amorous of my landlord's girls.

"Well, let them think so," said I; "they are worthy of love, though not to be named in the same breath with one past compare, but who leaves me no hope."

"Let me tell Madame d'Urfé all about it."

"Certainly; I shall be delighted."

M. and Madame Morin and their niece came at noon, and we spent the hour before dinner in reading the horoscope. It would be impossible to describe the four distinct sorts of surprise which I saw before me. The interesting Mdlle. Roman looked very grave, and, not knowing whether she had a will of her own, listened to what was said in silence. M. Morin looked at me now and again, and seeing that I kept a serious countenance did not dare to laugh. Valenglard shewed fanatic belief in astrology in every feature. Madame Morin seemed struck as by a miracle, and, far from thinking the fact prophesied too improbable, remarked that her niece was much more worthy of becoming her sovereign's wife or mistress than the bigoted Maintenon had been.

"She would never have done anything," said Madame

Morin, "if she had not left America and come to France;
and if my niece does not go to Paris nobody can say that
the horoscope has prophesied falsely. We should therefore go to Paris, but how is it to be done? I don't see my
way to it. The prediction of the birth of a son has
something divine and entrancing about it. I don't wish
to seem prejudiced, but my niece has certainly more
qualifications for gaining the king's affection than the
Maintenon had: my niece is a good girl and young, while
the Maintenon was no longer as young as she had been,
and had led a strange life before she became a devotee.
But we shall never accomplish this journey to Paris."

"Nay," said Valenglard, in a serious tone, which struck
me as supremely ridiculous, "she must go; her fate
must be fulfilled."

The fair Mdlle. Roman seemed all amazed. I let
them talk on, and we sat down to dinner.

At first silence reigned, and then the conversation ran
on a thousand trifles, as is usual in good society, but by
degrees, as I had thought, they returned to the horoscope.

"According to the horoscope," said the aunt, "the king
is to fall in love with my niece in her eighteenth year;
she is now close on it. What are we to do? Where are
we to get the hundred louis necessary? And when she
gets to Paris is she to go to the king and say, 'Here I am,
your majesty'? And who is going to take her there? I
can't."

"My aunt Roman might," said the young lady, blushing up to her eyes at the roar of laughter which none of
us could restrain.

"Well," said Madame Morin, "there is Madame
Varnier, of the Rue de Richelieu; she is an aunt of yours.
She has a good establishment, and knows everybody."

"See," said Valenglard, "how the ways of destiny are

made plain. You talk of a hundred louis; twelve will be sufficient to take you to Madame Varnier's. When you get there, leave the rest to your fate, which will surely favour you."

"If you do go to Paris," said I, "say nothing to Madame Roman or Madame Varnier about the horoscope."

"I will say nothing to anyone about it; but, after all, it is only a happy dream. I shall never see Paris, still less Louis XV."

I arose, and going to my cash-box I took out a roll of a hundred and fifty louis, which I gave to her, saying it was a packet of sweetmeats. It felt rather heavy, and on opening it she found it to contain fifty pieces-of-eight, which she took for medals.

"They are gold," said Valenglard.

"And the goldsmith will give you a hundred and fifty louis for them," added M. Morin.

"I beg you will keep them; you can give me a bill payable at Paris when you become rich."

I knew she would refuse to accept my present, although I should have been delighted if she had kept the money. But I admired her strength of mind in restraining her tears, and that without disturbing for a moment the smile on her face.

We went out to take a turn in the garden. Valenglard and Madame Morin began on the topic of the horoscope anew, and I left them, taking Mdlle. Roman with me.

"I wish you would tell me," said she, when we were out of hearing of the others, "if this horoscope is not all a joke."

"No," I answered, "it is quite serious, but it all depends on an *if*. *If* you do not go to Paris the prophecy will never be fulfilled."

"You must think so, certainly, or you would never have offered me those fifty medals."

"Do me the pleasure of accepting them now; nobody will know anything about it."

"No, I cannot, though I am much obliged to you. But why should you want to give me such a large sum?"

"For the pleasure of contributing to your happiness, and in the hope that you will allow me to love you."

"If you really love me, why should I oppose your love? You need not buy my consent; and to be happy I do not want to possess the King of France, if you did but know to what my desires are limited."

"Tell me."

"I would fain find a kind husband, rich enough for us not to lack the necessaries of life."

"But how if you did not love him?"

"If he was a good, kind man how could I help loving him?"

"I see that you do not know what love is."

"You are right. I do not know the love that maddens, and I thank God for it."

"Well, I think you are wise; may God preserve you from that love."

"You say, that as soon as the king sees me he will fall in love with me, and to tell you the truth that strikes me as vastly improbable; for though it is quite possible that he may not think me plain, or he might even pronounce me pretty, yet I do not think he will become so madly in love as you say."

"You don't? Let us sit down. You have only got to fancy that the king will take the same liking to you that I have done; that is all."

"But what do you find in me that you will not find in most girls of my age? I certainly may have struck you;

but that only proves that I was born to exercise this sway over you, and not at all that I am to rule the king in like manner. Why should I go and look for the king, if you love me yourself?"

"Because I cannot give you the position you deserve."

"I should have thought you had plenty of money."

"Then there's another reason: you are not in love with me."

"I love you as tenderly as if I were your wife. I might then kiss you, though duty now forbids my doing so."

"I am much obliged to you for not being angry with me for being so happy with you!"

"On the contrary, I am delighted to please you."

"Then you will allow me to call on you at an early hour to-morrow, and to take coffee at your bedside."

"Do not dream of such a thing. If I would I could not. I sleep with my aunt, and I always rise at the same time she does. Take away your hand; you promised not to do it again. In God's name, let me alone."

Alas! I had to stop; there was no overcoming her. But what pleased me extremely was that in spite of my amorous persecution she did not lose that smiling calm which so became her. As for myself I looked as if I deserved that pardon for which I pleaded on my knees, and in her eyes I read that she was sorry that she could not grant what I required of her.

I could no longer stay beside her, my senses were too excited by her beauty. I left her and went to my room where I found the kind Manon busying herself on my cuffs, and she gave me the relief I wanted, and when we were both satisfied made her escape. I reflected that I should never obtain more than I had obtained hitherto from young Mdlle. Roman—at least, unless I gave the lie to my horoscope by marrying her, and I decided that I would not take any further steps in the matter.

I returned to the garden, and going up to the aunt I begged her to walk with me. In vain I urged the worthy woman to accept a hundred louis for her niece's journey from me. I swore to her by all I held sacred that no one else should ever know of the circumstance. All my eloquence and all my prayers were in vain. She told me that if her niece's destiny only depended on that journey all would be well, for she had thought over a plan which would, with her husband's consent, enable Mdlle. Roman to go to Paris. At the same time she gave me her sincerest thanks, and said that her niece was very fortunate to have pleased me so well.

"She pleased me so well," I replied, "that I have resolved to go away to-morrow to avoid making proposals to you which would bring the great fortune that awaits her to nought. If it were not for that I should have been happy to have asked her hand of you."

"Alas! her happiness would, perhaps, be built on a better foundation. Explain yourself."

"I dare not wage war with fate."

"But you are not going to-morrow?"

"Excuse me, but I shall call to take leave at two o'clock."

The news of my approaching departure saddened the supper-table. Madame Morin, who, for all I know, may be alive now, was a most kind-hearted woman. At table she announced her resolve that as I had decided on going, and as I should only leave my house to take leave of her, she would not force me to put myself out to such an extent, and ordained that our farewells should be said that evening.

"At least," I said, "I may have the honour of escorting you to your door?"

"That will protract our happiness for some minutes."

Valenglard went away on foot, and the fair Mdlle. Roman sat on my knee. I dared to be bold with her, and contrary to expectation she shewed herself so kind that I was half sorry I was going; but the die was cast.

A carriage lying overturned on the road outside an inn made my coachman stop a short while, and this accident which made the poor driver curse overwhelmed me with joy, for in these few moments I obtained all the favours that she could possibly give under the circumstances.

Happiness enjoyed alone is never complete. Mine was not until I assured myself, by looking at my sweetheart's features, that the part she had taken had not been an entirely passive one; and I escorted the ladies to their room. There, without any conceit, I was certain that I saw sadness and love upon that fair creature's face. I could see that she was neither cold nor insensible, and that the obstacles she had put in my way were only suggested by fear and virtue. I gave Madame Morin a farewell kiss, and she was kind enough to tell her niece to give me a similar mark of friendship, which she did in a way that shewed me how completely she had shared my ardour.

I left them, feeling amorous and sorry I had obliged myself to go. On entering my room I found the three nymphs together, which vexed me as I only wanted one. I whispered my wishes to Rose as she curled my hair, but she told me it was impossible for her to slip away as they all slept in one room. I then told them that I was going away the next day, and that if they would pass the night with me I would give them a present of six louis each. They laughed at my proposal and said it couldn't possibly be done. I saw by this they had not

made confidantes of one another, as girls mostly do, and
I also saw that they were jealous of each other. I wished
them a good night, and as soon as I was in bed the god
of dreams took me under his care, and made me pass
the night with the adorable Mdlle. Roman.

I rang rather late in the morning, and the cousin came
in and said that Rose would bring my chocolate, and
that M. Charles Ivanoff wanted to speak to me. I
guessed that this was the Russian, but as he had not
been introduced to me I thought I might decline to see
him.

"Tell him I don't know his name."

Rose went out, and came in again saying he was the
gentleman who had had the honour of supping with
me at Madame Morin's.

"Tell him to come in."

"Sir," said he, "I want to speak with you in private."

"I cannot order these young ladies to leave my room,
sir. Be kind enough to wait for me outside till I have
put on my dressing-gown, and then I shall be ready to
speak to you."

"If I am troubling you, I will call again to-morrow."

"You would not find me, as I am leaving Grenoble
to-day."

"In that case I will wait."

I got up in haste and went out to him.

"Sir," said he, "I must leave this place, and I have
not a penny to pay my landlord. I beg of you to come
to my aid. I dare not have recourse to anyone else in
the town for fear of exposing myself to the insult of a
refusal."

"Perhaps I ought to feel myself flattered at the preference you have shewn me, but without wishing to insult

you in any way I am afraid I shall be obliged to refuse
your request."

"If you knew who I am I am sure you would not refuse me some small help."

"If you think so, tell me who you are; you may count
on my silence."

"I am Charles, second son of Ivan, Duke of Courland,
who is in exile in Siberia. I made my escape."

"If you go to Genoa you will find yourself beyond the
reach of poverty; for no doubt the brother of your
lady-mother would never abandon you."

"He died in Silesia."

"When?"

"Two years ago, I believe."

"You have been deceived, for I saw him at Stuttgart
scarcely six months ago. He is the Baron de Treiden."

It did not cost me much to get wind of the adventurer,
but I felt angry that he had had the impudence to try
and dupe me. If it had not been for that I would willingly have given him six louis, for it would have been
bad form on my part to declare war against adventurers,
as I was one myself, and I ought to have pardoned his
lies as nearly all adventurers are more or less impostors.

I gave a glance at his diamond buckles, which were
considered real at Grenoble, and I saw directly that they
were counterfeits of a kind made in Venice, which imitate the facets of the diamonds in perfection, except to
people who are experienced in diamonds.

"You have diamond buckles," said I. "Why don't you
sell them?"

"It's the last piece of jewellery I possess out of all my
mother gave me, and I promised her never to part with
them."

"I would not shew those buckles if I were you; your pocket would be a better place for them. I may tell you frankly that I believe the stones to be counterfeit, and that your lie displeases me."

"Sir, I am not a liar."

"We shall see. Prove that the stones are genuine, and I will give you six louis. I shall be delighted if I am in the wrong. Farewell."

Seeing M. de Valenglard coming up to my door, he begged me not to tell him of what had passed between us; and I promised that I would tell no one.

Valenglard came to wish me a prosperous journey; he himself was obliged to go with M. Monteinard. He begged me to correspond constantly with him; and I had been intending to prefer the same request, as I took too great an interest in the fair Mdlle. Roman not to wish to hear of her fate, and the correspondence the worthy officer desired was the best way possible for me to hear about her. As will be imagined, I promised what he asked without making any difficulty. He shed tears as he embraced me, and I promised to be his friend.

CHAPTER II

My Departure from Grenoble—Avignon—The Fountain of Vaucluse—The False Astrodi and the Humpback—Gaetan Costa—I Arrive at Marseilles

WHILE the three girls were helping Le Duc to pack my mails my landlord entered, gave me his bill, and finding everything correct I paid him, much to his satisfaction. I owed him a compliment, too, at which he seemed extremely gratified.

"Sir," said I, "I do not wish to leave your house without having the pleasure of dining with your charming girls, to shew them how I appreciate the care they have taken of me. Let me have, then, a delicate repast for four, and also order post horses, that I may start in the evening."

"Sir," broke in Le Duc, "I entreat you to order a saddle-horse besides; I was not made for a seat behind a chaise."

The cousin laughed openly at his vain boasting, and to avenge himself the rascal told her that he was better than she.

"Nevertheless, M. le Duc, you will have to wait on her at table."

"Yes, as she waits on you in bed."

I ran for my stick, but the rogue, knowing what was going to happen, opened the window and jumped into the courtyard. The girls gave a shriek of terror, but when we looked out we saw him jumping about and performing a thousand apish tricks.

37

Very glad to find that he had not broken a limb, I called out, "Come back, I forgive you." The girls, and the man himself who escaped so readily, were as delighted as I. Le Duc came in in high spirits, observing that he did not know he was such a good jumper.

"Very good, but don't be so impudent another time. Here, take this watch."

So saying, I gave him a valuable gold watch, which he received, saying,——

"I would jump again for another watch like this."

Such was my Spaniard, whom I had to dismiss two years afterwards. I have often missed him.

The hours went by with such speed when I was seated at table with the three girls, whom I vainly endeavoured to intoxicate, that I decided that I would not leave till the next day. I was tired of making mysteries and wanted to enjoy them all together, and resolved that the orgy should take place that night. I told them that if they would pass the night in my room I would not go till the next day. This proposition was received with a storm of exclamations and with laughter, as at an impossibility, while I endeavoured to excite them to grant my request. In the midst of this the door-keeper came in, advising me not to travel by night, but to go to Avignon by a boat in which I could ship my carriage.

"You will save time and money," said he.

"I will do so," I answered, "if these girls of yours will keep me company all night, as I am determined I will not go to bed."

"O Lord!" said he with a laugh, "that's their business."

This decided them and they gave in. The door-keeper sent to order the boat, and promised to let me have a dainty supper by midnight.

The hours passed by in jests and merriment, and when we sat down to supper I made the champagne corks fly to such an extent that the girls began to get rather gay. I myself felt a little heated, and as I held each one's secret I had the hardihood to tell them that their scruples were ridiculous, as each of them had shewn no reserve to me in private.

At this they gazed at one another in a kind of blank surprise, as if indignant at what I had said. Foreseeing that feminine pride might prompt them to treat my accusation as an idle calumny, I resolved not to give them time, and drawing Manon on to my knee I embraced her with such ardour that she gave in and abandoned herself to my passion. Her example overcame the others, and for five hours we indulged in every kind of voluptuous enjoyment. At the end of that time we were all in need of rest, but I had to go. I wanted to give them some jewels, but they said they would rather I ordered gloves to the amount of thirty louis, the money to be paid in advance, and the gloves not to be called for.

I went to sleep on board the boat, and did not awake till we got to Avignon. I was conducted to the inn of "St. Omer," and supped in my room in spite of the marvellous tales which Le Duc told me of a young beauty at the public table.

Next morning my Spaniard told me that the beauty and her husband slept in a room next to mine. At the same time he brought me a bill of the play, and I saw *Company from Paris,* with Mdlle. Astrodi, who was to sing and dance. I gave a cry of wonder, and exclaimed,——

"The famous Astrodi at Avignon—how she will be astonished to see me!"

Not wanting to live in hermit fashion, I went down-

stairs to dine at the public table, and I found a score of
people sitting down to such a choice repast that I could
not conceive how it could be done for forty sous a head.
The fair stranger drew all eyes, and especially mine, towards her. She was a young and perfect beauty, silent,
her eyes fixed on a napkin, replying in monosyllables to
those who addressed her, and glancing at the speaker
with large blue eyes, the beauty of which it would be
difficult to describe. Her husband was seated at the
other end of the table—a man of a kind that inspires
contempt at the first glance. He was young, marked
with the small-pox, a greedy eater, a loud talker, laughing and speaking at random, and altogether I took him
for a servant in disguise. Feeling sure that such a fellow
did not know how to refuse, I sent him a glass of
champagne, which he drank off to my health forthwith.
"May I have the pleasure of sending a glass to your
wife?" He replied, with a roar of laughter, to ask her
myself; and with a slight bow she told me that she
never took anything to drink. When the dessert came in
she rose, and her husband followed her to their room.

A stranger who like myself had never seen her before,
asked me who she was. I said I was a newcomer and
did not know, and somebody else said that her husband
called himself the Chevalier Stuard, that he came from
Lyons, and was going to Marseilles; he came, it appeared, to Avignon a week ago, without servants, and in a
very poor carriage.

I intended staying at Avignon only as long as might
be necessary to see the Fountain or Fall of Vaucluse, and
so I had not got any letters of introduction, and had
not the pretext of acquaintance that I might stay and
enjoy her fine eyes. But an Italian who had read and
enjoyed the divine Petrarch would naturally wish to see

the place made divine by the poet's love for Laura.

I went to the theatre, where I saw the vice-legate Salviati, women of fashion, neither fair nor foul, and a wretched comic opera; but I neither saw Astrodi nor any other actor from the Comédie Italienne at Paris.

"Where is the famous Astrodi?" said I, to a young man sitting by me, "I have not seen her yet."

"Excuse me, she has danced and sang before your eyes."

"By Jove, it's impossible! I know her perfectly, and if she has so changed as not to be recognized she is no longer herself."

I turned to go, and two minutes after the young man I had addressed came up and begged me to come back, and he would take me to Astrodi's dressing-room, as she had recognized me. I followed him without saying a word, and saw a plain-looking girl, who threw her arms round my neck and addressed me by my name, though I could have sworn I had never seen her before, but she did not leave me time to speak. Close by I saw a man who gave himself out as the father of the famous Astrodi, who was known to all Paris, who had caused the death of the Comte d'Egmont, one of the most amiable noblemen of the Court of Louis XV. I thought this ugly female might be her sister, so I sat down and complimented her on her talents. She asked if I would mind her changing her dress; and in a moment she was running here and there, laughing and shewing a liberality which possibly might have been absent if what she had to display had been worth seeing.

I laughed internally at her wiles, for after my experiences at Grenoble she would have found it a hard task to arouse my desires if she had been as pretty as she was ugly. Her thinness and her tawny skin could

not divert my attention from other still less pleasing
features about her. I admired her confidence in spite
of her disadvantages. She must have credited me with a
diabolic appetite, but these women often contrive to ex-
tract charms out of their depravity which their delicacy
would be impotent to furnish. She begged me to sup
with her, and as she persisted I was obliged to refuse her
in a way I should not have allowed myself to use with
any other woman. She then begged me to take four
tickets for the play the next day, which was to be for
her benefit. I saw it was only a matter of twelve francs,
and delighted to be quit of her so cheaply I told her to
give me sixteen. I thought she would have gone mad
with joy when I gave her a double louis. She was not
the real Astrodi. I went back to my inn and had a delicious supper in my own room.

While Le Duc was doing my hair before I went to bed,
he told me that the landlord had paid a visit to the
fair stranger and her husband before supper, and had
said in clear terms that he must be paid next morning;
and if he were not, no place would be laid for them at
table, and their linen would be detained.

"Who told you that?"

"I heard it from here; their room is only separated
from this by a wooden partition. If they were in it
now, I am sure they could hear all we are saying."

"Where are they, then?"

"At table, where they are eating for to-morrow,
but the lady is crying. There's a fine chance for you,
sir."

"Be quiet; I shan't have anything to do with it. It's
a trap, for a woman of any worth would die rather than
weep at a public table."

"Ah, if you saw how pretty she looks in tears! I am

only a poor devil, but I would willingly give her two
louis if she would earn them."

"Go and offer her the money."

A moment after the gentleman and his wife came back
to their room, and I heard the loud voice of the one and
the sobs of the other, but as he was speaking Walloon
I did not understand what he said.

"Go to bed," said I to Le Duc, "and next morning tell
the landlord to get me another room, for a wooden partition is too thin a barrier to keep off people whom despair
drive to extremities."

I went to bed myself, and the sobs and muttering did
not die away till midnight.

I was shaving next morning, when Le Duc announced
the Chevalier Stuard.

"Say I don't know anybody of that name."

He executed my orders, and returned saying that the
chevalier on hearing my refusal to see him had stamped
with rage, gone into his chamber, and come out again
with his sword beside him.

"I am going to see," added Le Duc, "that your pistols
are well primed for the future."

I felt inclined to laugh, but none the less I admired
the foresight of my Spaniard, for a man in despair is
capable of anything.

"Go," said I, "and ask the landlord to give me another
room."

In due course the landlord came himself and told me
that he could not oblige me until the next day.

"If you don't get me another room I shall leave your
house on the spot, because I don't like hearing sobs and
reproaches all night."

"Can you hear them, sir?"

"You can hear them yourself now. What do you think

of it? The woman will kill herself, and you will be the cause of her death."

"I, sir? I have only asked them to pay me my just debts."

"Hush! there goes the husband. I am sure he is telling his wife in his language that you are an unfeeling monster."

"He may tell her what he likes so long as he pays me."

"You have condemned them to die of hunger. How much do they owe you?"

"Fifty francs."

"Aren't you ashamed of making such a row for a wretched sum like that?"

"Sir, I am only ashamed of an ill deed, and I do not commit such a deed in asking for my own."

"There's your money. Go and tell them that you have been paid, and that they may eat again; but don't say who gave you the money."

"That's what I call a good action," said the fellow; and he went and told them that they did not owe him anything, but that they would never know who paid the money.

"You may dine and sup," he added, "at the public table, but you must pay me day by day."

After he had delivered this speech in a high voice, so that I could hear as well as if I had been in the room, he came back to me.

"You stupid fool!" said I, pushing him away, "they will know everything." So saying I shut my door.

Le Duc stood in front of me, staring stupidly before him.

"What's the matter with you, idiot?" said I.

"That's fine. I see. I am going on the stage. You would do well to become an actor."

"You are a fool."

"Not so big a fool as you think."

"I am going for a walk; mind you don't leave my room for a moment."

I had scarcely shut the door when the chevalier accosted me and overwhelmed me with thanks.

"Sir, I don't know to what you are referring."

He thanked me again and left me, and walking by the banks of the Rhone, which geographers say is the most rapid river in Europe, I amused myself by looking at the ancient bridge. At dinner-time I went back to the inn, and as the landlord knew that I paid six francs a meal he treated me to an exquisite repast. Here, I remember, I had some exceedingly choice Hermitage. It was so delicious that I drank nothing else. I wished to make a pilgrimage to Vaucluse and begged the landlord to procure me a good guide, and after I had dressed I went to the theatre.

I found the Astrodi at the door, and giving her my sixteen tickets, I sat down near the box of the vicelegate Salviati, who came in a little later, surrounded by a numerous train of ladies and gentlemen bedizened with orders and gold lace.

The so-called father of the false Astrodi came and whispered that his daughter begged me to say that she was the celebrated Astrodi I had known at Paris. I replied, also in a whisper, that I would not run the risk of being posted as a liar by bolstering up an imposture. The ease with which a rogue invites a gentleman to share in a knavery is astonishing; he must think his confidence confers an honour.

At the end of the first act a score of lackeys in the prince's livery took round ices to the front boxes. I thought it my duty to refuse. A young gentleman, as fair as love, came up to me, and with easy politeness asked me why I had refused an ice.

"Not having the honour to know anyone here, I did not care that anyone should be able to say that he had regaled one who was unknown to him."

"But you, sir, are a man who needs no introduction."

"You do me too much honour."

"You are staying at the 'St. Omer'!"

"Yes; I am only stopping here to see Vaucluse, where I think of going to-morrow if I can get a good guide."

"If you would do me the honour of accepting me, I should be delighted. My name is Dolci, I am son of the captain of the vice-legate's guard."

"I feel the honour you do me, and I accept your obliging offer. I will put off my start till your arrival."

"I will be with you at seven."

I was astonished at the easy grace of this young Adonis, who might have been a pretty girl if the tone of his voice had not announced his manhood. I laughed at the false Astrodi, whose acting was as poor as her face, and who kept staring at me all the time. While she sang she regarded me with a smile and gave me signs of an understanding, which must have made the audience notice me, and doubtless pity my bad taste. The voice and eyes of one actress pleased me; she was young and tall, but hunchbacked to an extraordinary degree. She was tall in spite of her enormous humps, and if it had not been for this malformation she would have been six feet high. Besides her pleasing eyes and very tolerable voice I fancied that, like all hunchbacks, she was intelligent. I found her at the door with the ugly Astrodi when I was leaving the theatre. The latter was waiting to thank me, and the other was selling tickets for her benefit.

After the Astrodi had thanked me, the hunchbacked girl turned towards me, and with a smile that stretched from ear to ear and displayed at least twenty-four exquisite teeth, she said that she hoped I would honour her by being present at her benefit.

"If I don't leave before it comes off, I will," I replied.

At this the impudent Astrodi laughed, and in the hearing of several ladies waiting for their carriages told me that her friend might be sure of my presence, as she would not let me go before the benefit night. "Give him sixteen tickets," she added. I was ashamed to refuse, and gave her two louis. Then in a lower voice the Astrodi said, "After the show we will come and sup with you, but on the condition that you ask nobody else, as we want to be alone."

In spite of a feeling of anger, I thought that such a supper-party would be amusing, and as no one in the town knew me I resolved to stay in the hope of enjoying a hearty laugh.

I was having my supper when Stuard and his wife went to their room. This night I heard no sobs nor reproaches, but early next morning I was surprised to see the chevalier who said, as if we had been old friends, that he had heard that I was going to Vaucluse, and that as I had taken a carriage with four places he would be much obliged if I would allow him and his wife, who wanted to see the fountain, to go with me. I consented.

Le Duc begged to be allowed to accompany me on horseback, saying that he had been a true prophet. In fact it seemed as if the couple had agreed to repay me for my expenditure by giving me new hopes. I was not displeased with the expedition, and it was all to my advantage, as I had had recourse to no stratagems to obtain it.

Dolci came, looking as handsome as an angel; my neighbours were ready, and the carriage loaded with the best provisions in food and drink that were obtainable; and we set off, Dolci seated beside the lady and I beside the chevalier.

I had thought that the lady's sadness would give place, if not to gaiety, at least to a quiet cheerfulness, but I was mistaken; for, to all my remarks, grave or gay, she replied, either in monosyllables or in a severely laconic style. Poor Dolci, who was full of wit, was stupefied. He thought himself the cause of her melancholy, and was angry with himself for having innocently cast a shadow on the party of pleasure. I relieved him of his fears by telling him that when he offered me his pleasant society I was not aware that I was to be of service to the fair lady. I added that when at day-break I received this information, I was pleased that he would have such good company. The lady did not say a word. She kept silent and gloomy all the time, and gazed to right and left like one who does not see what is before his eyes.

Dolci felt at ease after my explanation, and did his best to arouse the lady, but without success. He talked on a variety of topics to the husband, always giving her an opportunity of joining in, but her lips remained motionless. She looked like the statue of Pandora before it had been quickened by the divine flame.

The beauty of her face was perfect; her eyes were of a brilliant blue, her complexion a delicate mixture of white and red, her arms were as rounded as a Grace's, her hands plump and well shaped, her figure was that of a nymph's, giving delightful hints of a magnificent breast; her hair was a chestnut brown, her foot small: she had all that constitutes a beautiful woman save that gift of intellect, which makes beauty more beautiful, and gives a charm to ugliness itself. My vagrant fancy shewed me her naked form, all seemed ravishing, and yet I thought that though she might inspire a passing fancy she could not arouse a durable affection. She might minister to a man's pleasures, she could not make him happy.

I arrived at the isle resolved to trouble myself about her no more; she might, I thought, be mad, or in despair at finding herself in the power of a man whom she could not possibly love. I could not help pitying her, and yet I could not forgive her for consenting to be of a party which she knew she must spoil by her morose behaviour.

As for the self-styled Chevalier Stuard, I did not trouble my head whether he were her husband or her lover. He was young, commonplace-looking, he spoke affectedly; his manners were not good, and his conversation betrayed both ignorance and stupidity. He was a beggar, devoid of money and wits, and I could not make out why he took with him a beauty who, unless she were over-kind, could add nothing to his means of living. Perhaps he expected to live at the expense of simpletons, and had come to the conclusion, in spite of his ignorance, that the world is full of such; however, experience must have taught him that this plan cannot be relied on.

When we got to Vaucluse I let Dolci lead; he had been there a hundred times, and his merit was enhanced in my eyes by the fact that he was a lover of the lover of Laura. We left the carriage at Apt, and wended our way to the fountain which was honoured that day with a numerous throng of pilgrims. The stream pours forth from a vast cavern, the handiwork of nature, inimitable

by man. It is situated at the foot of a rock with a
sheer descent of more than a hundred feet. The cavern
is hardly half as high, and the water pours forth from
it in such abundance that it deserves the name of river
at its source. It is the Sorgue which falls into the Rhone
near Avignon. There is no other stream as pure and
clear, for the rocks over which it flows harbour no de-
posits of any kind. Those who dislike it on account of
its apparent blackness should remember that the extreme
darkness of the cavern gives it that gloomy tinge.

> *Chiare fresche e dolce aque*
> *Ove le belle membra*
> *Pose colei che sola a me par donna.*

I wished to ascend to that part of the rock where Petrarch's house stood. I gazed on the remains with tears
in my eyes, like Leo Allatius at Homer's grave. Sixteen years later I slept at Arqua, where Petrarch died,
and his house still remains. The likeness between the
two situations was astonishing, for from Petrarch's study
at Arqua a rock can be seen similar to that which may
be viewed at Vaucluse; this was the residence of Madonna Laura.

"Let us go there," said I, "it is not far off."

I will not endeavour to delineate my feelings as I
contemplated the ruins of the house where dwelt the
lady whom the amorous Petrarch immortalised in his
verse—verse made to move a heart of stone:

> *"Morte bella parea nel suo bel viso."*

I threw myself with arms outstretched upon the
ground as if I would embrace the very stones. I kissed
them, I watered them with my tears. I strove to breathe

the holy breath they once contained. I begged Madame Stuard's pardon for having left her arm to do homage to the spirit of a woman who had quickened the profoundest soul that ever lived.

I say soul advisedly, for after all the body and the senses had nothing to do with the connection.

"Four hundred years have past and gone," said I to the statue of a woman who gazed at me in astonishment, "since Laura de Sade walked here; perhaps she was not as handsome as you, but she was lively, kindly, polite, and good of heart. May this air which she breathed and which you breathe now kindle in you the spark of fire divine; that fire that coursed through her veins, and made her heart beat and her bosom swell. Then you would win the worship of all worthy men, and from none would you receive the least offence. Gladness, madam, is the lot of the happy, and sadness the portion of souls condemned to everlasting pains. Be cheerful, then, and you will do something to deserve your beauty."

The worthy Dolci was kindled by my enthusiasm. He threw himself upon me, and kissed me again and again; the fool Stuard laughed; and his wife, who possibly thought me mad, did not evince the slightest emotion. She took my arm, and we walked slowly towards the house of Messer Francesco d'Arezzo, where I spent a quarter of an hour in cutting my name. After that we had our dinner.

Dolci lavished more attention on the extraordinary woman than I did. Stuard did nothing but eat and drink, and despised the Sorgue water, which, said he, would spoil the Hermitage; possibly Petrarch may have been of the same opinion. We drank deeply without impairing our reason, but the lady was very temperate. When we reached Avignon we bade her farewell, declining the invitation of her foolish husband to come and rest in his rooms.

I took Dolci's arm and we walked beside the Rhone as the sun went down. Among other keen and witty observations the young man said,——

"That woman is an old hand, infatuated with a sense of her own merit. I would bet that she has only left her own country because her charms, from being too freely displayed, have ceased to please there. She must be sure of making her fortune out of anybody she comes across. I suspect that the fellow who passes for her husband is a rascal, and that her pretended melancholy is put on to drive a persistent lover to distraction. She has not yet succeeded in finding a dupe, but as she will no doubt try to catch a rich man, it is not improbable that she is hovering over you."

When a young man of Dolci's age reasons like that, he is bound to become a great master. I kissed him as I bade him good-night, thanked him for his kindness, and we agreed that we would see more of one another.

As I came back to my inn I was accosted by a fine-looking man of middle age, who greeted me by name and asked with great politeness if I had found Vaucluse as fine as I had expected. I was delighted to recognize the Marquis of Grimaldi, a Genoese, a clever and good-natured man, with plenty of money, who always lived at Venice because he was more at liberty to enjoy himself there than in his native country; which shews that there is no lack of freedom at Venice.

After I had answered his question I followed him into his room, where having exhausted the subject of the fountain he asked me what I thought of my fair companion.

"I did not find her satisfactory in all respects," I answered; and noticing the reserve with which I spoke, he tried to remove it by the following confession:

"There are some very pretty women in Genoa, but not one to compare with her whom you took to Vaucluse to-day. I sat opposite to her at table yesterday evening, and I was struck with her perfect beauty. I offered her my arm up the stair; I told her that I was sorry to see her so sad, and if I could do anything for her she had only to speak. You know I was aware she had no money. Her husband, real or pretended, thanked me for my offer, and after I had wished them a good night I left them.

"An hour ago you left her and her husband at the door of their apartment, and soon afterwards I took the liberty of calling. She welcomed me with a pretty bow, and her husband went out directly, begging me to keep her company till his return. The fair one made no difficulty in sitting next to me on a couch, and this struck me as a good omen, but when I took her hand she gently drew it away. I then told her, in as few words as I could, that her beauty had made me in love with her, and that if she wanted a hundred louis they were at her service, if she would drop her melancholy, and behave in a manner suitable to the feelings with which she had inspired me. She only replied by a motion of the head, which shewed gratitude, but also an absolute refusal of my offer. 'I am going to-morrow,' said I. No answer. I took her hand again, and she drew it back with an air of disdain which wounded me. I begged her to excuse me, and I left the room without more ado.

"That's an account of what happened an hour ago. I am not amorous of her, it was only a whim; but knowing, as I do, that she has no money, her manner astonished me. I fancied that you might have placed her in a position to despise my offer, and this would explain her conduct, in a measure; otherwise I can't understand it at all. May I ask you to tell me whether you are more fortunate than I?"

I was enchanted with the frankness of this noble gentleman, and did not hesitate to tell him all, and we laughed together at our bad fortune: I had to promise to call on him at Genoa, and tell him whatever happened between us during the two days I purposed to remain at Avignon. He asked me to sup with him and admire the fair recalcitrant.

"She has had an excellent dinner," said I, "and in all probability she will not have any supper."

"I bet she will," said the marquis; and he was right, which made me see clearly that the woman was playing a part. A certain Comte de Bussi, who had just come, was placed next to her at table. He was a good-looking young man with a fatuous sense of his own superiority, and he afforded us an amusing scene.

He was good-natured, a wit, and inclined to broad jokes, and his manner towards women bordered on the impudent. He had to leave at midnight and began to make love to his fair neighbour forthwith, and teased her in a thousand ways; but she remained as dumb as a statue, while he did all the talking and laughing, not regarding it within the bounds of possibility that she might be laughing at him.

I looked at M. Grimaldi, who found it as difficult to keep his countenance as I did. The young *roué* was hurt at her silence, and continued pestering her, giving her all the best pieces on his plate after tasting them first. The lady refused to take them, and he tried to put them into her mouth, while she repulsed him in a rage. He saw that no one seemed inclined to take her part, and determined to continue the assault, and taking her hand he kissed it again and again. She tried to draw it away, and as she rose he put his arm round her waist and made her sit down on his knee; but at this point the husband took her arm and led her out of the room. The attacking party looked rather taken aback for a moment as he followed her with his eyes, but sat down again and began to eat and laugh afresh, while everybody else kept a profound silence. He then turned to the footman behind his chair and asked him if his sword was upstairs. The footman said no, and then the fatuous young man turned to an abbé who sat near me, and enquired who had taken away his mistress.

"It was her husband," said the abbé.

"Her husband! Oh, that's another thing; husbands don't fight—a man of honour always apologises to them."

With that he got up, went upstairs, and came down again directly, saying,——

"The husband's a fool. He shut the door in my face, and told me to satisfy my desires somewhere else. It isn't worth the trouble of stopping, but I wish I had made an end of it."

He then called for champagne, offered it vainly to everybody, bade the company a polite farewell and went upon his way.

As M. Grimaldi escorted me to my room he asked me what I had thought of the scene we had just witnessed. I told him I would not have stirred a finger, even if he had turned up her clothes.

"No more would I," said he, "but if she had accepted my hundred louis it would have been different. I am curious to know the further history of this siren, and I rely upon you to tell me all about it as you go through Genoa."

He went away at day-break next morning.

When I got up I received a note from the false Astrodi, asking me if I expected her and her great chum to supper. I had scarcely replied in the affirmative, when the sham Duke of Courland I had left at Grenoble appeared on the scene. He confessed in a humble voice that he was the son of a clock-maker at Narva, that his buckles were valueless, and that he had come to beg an alms of me. I gave him four louis, and he asked me to keep his secret. I replied that if anyone asked me about him I should say what was absolutely true, that I knew nothing about him.

"Thank you; I am now going to Marseilles."

"I hope you will have a prosperous journey."

Later on my readers will hear how I found him at Genoa. It is a good thing to know something about people of his kind, of whom there are far too many in the world.

I called up the landlord and told him I wanted a delicate supper for three in my own room.

He told me that I should have it, and then said, "I have just had a row with the Chevalier Stuard."

"What about?"

"Because he has nothing to pay me with, and I am going to turn them out immediately, although the lady is in bed in convulsions which are suffocating her."

"Take out your bill in her charms."

"Ah, I don't care for that sort of thing! I am getting on in life, and I don't want any more scenes to bring discredit on my house."

"Go and tell her that from henceforth she and her

husband will dine and sup in their own room and that
I will pay for them as long as I remain here."

"You are very generous, sir, but you know that meals
in a private room are charged double."

"I know they are."

"Very good."

I shuddered at the idea of the woman being turned
out of doors without any resources but her body, by
which she refused to profit. On the other hand I could
not condemn the inn-keeper who, like his fellows, was
not troubled with much gallantry. I had yielded to an
impulse of pity without any hopes of advantage for myself. Such were my thoughts when Stuard came to thank
me, begging me to come and see his wife and try and
persuade her to behave in a different manner.

"She will give me no answers, and you know that
that sort of thing is rather tedious."

"Come, she knows what you have done for her; she
will talk to you, for her feelings. . . ."

"What business have you to talk about feelings after
what happened yesterday evening?"

"It was well for that gentleman that he went away at
midnight, otherwise I should have killed him this morning."

"My dear sir, allow me to tell you that all that is
pure braggadocio. Yesterday, not to-day, was the time
to kill him, or to throw your plate at his head, at all
events. We will now go and see your wife."

I found her in bed, her face to the wall, the coverlet
right up to her chin, and her body convulsed with sobs.
I tried to bring her to reason, but as usual got no reply.
Stuard wanted to leave me, but I told him that if he
went out I would go too, as I could do nothing to console her, as he might know after her refusing the Mar-

quis of Grimaldi's hundred louis for a smile and her hand to kiss.

"A hundred louis!" cried the fellow with a sturdy oath; "what folly! We might have been at home at Liège by now. A princess allows one to kiss her hand for nothing, and she. . . . A hundred louis! Oh, damnable!"

His exclamations, very natural under the circumstances, made me feel inclined to laugh. The poor devil swore by all his gods, and I was about to leave the room, when all at once the wretched woman was seized with true or false convulsions. With one hand she seized a water-bottle and sent it flying into the middle of the room, and with the other she tore the clothes away from her breast. Stuard tried to hold her, but her disorder increased in violence, and the coverlet was disarranged to such a degree that I could see the most exquisite naked charms imaginable. At last she grew calm, and her eyes closed as if exhausted; she remained in the most voluptuous position that desire itself could have invented. I began to get very excited. How was I to look on such beauties without desiring to possess them? At this point her wretched husband left the room, saying he was gone to fetch some water. I saw the snare, and my self-respect prevented my being caught in it. I had an idea that the whole scene had been arranged with the intent that I should deliver myself up to brutal pleasure, while the proud and foolish woman would be free to disavow all participation in the fact. I constrained myself, and gently veiled what I would fain have revealed in all its naked beauty. I condemned to darkness these charms which this monster of a woman only wished me to enjoy that I might be debased.

Stuard was long enough gone. When he came back

with the water-bottle full, he was no doubt surprised to find me perfectly calm, and in no disorder of any kind, and a few minutes afterwards I went out to cool myself by the banks of the Rhone.

I walked along rapidly, feeling enraged with myself, for I felt that the woman had bewitched me. In vain I tried to bring myself to reason; the more I walked the more excited I became, and I determined that after what I had seen the only cure for my disordered fancy was enjoyment, brutal or not. I saw that I should have to win her, not by an appeal to sentiment but by hard cash, without caring what sacrifices I made. I regretted my conduct, which then struck me in the light of false delicacy, for if I had satisfied my desires and she chose to turn prude, I might have laughed her to scorn, and my position would have been unassailable. At last I determined on telling the husband that I would give him twenty-five louis if he could obtain me an interview in which I could satisfy my desires.

Full of this idea I went back to the inn, and had my dinner in my own room without troubling to enquire after her. Le Duc told me that she was dining in her room too, and that the landlord had told the company that she would not take her meals in public any more. This was information I possessed already.

After dinner I called on the good-natured Dolci, who introduced me to his father, an excellent man, but not rich enough to satisfy his son's desire of travelling. The young man was possessed of considerable dexterity, and performed a number of very clever conjuring tricks. He had an amiable nature, and seeing that I was curious to know about his love affairs he told me numerous little stories which shewed me that he was at that happy age when one's inexperience is one's sole misfortune.

There was a rich lady for whom he did not care, as she
wanted him to give her that which he would be ashamed
to give save for love, and there was a girl who required
him to treat her with respect. I thought I could give him
a piece of good advice, so I told him to grant his favours
to the rich woman, and to fail in respect now and
again to the girl, who would be sure to scold and then
forgive. He was no profligate, and seemed rather inclined to become a Protestant. He amused himself innocently with his friends of his own age, in a garden near
Avignon, and a sister of the gardener's wife was kind to
him when they were alone.

In the evening I went back to the inn, and I had not
long to wait for the Astrodi and the Lepi (so the hunchbacked girl was named); but when I saw these two
caricatures of women I felt stupefied. I had expected
them, of course, but the reality confounded me. The
Astrodi tried to counterbalance her ugliness by an out-
rageous freedom of manners; while the Lepi, who though
a hunchback was very talented and an excellent actress,
was sure of exciting desire by the rare beauty of her eyes
and teeth, which latter challenged admiration from her
enormous mouth by their regularity and whiteness.
The Astrodi rushed up to me and gave me an Italian embrace, to which, willy nilly, I was obliged to submit.
The quieter Lepi offered me her cheek, which I pretended to kiss. I saw that the Astrodi was in a fair
way to become intolerable, so I begged her to moderate
her transports, because as a novice at these parties I
wanted to get accustomed to them by degrees. She
promised that she would be very good.

While we were waiting for supper I asked her, for the
sake of something to say, whether she had found a lover
at Avignon.

"Only the vice-legate's auditor," she replied; "and though he makes me his pathic he is good-natured and generous. I have accustomed myself to his taste easily enough, though I should have thought such a thing impossible a year ago, as I fancied the exercise a harmful one, but I was wrong."

"So the auditor makes a boy of you?"

"Yes. My sister would have adored him, as that sort of love is her passion."

"But your sister has such fine haunches."

"So have I! Look here, feel me."

"You are right; but wait a bit, it is too soon for that kind of thing yet."

"We will be wanton after supper."

"I think you are wanton now," said the Lepi.

"Why?"

"Why? Ought you to shew your person like that?"

"My dear girl, you will be shewing yourself soon. When one is in good company, one is in the golden age."

"I wonder at your telling everyone what sort of a connection you have with the auditor," said I.

"Nonsense! I don't tell everyone, but everyone tells me and congratulates me too. They know the worthy man never cared for women, and it would be absurd to deny what everybody guesses. I used to be astonished at my sister, but the best plan in this world is to be astonished at nothing. But don't you like that?"

"No, I only like this."

As I spoke I laid hands on the Lepi, on the spot where one usually finds what I called "this;" but the Astrodi, seeing that I found nothing, burst into a roar of laughter, and taking my hand put it just under her front hump, where at last I found what I wanted. The reader will guess my surprise. The poor creature, too ashamed to be prudish, laughed too. My spirits also begin to rise, as I thought of the pleasure I should get out of this new discovery after supper.

"Have you never had a lover?" said I to the Lepi.

"No," said the Astrodi, "she is still a maid."

"No, I am not," replied the Lepi, in some confusion, "I had a lover at Bordeaux, and another at Montpellier."

"Yes, I know, but you are still as you were born."

"I can't deny it."

"What's that? Two lovers and still a maid! I don't understand; please tell me about it, for I have never heard of such a thing."

"Before I satisfied my first lover which happened when I was only twelve, I was just the same as I am now."

"It's wonderful. And what did he say when he saw it?"

"I swore that he was my first, and he believed me, putting it down to the peculiar shape of my body."

"He was a man of spirit; but didn't he hurt you?"

"Not a bit; but then he was very gentle."

"You must have a try after supper," said the Astrodi to me, "that would be fine fun."

"No, no," said the Lepi, "the gentleman would be too big for me."

"Nonsense! You don't want to take in all of him. I will show you how it is."

With these words the impudent hussy proceeded to exhibit me, and I let her do what she liked.

"That's just what I should have thought," cried the Lepi; "it could never be done."

"Well, he is rather big," answered the Astrodi; "but there's a cure for everything, and he will be content with half-measures."

"It's not the length, my dear, but the thickness which frightens me; I am afraid the door is too narrow."

"All the better for you, for you can sell your maidenhead after having had two lovers."

This conversation, not devoid of wit, and still more the simplicity of the hunchback, had made me resolve to verify things for myself.

Supper came up, and I had the pleasure of seeing the two nymphs eat like starving savages, and drink still better. When the Hermitage had done its work the Astrodi proposed that we should cast off the clothes which disfigure nature.

"Certainly," said I; "and I will turn away while you are getting ready."

I went behind the curtains, took off my clothes, and went to bed with my back to them. At last the Astrodi told me that they were ready, and when I looked the Lepi took up all my attention. In spite of her double deformity she was a handsome woman. My glances frightened her, for she was doubtless taking part in an orgy for the first time. I gave her courage, however, by dint of praising those charms which the white and beautiful hands could not hide, and at last I persuaded her to come and lie beside me. Her hump prevented her lying on her back, but the ingenious Astrodi doubled up the pillows and succeeded in placing her in a position similar to that of a ship about to be launched. It was also by the tender care of the Astrodi that the introduction of the knife was managed, to the great delight of priest and victim. After the operation was over she got up and kissed me, which she could not do before, for her mouth reached to the middle of my chest, while my feet were scarcely down to her knees. I would have given ten louis to have been able to see the curious sight we must have presented at work.

"Now comes my turn," said the Astrodi; "but I don't want you to infringe on the rights of my auditor, so come and look round and see where the path lies. Take that."

"What am I to do with this slice of lemon?"

"I want you to try whether the place is free from infection, or whether it would be dangerous for you to pay it a visit."

"Is that a sure method?"

"Infallible; if everything were not right I could not bear the smart."

"There you are. How's that?"

"All right; but don't deceive me, I want no half measures. My reputation would be made if I became with child."

I ask my reader's leave to draw a veil over some incidents of this truly scandalous orgy, in which the ugly woman taught me some things I did not know before. At last, more tired than exhausted, I told them to begone, but the Astrodi insisted on finishing up with a bowl of punch. I agreed, but not wishing to have anything more to do with either of them I dressed myself again. However, the champagne punch excited them to such an extent that at last they made me share their transports. The Astrodi placed her friend in such a singular position that the humps were no longer visible, and imagining that I had before me the high priestess of Jove, I paid her a long sacrifice, in which death and resurrection followed one another in succession. But I felt disgusted with myself, and drew away from their lascivious frenzies, and gave them ten louis to get rid of them. The Astrodi fell on her knees, blessed me, thanked me, called me her god; and the Lepi wept and laughed for joy at the same time; and thus for a quarter of an hour I was treated to a scene of an extraordinary kind.

I had them taken home in my carriage, and slept till ten o'clock next morning. Just as I was going out for a walk Stuard came to my room and told me, with an air of despair, that if I did not give him the means of going away before I left he would throw himself in the Rhine.

"That's rather tragic," said I, "but I can find a cure. I will disburse twenty-five louis, but it is your wife who must receive them; and the only condition is that she must receive me alone for an hour, and be entirely kind."

"Sir, we need just that sum; my wife is disposed to receive you; go and talk to her. I shall not be in till noon."

I put twenty-five louis in a pretty little purse, and left my room thinking that the victory was won. I I entered her room and approached her bed respectfully. When she heard me she sat up in bed without taking the trouble to cover her breast, and before I could wish her good-day she spoke to me as follows:

"I am ready, sir, to pay with my body for the wretched twenty-five louis of which my husband is in need. You can do what you like with me; but remember that in taking advantage of my position to assuage your brutal lust you are the viler of the two, for I only sell myself so cheaply because necessity compels me to do so. Your baseness is more shameful than mine. Come on; here I am."

With this flattering address she threw off the coverlet

with a vigorous gesture, and displayed all her beauties, which I might have gazed on with such different feelings from those which now filled my breast. For a moment I was silent with indignation. All my passion had evaporated; in those voluptuous rounded limbs I saw now only the covering of a wild beast's soul. I put back the coverlet with the greatest calmness, and addressed her in a tone of cold contempt:

"No, madam, I shall not leave this room degraded because you have told me so, but I shall leave it after imparting to you a few degrading truths, of which you cannot be ignorant if you are a woman of any decency whatever. Here are twenty-five louis, a wretched sum to give a virtuous woman in payment of her favours, but much more than you deserve. I am not brutal, and to convince you of the fact I am going to leave you in the undisturbed possession of your charms, which I despise as heartily as I should have admired them if your behaviour had been different. I only give you the money from a feeling of compassion which I cannot overcome, and which is the only feeling I now have for you. Nevertheless, let me tell you that whether a woman sells herself for twenty-five louis or twenty-five million louis she is as much a prostitute in the one case as in the other, if she does not give her love with herself, or at all events the semblance of love. Farewell."

I went back to my room, and in course of time Stuard came to thank me.

"Sir," said I, "let me alone; I wish to hear no more about your wife."

They went away the next day for Lyons, and my readers will hear of them again at Liège.

In the afternoon Dolci took me to his garden that I

might see the gardener's sister. She was pretty, but not so pretty as he was. He soon got her into a good humour, and after some trifling objection she consented to be loved by him in my presence. I saw that this Adonis had been richly dowered by nature, and I told him that with such a physical conformation he had no need of emptying his father's purse to travel, and before long he took my advice. This fair Ganymede might easily have turned me into Jove, as he struggled amorously with the gardener's sister.

As I was going home I saw a young man coming out of a boat; he was from twenty to twenty-five years old, and looked very sad. Seeing me looking at him, he accosted me, and humbly asked for alms, shewing me a document authorizing him to beg, and a passport stating he had left Madrid six weeks before. He came from Parma, and was named Costa. When I saw Parma my national prejudice spoke in his favour, and I asked him what misfortune had reduced him to beggary.

"Only lack of money to return to my native country," said he.

"What were you doing at Madrid, and why did you leave?"

"I was there four years as valet to Dr. Pistoria, physician to the King of Spain, but on my health failing I left him. Here is a certificate which will shew you that I gave satisfaction."

"What can you do?"

"I write a good hand, I can assist a gentleman as his secretary, and I intend being a scribe when I get home. Here are some verses I copied yesterday."

"You write well; but can you write correctly without a book?"

"I can write from dictation in French, Latin, and Spanish."

"Correctly?"

"Yes, sir, if the dictation is done properly, for it is the business of the one who dictates to see that everything is correct."

I saw that Master Gaetan Costa was an ignoramus, but in spite of that I took him to my room and told Le Duc to address him in Spanish. He answered well enough, but on my dictating to him in Italian and French I found he had not the remotest ideas on orthography. "But you can't write," said I to him. However, I saw he was mortified at this, and I consoled him by saying that I would take him to his own country at my expense. He kissed my hand, and assured me that I should find a faithful servant in him.

This young fellow took my fancy by his originality; he had probably assumed it to distinguish himself from the blockheads amongst whom he had hitherto lived, and now used it in perfect good faith with everybody. He thought that the art of a scribe solely consisted in possessing a good hand, and that the fairest writer would be the best scribe. He said as much while he was examining a paper I had written, and as my writing was not as legible as his he tacitly told me I was his inferior, and that I should therefore treat him with some degree of respect. I laughed at this fad, and, not thinking him incorrigible I took him into my service. If it had not been for that odd notion of his I should probably have merely given him a louis, and no more. He said that spelling was of no consequence, as those who knew how to spell could easily guess the words, while those who did not know were unable to pick out the mistakes. I laughed, but as I said nothing he thought the laugh

signified approval. In the dictation I gave him the
Council of Trent happened to occur. According to his
system he wrote Trent by a three and a nought. I burst
out laughing; but he was not in the least put out, only
remarking that the pronunciation being the same it was
of no consequence how the word was spelt. In point of
fact this lad was a fool solely through his intelligence,
matched with ignorance and unbounded self-confidence.
I was pleased with his originality and kept him, and was
thus the greater fool of the two, as the reader will see.

I left Avignon next day, and went straight to Marseilles, not troubling to stop at Aix. I halted at the
"Treize Cantons," wishing to stay for a week at least
in this ancient colony of the Phocæans, and to do as I
liked there. With this idea I took no letter of introduction; I had plenty of money, and needed nobody's help.
I told my landlord to give me a choice fish dinner in
my own room, as I was aware that the fish in those parts
is better than anywhere else.

I went out the next morning with a guide, to take me
back to the inn when I was tired of walking. Not heeding where I went, I reached a fine quay; I thought I
was at Venice again, and I felt my bosom swell, so
deeply is the love of fatherland graven on the heart of
every good man. I saw a number of stalls where Spanish
and Levantine wines were kept, and a number of people
drinking in them. A crowd of business men went hither
and thither, running up against each other, crossing each
other's paths, each occupied with his own business, and
not caring whose way he got into. Hucksters, well
dressed and ill dressed, women, pretty and plain, women
who stared boldly at everyone, modest maidens with
downcast eyes, such was the picture I saw.

The mixture of nationalities, the grave Turk and the

glittering Andalusian, the French dandy, the gross Negro, the crafty Greek, the dull Hollander; everything reminded me of Venice, and I enjoyed the scene.

I stopped a moment at a street corner to read a play-bill, and then I went back to the inn and refreshed my weary body with a delicious dinner, washed down with choice Syracusan wine. After dinner I dressed and took a place in the amphitheatre of the theatre.

CHAPTER III

Rosalie—Toulon—Nice—I Arrive at Genoa—M. Grimaldi—Véronique and Her Sister

I NOTICED that the four principal boxes on both sides of the proscenium were adorned with pretty women, but not a single gentleman. In the interval between the first and second acts I saw gentlemen of all classes paying their devoirs to these ladies. Suddenly I heard a Knight of Malta say to a girl, who was the sole occupant of a box next to me,——

"I will breakfast with you to-morrow."

This was enough for me. I looked at her more closely and finding her to be a dainty morsel I said, as soon as the knight had gone,——

"Will you give me my supper?"

"With pleasure; but I have been taken in so often that I shan't expect you without an earnest."

"How can I give you an earnest? I don't understand."

"You must be a new-comer here."

"Just arrived."

She laughed, called the knight, and said,——

"Be pleased to explain to this gentleman, who has just asked me for supper, the meaning of the word 'earnest.'"

The good-natured knight explained, with a smile, that the lady, fearing lest my memory should prove defective, wanted me to pay for my supper in advance. I thanked him, and asked her if a louis would be enough; and on her replying in the affirmative, I gave her the louis and asked for her address. The knight told me politely that he would take me there himself after the theatre, adding,——

"She's the wantonest wench in all Marseilles."

He then asked me if I knew the town, and when I told him that I had only come that day he said he was glad to be the first to make my acquaintance. We went to the middle of the amphitheatre and he pointed out a score of girls to right and left, all of them ready to treat the first comer to supper. They are all on the free list, and the manager finds they serve his ends as respectable women will not sit in their boxes, and they draw people to the theatre. I noticed five or six of a better type than the one I had engaged, but I resolved to stick to her for the evening, and to make the acquaintance of the others another time.

"Is your favourite amongst them?" I said to the knight.

"No, I keep a ballet-girl, and I will introduce you to her, as I am glad to say that I am free from all jealousy."

When the play came to an end he took me to my nymph's lodging, and we parted with the understanding that we were to see more of one another.

I found the lady in undress—a circumstance which went against her, for what I saw did not please me. She gave me a capital supper, and enlivened me by some witty and wanton sallies which made me regard her in a more favourable light. When we had supper she got into bed, and asked me to follow her example; but I told her that I never slept out. She then offered me the English article which brings peace to the soul, but I did not accept the one she offered as I thought it looked of a common make.

"I have finer ones, but they are three francs each, and

the maker only sells them by the dozen," she said.

"I will take a dozen if they are really good," I replied.

She rang the bell, and a young, charming, and modest-looking girl came in. I was struck with her.

"You have got a nice maid," I remarked, when the girl had gone for the protective sheaths.

"She is only fifteen," she said, "and won't do anything, as she is new to it."

"Will you allow me to see for myself?"

"You may ask her if you like, but I don't think she will consent."

The girl came back with the packet, and putting myself in a proper position I told her to try one on. She proceeded to do so with a sulky air and with a kind of repugnance which made me feel interested in her. Number one would not go on, so she had to try on a second, and the result was that I besprinkled her plentifully. The mistress laughed, but she was indignant, threw the whole packet in my face, and ran away in a rage. I wanted nothing more after this, so I put the packet in my pocket, gave the woman two louis, and left the room. The girl I had treated so cavalierly came to light me downstairs, and thinking I owed her an apology I gave her a louis and begged her pardon. The poor girl was astonished, kissed my hand, and begged me to say nothing to her mistress.

"I will not, my dear, but tell me truly whether you are still a *virgo intacta.*"

"Certainly, sir."

"Wonderful! but tell me why you wouldn't let me see for myself?"

"Because it revolted me."

"Nevertheless you will have to do so, for otherwise, in spite of your prettiness, people will not know what to make of you. Would you like to let me try?"

"Yes, but not in this horrible house."

"Where, then?"

"Go to my mother's to-morrow, I will be there. Your guide knows where she lives."

When I got outside, I asked the man if he knew her. He replied in the affirmative, and said he believed her to be an honest girl.

"You will take me to-morrow to see her mother," I said.

Next morning he took me to the end of the town, to a poor house, where I found a poor woman and poor children living on the ground floor, and eating hard black bread.

"What do you want?" said she.

"Is you daughter here?"

"No, and what if she were? I am not her bawd."

"No, of course not, my good woman."

Just then the girl came in, and the enraged mother flung an old pot which came handy, at her head. Luckily it missed, but she would not have escaped her mother's talons if I had not flung myself between them. However, the old woman set up a dismal shriek, the children imitated her, and the poor girl began to cry. This hubbub made my man come in.

"You hussy!" screamed the mother, "you are bringing disgrace on me; get out of my house. You are no longer my daughter!"

I was in a difficult position. The man begged her not to make such a noise, as it would draw all the neighbours about the house; but the enraged woman answered only by abuse. I drew six francs from my pocket and gave them to her, but she flung them in my face. At last I

went out with the daughter, whose hair she attempted
to pull out by the roots, which project was defeated by
the aid of my man. As soon as we got outside, the mob
which the uproar had attracted hooted me and followed
me, and no doubt I should have been torn to pieces if
I had not escaped into a church, which I left by another
door a quarter of an hour later. My fright saved me,
for I knew the ferocity of the Provençals, and I took
care not to reply a word to the storm of abuse which
poured on me. I believe that I was never in greater
danger than on that day.

Before I got back to my inn I was rejoined by the
servant and the girl.

"How could you lead me into such a dangerous position?" said I. "You must have known your mother was
savage."

"I hoped she would behave respectfully to you."

"Be calm; don't weep any more. Tell me how I can
serve you."

"Rather than return to that horrible house I was in
yesterday I would throw myself into the sea."

"Do you know of any respectable house where I can
keep her?" said I to the man.

He told me he did know a respectable individual who
let furnished apartments.

"Take me to it, then."

The man was of an advanced age, and he had rooms
to let on all the floors.

"I only want a little nook," said the girl; and the old
man took us to the highest story, and opened the door
of a garret, saying,——

"This closet is six francs a month, a month's rent to
be paid in advance, and I may tell you that my door is

always shut at ten o'clock, and that nobody can come
and pass the night with you."

The room held a bed with coarse sheets, two chairs,
a little table, and a chest of drawers.

"How much will you board this young woman for?"
said I.

He asked twenty sous, and two sous for the maid who
would bring her meals and do her room.

"That will do," said the girl, and she paid the month's
rent and the day's board.   I left her telling her I would
come back again.

As I went down the stairs I asked the old man to shew
me a room for myself.   He shewed me a very nice one
at a louis a month, and I paid in advance.   He then
gave me a latch-key, that I might go and come when I
liked.

"If you wish to board here," said he, "I think I could
give satisfaction."

Having done this good work, I had my dinner by myself, and then went to a coffee-house where I found the
amiable Knight of Malta who was playing.   He left the
game as soon as he saw me, put the fistfull of gold he
had won into his pocket, accosted me with the politeness
natural to a Frenchman, and asked me how I had liked
the lady who had given me my supper.   I told him what
had happened, at which he laughed, and asked me to
come and see his ballet-girl.   We found her under the
hairdresser's hands, and she received me with the play-
ful familiarity with which one greets an old acquaintance.   I did not think much of her, but I pretended to be
immensely struck, with the idea of pleasing the good-
natured knight.

When the hairdresser left her, it was time for her to

get ready for the theatre, and she dressed herself, without caring who was present. The knight helped her to change her chemise, which she allowed him to do as a matter of course, though indeed she begged me to excuse her.

As I owed her a compliment, I could think of nothing better than to tell her that though she had not offended me she had made me feel very uncomfortable.

"I don't believe you," said she.

"It's true all the same."

She came up to me to verify the fact, and finding I had deceived her, she said half crossly,——

"You are a bad fellow."

The women of Marseilles are undoubtedly the most profligate in France. They not only pride themselves on never refusing, but also on being the first to propose. This girl shewed me a repeater, for which she had got up a lottery at twelve francs a ticket. She had ten tickets left; I took them all, and so delighted was she to touch my five louis that she came and kissed me, and told the knight that her unfaithfulness to him rested only with me.

"I am charmed to hear it," said the Maltese. He asked me to sup with her, and I accepted the invitation, but the sole pleasure I had was looking at the knight at work. He was far inferior to Dolci!

I wished them good night, and went to the house where I had placed the poor girl. The maid shewed me to my room, and I asked her if I might go to the garret. She took the light, I followed her up, and Rosalie, as the poor girl was named, heard my voice and opened the door. I told the maid to wait for me in my room, and I went in and sat down on the bed.

"Are you contented, dear?" I said.

"I am quite happy."

"Then I hope you will be kind, and find room for me in your bed."

"You may come if you like, but I must tell you that you will not find me a maid, as I have had one lover."

"You told me a lie, then?"

"Forgive me, I could not guess you would be my lover."

"I forgive you willingly; all the more so as I am no great stickler for maidenheads."

She was as gentle as a lamb, and allowed me to gaze on all those charms of which my hands and my lips disputed the possession; and the notion that I was master of all these treasures put fire in all my veins, but her submissive air distressed me.

"How is it you do not partake my desires?" said I.

"I dare not, lest you take me for a pretender."

Artifice or studied coquetry might have prompted such an answer, but the real timidity and the frankness with which these words were uttered could not have been assumed. Impatient to gain possession of her I took off my clothes, and on getting into bed to her I was astonished to find her a maid.

"Why did you tell me you had a lover?" said I. "I never heard of a girl telling a lie of that sort before."

"All the same I did not tell a lie, but I am very glad that I seem as if I had done so."

"Tell me all about it."

"Certainly I will, for I want to win your confidence. This is the story:

"Two years ago my mother, though she was hot-tempered, still loved me. I was a needle-woman, and earned from twenty to thirty sous a day. Whatever I earned I gave my mother. I had never had a lover, never thought of such a thing, and when my goodness was praised I felt inclined to laugh. I had been brought up from a child never to look at young men when I met them in the street, and never to reply to them when they addressed any impudence to me.

"Two months ago a fine enough looking young man, a native of Genoa, and a merchant in a small way, came to my mother to get her to wash some very fine cotton stockings which the sea-water had stained. When he saw me he was very complimentary, but in an honest way. I liked him, and, no doubt seeing it, he came and came again every evening. My mother was always present at our interviews, and he looked at me and talked to me, but did not so much as ask to kiss my hand. My mother was very pleased to notice that the young man liked me, and often scolded me because I was not polite enough to him. In time he had to go to Genoa in a small ship which belonged to him, and which was laden with goods. He assured us that he would return again the next spring and declare his intentions. He said he hoped he should find me as good as ever, and still without any lover. This was enough; my mother looked upon him as my betrothed, and let us talk together at the door till midnight. When he went I would shut the door and lie down beside my mother, who was always asleep.

"Four or five days before his departure, he took my arm and got me to go with him to a place about fifty paces from the house to drink a glass of Muscat at a Greek's, who kept his tavern open all night. We were only away for half an hour, and then it was that he first kissed me. When I got home I found my mother awake, and told her all; it seemed so harmless to me.

"Next day, excited by the recollection of what had happened the night before, I went with him again, and love began to gain ground. We indulged in caresses which were no longer innocent, as we well knew. However, we forgave each other, as we had abstained from the chief liberty.

"The day after, my lover—as he had to journey in the night—took leave of my mother, and as soon as she was in bed I was not longer in granting what I desired as much as he. We went to the Greek's, ate and drank, and our heated senses gained love's cause; we forgot our duty, and fancied our misdemeanour a triumph.

"Afterwards we fell asleep, and when we awoke we saw our fault in the clear, cold light of day. We parted sorrowful rather than rejoicing, and the reception my mother gave me was like that you witnessed this morning. I assured her that marriage would take away the shame of my sin, and with this she took up a stick and would have done for me, if I had not taken to my heels, more from instinct than from any idea of what I was doing.

"Once in the street I knew not where to turn, and taking refuge in a church I stayed there like one in a dream till noon. Think of my position. I was hungry, I had no refuge, nothing but the clothes I wore, nothing that would get me a morsel of bread. A woman accosted me in the street. I knew her and I also knew that she kept a servants' agency. I asked her forthwith if she could get me a place.

"'I had enquiries about a maid this morning,' said she, 'but it is for a gay woman, and you are pretty. You would have a good deal of difficulty in remaining virtuous.'

"'I can keep off the infection,' I answered, 'and in the position I am in I cannot pick and choose.'

"She thereupon took me to the lady, who was delighted

to see me, and still more delighted when I told her that I had never had anything to do with a man. I have repented of this lie bitterly enough, for in the week I spent at that profligate woman's house I have had to endure the most humiliating insults that an honest girl ever suffered. No sooner did the men who came to the house hear that I was a maid than they longed to slake their brutal lust upon me, offering me gold if I would submit to their caresses. I refused and was reviled, but that was not all. Five or six times every day I was obliged to remain a witness of the disgusting scenes enacted between my mistress and her customers, who, when I was compelled to light them about the house at night, overwhelmed me with insults, because I would not do them a disgusting service for a twelve-sous piece. I could not bear this sort of life much longer, and I was thinking of drowning myself. When you came you treated me so ignominiously that my resolve to die was strengthened, but you were so kind and polite as you went away that I fell in love with you directly, thinking that Providence must have sent you to snatch me away from the abyss. I thought your fine presence might calm my mother and persuade her to take me back till my lover came to marry me. I was undeceived, and I saw that she took me for a prostitute. Now, if you like, I am altogether yours, and I renounce my lover of whom I am no longer worthy. Take me as your maid, I will love you and you only; I will submit myself to you and do whatever you bid me."

Whether it were weakness or virtue on my part, this tale of woe and a mother's too great severity drew tears from my eyes, and when she saw my emotion she wept profusely, for her heart was in need of some relief.

"I think, my poor Rosalie, you have only one chemise."

"Alas! that is all."

Comfort yourself, my dear; all your wants shall be supplied to-morrow, and in the evening you shall sup with me in my room on the second floor. I will take care of you."

"You pity me, then?"

"I fancy there is more love than pity in it."

"Would to God it were so!"

This "would to God," which came from the very depths of her soul, sent me away in a merry mood. The servant who had been waiting for me for two hours, and was looking rather glum, relaxed when she saw the colour of a crown which I gave her by way of atonement.

"Tell your master," said I, "that Rosalie will sup with me to-morrow; let us have a fasting dinner, but let it be a good one."

I returned to my inn quite in love with Rosalie, and I congratulated myself on having at last heard a true tale from a pretty mouth. She appeared to me so well disposed that her small failing seemed to make her shine the more. I resolved never to abandon her, and I did so in all sincerity; was I not in love?

After I had had my chocolate next morning I went out with a guide to the shops, where I got the necessary articles, paying a good but not an excessive price. Rosalie was only fifteen, but with her figure, her well-formed breasts, and her rounded arms, she would have been taken for twenty. Her shape was so imprinted on my brain that everything I got for her fitted as if she had been measured for it. This shopping took up all the morning, and in the afternoon the man took her a small trunk containing two dresses, chemises, petticoats, handkerchiefs, stockings, gloves, caps, a pair of slippers, a fan, a work-bag, and a mantle. I was pleased at giving

her such a delightful surprise, and I longed for supper-
time that I might enjoy the sight of her pleasure.

The Knight of Malta came to dine with me without
ceremony, and I was charmed to see him. After we had
dined he persuaded me to go to the theatre, as in consequence of the suspense of the subscription arrangements the boxes would be filled with all the quality in
Marseilles.

"There will be no loose women in the amphitheatre,"
said he, "as everybody has to pay."

That decided me and I went. He presented me to a
lady with an excellent connection, who asked me to come
and see her. I excused myself on the plea that I was
leaving so shortly. Nevertheless she was very useful to
me on my second visit to Marseilles. Her name was
Madame Audibert.

I did not wait for the play to end, but went where
love called me. I had a delightful surprise when I saw
Rosalie; I should not have known her. But I cannot
resist the pleasure of recalling her picture as she stood
before me then, despite the years that have rolled by
since that happy moment.

Rosalie was an enticing-looking brunette, above the
middle height. Her face was a perfect oval, and exquisitely proportioned. Two fine black eyes shed a soft
and ravishing light around. Her eyebrows were arched,
and she had a wealth of hair, black and shining as ebony;
her skin was while and lightly tinged with colour. On
her chin was a dimple, and her slightest smile summoned
into being two other dimples, one on each cheek. Her
mouth was small, disclosing two rows of fairest orient
pearls, and from her red lips flowed forth an indefinable
sweetness. The lower lip projected ever so lightly, and
seemed designed to hold a kiss. I have spoken of her

arms, her breast, and her figure, which left nothing to
be desired, but I must add to this catalogue of her
charms, that her hand was exquisitely shaped, and
that her foot was the smallest I have ever seen. As
to her other beauties, I will content myself with saying that they were in harmony with those I have described.

To see her at her best, one had to see her smiling; and
hitherto she had been sad or vexed—states of mind which
detract from a woman's appearance. But now sadness
was gone, and gratitude and pleasure had taken its place.
I examined her closely, and felt proud, as I saw what a
transformation I had effected; but I concealed my
surprise, lest she should think I had formed an unfavourable impression of her. I proceeded, therefore, to tell
her that I should expose myself to ridicule if I attempted
to keep a beauty like herself for a servant.

"You shall be my mistress," I said, "and my servants
shall respect you as if you were my wife."

At this Rosalie, as if I had given her another being,
began to try and express her gratitude for what I had
done. Her words, which passion made confused, increased my joy; here was no art nor deceit, but simple
nature.

There was no mirror in her garret, so she had dressed
by her sense of touch, and I could see that she was
afraid to stand up and look at herself in the mirror in
my room. I knew the weak spot in all women's hearts
(which men are very wrong in considering as matter for
reproach), and I encouraged her to admire herself, whereupon she could not restrain a smile of satisfaction.

"I think I must be in disguise," said she, "for I have
never seen myself so decked out before."

She praised the tasteful simplicity of the dress I had

chosen, but was vexed at the thought that her mother would still be displeased.

"Think no more of your mother, dearest one. You look like a lady of quality, and I shall be quite proud when the people at Genoa ask me if you are my daughter."

"At Genoa?"

"Yes, at Genoa. Why do you blush?"

"From surprise; perhaps I may see there one whom I have not yet forgotten."

"Would you like to stay here better?"

"No, no! Love me and be sure that I love you and for your own sake, not from any thought of my own interests."

"You are moved, my angel; let me wipe away your tears with kisses."

She fell into my arms, and she relieved the various feelings of which her heart was full by weeping for some time. I did not try to console her, for she had not grief; she wept as tender souls, and women, more especially, often will. We had a delicious supper to which I did honour for two, for she ate nothing. I asked her if she was so unfortunate as not to care for good food.

"I have as good an appetite as anyone," she replied, "and an excellent digestion. You shall see for yourself when I grow more accustomed to my sudden happiness."

"At least you can drink; this wine is admirable. If you prefer Greek muscat I will send for some. It will remind you of your lover."

"If you love me at all, I beg you will spare me that mortification."

"You shall have no more mortification from me, I promise you. It was only a joke, and I beg your pardon for it."

"As I look upon you I feel in despair at not having known you first."

"That feeling of yours, which wells forth from the depths of your open soul, is grand. You are beautiful and good, for you only yielded to the voice of love with the prospect of becoming his wife; and when I think what you are to me I am in despair at not being sure you love me. An evil genius whispers in my ear that you only bear with me because I had the happiness of helping you."

"Indeed, that is an evil genius. To be sure, if I had met you in the street I should not have fallen head over ears in love with you, like a wanton, but you would certainly have pleased me. I am sure I love you, and not for what you have done for me; for if I were rich and you were poor, I would do anything in the world for you. But I don't want it to be like that, for I had rather be your debtor than for you to be mine. These are my real feelings, and you can guess the rest."

We were still talking on the same subject when midnight struck, and my old landlord came and asked me if I were pleased.

"I must thank you," I replied, "I am delighted. Who cooked this delicious supper?"

"My daughter."

"She understands her craft; tell her I thought it excellent."

"Yes, sir, but it is dear."

"Not too dear for me. You shall be pleased with me as I with you, and take care to have as good a supper to-morrow evening, as I hope the lady will be well enough to do justice to the products of your daughter's culinary skill."

"Bed is a capital place to get an appetite. Ah! it is

sixty years since I have had anything to do with that sort of thing. What are you laughing at, mademoiselle?"

"At the delight with which you must recollect it."

"You are right, it is a pleasant recollection; and thus I am always ready to forgive young folks the peccadilloes that love makes them commit."

"You are a wise old man," said I, "everyone should sympathise with the tenderest of all our mortal follies."

"If the old man is wise," said Rosalie, when he had left the room, "my mother must be very foolish."

"Would you like me to take you to the play to-morrow?"

"Pray do not. I will come if you like, but it will vex me very much. I don't want to walk out with you or to go to the theatre with you here. Good heavens! What would people say. No, neither at Marseilles; but elsewhere, anything you please and with all my heart."

"Very good, my dear, just as you please. But look at your room; no more garret for you; and in three days we will start."

"So soon?"

"Yes; tell me to-morrow what you require for the journey, for I don't want you to lack for anything, and if you leave it all to me I might forget something which would vex me."

"Well, I should like another cloak, a cloak with a lining, some boots, a night-cap, and a prayer-book."

"You know how to read, do you?"

"Certainly; and I can write fairly well."

"I am glad to hear it. Your asking me so freely for what you want is a true proof of your love; where confidence dwells not there is no love. I will not forget anything, but your feet are so small that I should advise you to get your boots yourself."

Our talk was so pleasant, and I experienced such delight in studying her disposition, that we did not go to bed till five o'clock. In the arms of love and sleep we spent seven delicious hours, and when we rose at noon we were fast lovers. She called me *thou*, talked of love and not of gratitude, and, grown more familiar with her new estate, laughed at her troubles. She kissed me at every opportunity, called me her darling boy, her joy, and as the present moment is the only real thing in this life, I enjoyed her love, I was pleased with her caresses, and put away all ideas of the dreadful future, which has only one certainty—death, *ultima linea rerum*.

The second night was far sweeter than the first; she had made a good supper, and drunk well, though moderately; thus she was disposed to refine on her pleasure, and to deliver herself with greater ardour to all the voluptuous enjoyments which love inspires.

I gave her a pretty watch and a gold shuttle for her to amuse herself with.

"I wanted it," said she, "but I should never have dared to ask for it."

I told her that this fear of my displeasure made me doubt once more whether she really loved me. She threw herself into my arms, and promised that henceforth she would shew me the utmost confidence.

I was pleased to educate this young girl, and I felt that when her mind had been developed she would be perfect.

On the fourth day I warned her to hold herself in readiness to start at a moment's notice. I had said nothing about my plans to Costa or Le Duc, but Rosalie knew that I had two servants, and I told her that I should often make them talk on the journey for the sake of the laughter their folly would afford me.

"You, my dear," I had said to her, "must be very reserved with them, and not allow them to take the slightest liberty. Give them your orders as a mistress, but without pride, and you will be obeyed and respected. If they forget themselves in the slightest particular, tell me at once."

I started from the hotel of the "Treize Cantons" with four post-horses, Le Duc and Costa sitting on the coachman's seat. The guide, whom I had paid well for his services, took us to Rosalie's door. I got out of the carriage, and after thanking the kindly old landlord, who was sorry to lose so good a boarder, I made her get in, sat down beside her, and ordered the postillions to go to Toulon, as I wished to see that fine port before returning to Italy. We got to Toulon at five o'clock.

My Rosalie behaved herself at supper like the mistress of a house accustomed to the best society. I noticed that Le Duc as head man made Costa wait upon her, but I got over him by telling my sweetheart that he would have the honour of doing her hair, as he could do it as well as the best barber in Paris. He swallowed the golden pill, and gave in with a good grace, and said, with a profound bow, that he hoped to give madam satisfaction.

We went out next morning to see the port, and were shewn over the place by the commandant, whose acquaintance we made by a lucky chance. He offered his arm to Rosalie, and treated her with the consideration she deserved for her appearance and the good sense of her questions. The commandant accepted my invitation to dinner, at which Rosalie spoke to the point though not to excess, and received the polite compliments of our worthy guest with much grace. In the afternoon he took us over the arsenal, and after having him to dinner I could not refuse his invitation to supper. There was no difficulty about Rosalie; the commandant introduced her immediately to his wife, his daughter, and his son. I was delighted to see that her manner with ladies even surpassed her manner with gentlemen. She was one of Nature's own ladies. The commandant's wife and daughter caressed her again and again, and she received their attentions with that modest sensibility which is the seal of a good education.

They asked me to dinner the next day, but I was satisfied with what I had seen, so I took leave, intending to start on the morrow.

When we got back to the inn I told her how pleased I was with her, and she threw her arms round my neck for joy.

"I am always afraid," said she, "of being asked who I am."

"You needn't be afraid, dearest; in France no gentleman or lady would think of asking such a question."

"But if they did, what ought I to do?"

"You should make use of an evasion."

"What's an evasion?"

"A way of escaping from a difficulty without satisfying impertinent curiosity."

"Give me an example."

"Well, if such a question were asked you, you might say, 'You had better ask this gentleman.'"

"I see, the question is avoided; but is not that impolite?"

"Yes; but not so impolite as to ask an embarrassing question."

"And what would you say if the question was passed on to you?"

"Well, my answer would vary in a ratio with the

respect in which I held the questioner. I would not tell the truth, but I should say something. And I am glad to see you attentive to my lessons. Always ask questions, and you will always find me ready to answer, for I want to teach you. And now let us to bed; we have to start for Antibes at an early hour, and love will reward you for the pleasure you have given me to-day."

At Antibes I hired a felucca to take me to Genoa, and as I intended to return by the same route I had my carriage warehoused for a small monthly payment. We started early with a good wind, but the sea becoming rough, and Rosalie being mortally afraid, I had the felucca rowed into Villafranca, where I engaged a carriage to take me to Nice. The weather kept us back for three days, and I felt obliged to call on the commandant, an old officer named Peterson.

He gave me an excellent reception, and after the usual compliments had passed, said,——

"Do you know a Russian who calls himself Charles Ivanoff?"

"I saw him once at Grenoble."

"It is said that he has escaped from Siberia, and that he is the younger son of the Duke of Courland."

"So I have heard, but I know no proof of his claim to the title."

"He is at Genoa, where it is said a banker is to give him twenty thousand crowns. In spite of that, no one would give him a sou here, so I sent him to Genoa at my own expense, to rid the place of him."

I felt very glad that the Russian had gone away before my arrival. An officer named Ramini, who was staying at the same inn as myself, asked if I would mind taking charge of a packet which M. de St. Pierre, the Spanish consul, had to send to the Marquis Grimaldi, at

Genoa. It was the nobleman I had just seen at Avignon, and I was pleased to execute the commission. The same officer asked me whether I had ever seen a certain Madame Stuard.

"She came here a fortnight ago with a man who calls himself her husband. The poor devils hadn't a penny, and she, a great beauty, enchanted everybody, but would give no one a smile or a word."

"I have both seen and know her," I answered. "I furnished her with the means to come here. How could she leave Nice without any money?"

"That's just what no one can understand. She went off in a carriage, and the landlord's bill was paid. I was interested in the woman. The Marquis Grimaldi told me that she had refused a hundred louis he offered her, and that a Venetian of his acquaintance had fared just as badly. Perhaps that is you?"

"It is, and I gave her some money despite my treatment."

M. Peterson came to see me, and was enchanted with Rosalie's amiable manner. This was another conquest for her, and I duly complimented her upon it.

Nice is a terribly dull place, and strangers are tormented by the midges, who prefer them to the inhabitants. However, I amused myself at a small bank at faro, which was held at a coffee-house, and at which Rosalie, whose play I directed, won a score of Piedmontese pistoles. She put her little earnings into a purse, and told me she liked to have some money of her own. I scolded her for not having told me so before, and reminded her of her promise.

"I don't really want it," said she, "it's only my thoughtlessness."

We soon made up our little quarrel.

In such ways did I make this girl my own, in the hope that for the remnant of my days she would be mine, and so I should not be forced to fly from one lady to another. But inexorable fate ordained it otherwise.

The weather grew fine again, and we got on board once more, and the next day arrived at Genoa, which I had never seen before. I put up at "St. Martin's Inn," and for decency's sake took two rooms, but they were adjoining one another. The following day I sent the packet to M. Grimaldi, and a little later I left my card at his palace.

My guide took me to a linen-draper's, and I bought some stuff for Rosalie, who was in want of linen. She was very pleased with it.

We were still at table when the Marquis Grimaldi was announced; he kissed me and thanked me for bringing the parcel. His next remark referred to Madame Stuard. I told him what had happened, and he laughed, saying that he was not quite sure what he would have done under the circumstances.

I saw him looking at Rosalie attentively, and I told him she was as good as she was beautiful.

"I want to find her a maid," I said, "a good seamstress, who could go out with her, and above all who could talk Italian to her, for I want her to learn the language that I may take her into society at Florence, Rome and Naples."

"Don't deprive Genoa of the pleasure of entertaining her," said the marquis. "I will introduce her under whatever name she pleases, and in my own house to begin with."

"She has good reasons for preserving her incognito here."

"Ah, I see! Do you think of staying here long?"

"A month, or thereabouts, and our pleasures will be limited to seeing the town and its surroundings and going to the theatre. We shall also enjoy the pleasures of the table. I hope to eat champignons every day, they are better here than anywhere else"

"An excellent plan. I couldn't suggest a better. I am going to see what I can do in the way of getting you a maid, mademoiselle."

"You sir? How can I deserve such great kindness?"

"My interest in you is the greater, as I think you come from Marseilles."

Rosalie blushed. She was not aware that she lisped, and that this betrayed her. I extricated her from her confusion by telling the marquis his conjecture was well founded.

I asked him how I could get the *Journal de Savans,* the *Mercure de France,* and other papers of the same description. He promised to send me a man who would get me all that kind of thing. He added that if I would allow him to send me some of his excellent chocolate he would come and breakfast with us. I said that both gift and guest were vastly agreeable to me.

As soon as he had gone Rosalie asked me to take her to a milliner's.

"I want ribbons and other little things," said she, "but I should like to bargain for them and pay for them out of my own money, without your having anything to do with it."

"Do whatever you like, my dear, and afterwards we will go to the play."

The milliner to whom we went proved to be a French-woman. It was a charming sight to see Rosalie shopping. She put on an important air, seemed to know all about it, ordered bonnets in the latest fashion, bargained, and contrived to spend five or six louis with great grandeur. As we left the shop I told her that I had been taken for her footman, and I meant to be revenged. So saying, I made her come into a jeweller's, where I bought her a necklace, ear-rings, and brooches in imitation diamonds, and without letting her say a word I paid the price and left the shop.

"You have bought me some beautiful things," said she, "but you are too lavish with your money; if you had bargained you might have saved four louis at least."

"Very likely, dearest, but I never was any hand at a bargain."

I took her to the play, but as she did not understand the language she got dreadfully tired, and asked me to take her home at the end of the first act, which I did very willingly. When we got in I found a box waiting for me from M. Grimaldi. It proved to contain twenty-four pounds of chocolate. Costa, who had boasted of his skill in making chocolate in the Spanish fashion, received orders to make us three cups in the morning.

At nine o'clock the marquis arrived with a tradesman, who sold me some beautiful oriental materials. I gave them to Rosalie to make two *mezzaro* for herself. The *mezzaro* is a kind of hooded cloak worn by the Genoese women, as the *cendal* is worn at Venice, and the *mantilla* at Madrid.

I thanked M. Grimaldi for the chocolate, which was excellent; Costa was quite proud of the praise the marquis gave him. Le Duc came in to announce a woman, whose name I did not know.

"It's the mother of the maid I have engaged," said M. Grimaldi.

She came in, and I saw before me a well-dressed woman, followed by a girl from twenty to twenty-four years old, who pleased me at the first glance. The mother thanked the marquis, and presented her daughter to Rosalie, enumerating her good qualities, and telling her that she would serve her well, and walk with her when she wished to go out.

"My daughter," she added, "speaks French, and you will find her a good, faithful, and obliging girl."

She ended by saying that her daughter had been in service lately with a lady, and that she would be obliged if she could have her meals by herself.

The girl was named Véronique. Rosalie told her that she was a good girl, and that the only way to be respected was to be respectable. Véronique kissed her hand, the mother went away, and Rosalie took the girl into her room to begin her work.

I did not forget to thank the marquis, for he had evidently chosen a maid more with a view to my likings than to those of my sweetheart. I told him that I should not fail to call on him, and he replied that he would be happy to see me at any hour, and that I should easily find him at his casino at St. Pierre d'Arena, where he often spent the night.

CHAPTER IV

The Play—The Russian—Petri—Rosalie at the Convent

WHEN the marquis had gone, seeing Rosalie engaged with Véronique, I set myself to translate the *Ecossaise* for the actors at Genoa, who seemed pretty good ones, to play.

I thought Rosalie looking sad at dinner, and said,——

"What is the matter, dearest? You know I do not like to see you looking melancholy."

"I am vexed at Véronique's being prettier than I."

"I see what you mean; I like that! But console your-self, Véronique is nothing compared to you, in my eyes at all events. You are my only beauty; but to reassure you I will ask M. de Grimaldi to tell her mother to come and fetch her away, and to get me another maid as ugly as possible."

"Oh, no! pray do not do so; he will think I am jealous, and I wouldn't have him think so for the world."

"Well, well, smile again if you do not wish to vex me."

"I shall soon do that, if, as you assure me, she will not make me lose your love. But what made the old gentleman get me a girl like that? Do you think he did it out of mischief?"

"No, I don't think so. I am sure, on the other hand, that he wanted to let you know that you need not fear being compared with anybody. Are you pleased with her in other respects?"

"She works well, and she is very respectful. She does not speak four words without addressing me as signora, and she is careful to translate what she says from Italian into French. I hope that in a month I shall speak well enough for us to dispense with her services when we go to Florence. I have ordered Le Duc to clear out the room I have chosen for her, and I will send her her dinner from our own table. I will be kind to her, but I hope you will not make me wretched."

"I could not do so; and I do not see what there can be in common between the girl and myself."

"Then you will pardon my fears."

"The more readily as they shew your love."

"I thank you, but keep my secret."

I promised never to give a glance to Véronique, of whom I was already afraid, but I loved Rosalie and would have done anything to save her the least grief.

I set to at my translation after dinner; it was work I liked. I did not go out that day, and I spent the whole of the next morning with M. de Grimaldi.

I went to the banker Belloni and changed all my gold into *gigliati* sequins. I made myself known after the money was changed, and the head cashier treated me with great courtesy. I had bills on this banker for forty thousand Roman crowns, and on Lepri bills for twenty thousand.

Rosalie did not want to go to the play again, so I got her a piece of embroidery to amuse her in the evening. The theatre was a necessity for me; I always went unless it interferred with some still sweeter pleasure. I went by myself, and when I got home I found the marquis talking to my mistress. I was pleased, and after I had embraced the worthy nobleman I complimented

Rosalie on having kept him till my arrival, adding gently that she should have put down her work.

"Ask him," she replied, "if he did not make me keep on. He said he would go if I didn't, so I gave in to keep him."

She then rose, stopped working, and in the course of an interesting conversation she succeeded in making the marquis promise to stay to supper, thus forestalling my intention. He was not accustomed to take anything at that hour, and ate little; but I saw he was enchanted with my treasure, and that pleased me, for I did not think I had anything to fear from a man of sixty; besides, I was glad at the opportunity of accustoming Rosalie to good society. I wanted her to be a little coquettish, as a woman never pleases in society unless she shews a desire to please.

Although the position was quite a strange one for her, she made me admire the natural aptitude of women, which may be improved or spoiled by art but which exists more or less in them all, from the throne to the milk-pail. She talked to M. de Grimaldi in a way that seemed to hint she was willing to give a little hope. As our guest did not eat, she said graciously that he must come to dinner some day that she might have an opportunity of seeing whether he really had any appetite.

When he had gone I took her on my knee, and covering her with kisses asked her where she had learnt to talk to great people so well.

"It's an easy matter," she replied. "Your eyes speak to my soul, and tell me what to do and what to say."

A professed rhetorician could not have answered more elegantly or more flatteringly.

I finished the translation; I had it copied out by Costa

and took it to Rossi, the manager, who said he would put
it on directly, when I told him I was going to make
him a present of the play. I named the actors of my
choice, and asked him to bring them to dine with me
at my inn, that I might read the play and distribute the
parts.

As will be guessed, my invitation was accepted, and
Rosalie enjoyed dining with the actors and actresses, and
especially hearing herself called Madame Casanova every
moment. Véronique explained everything she did not
understand.

When my actors were round me in a ring, they begged
me to tell them their parts, but I would not give in on
this point.

"The first thing to be done," said I, "is for you to listen
attentively to the whole piece without minding about
your parts. When you know the whole play I will satisfy your curiosity."

I knew that careless or idle actors often pay no attention to anything except their own parts, and thus a piece,
though well played in its parts, is badly rendered as a
whole.

They submitted with a tolerably good grace, which the
high and mighty players of the Comédie Française would
certainly not have done. Just as I was beginning my
reading the Marquis de Grimaldi and the banker Belloni
came in to call on me. I was glad for them to be present
at the trial, which only lasted an hour and a quarter.

After I had heard the opinion of the actors, who by
their praise of various situations shewed me that they
had taken in the plot, I told Costa to distribute the
parts; but no sooner was this done than the first actor
and the first actress began to express their displeasure;
she, because I had given her the part of Lady Alton; he,

because I had not given him Murray's part; but they had to bear it as it was my will. I pleased everybody by asking them all to dinner for the day after the morrow, after dinner the piece to be rehearsed for the first time.

The banker Belloni asked me to dinner for the following day, including my lady, who excused herself with great politeness, in the invitation; and M. Grimaldi was glad to take my place at dinner at her request.

When I got to M. Belloni's, I was greatly surprised to see the impostor Ivanoff, who instead of pretending not to know me, as he ought to have done, came forward to embrace me. I stepped back and bowed, which might be put down to a feeling of respect, although my coldness and scant ceremony would have convinced any observant eye of the contrary. He was well dressed, but seemed sad, though he talked a good deal, and to some purpose, especially on politics. The conversation turned on the Court of Russia, where Elizabeth Petrovna reigned; and he said nothing, but sighed and turned away pretending to wipe the tears from his eyes. At dessert, he asked me if I had heard anything of Madame Morin, adding, as if to recall the circumstance to my memory, that we had supped together there:

"I believe she is quite well," I answered.

His servant, in yellow and red livery, waited on him at table. After dinner he contrived to tell me that he had a matter of the greatest importance he wanted to discuss with me.

"My only desire sir, is to avoid all appearance of knowing anything about you."

"One word from you will gain me a hundred thousand crowns, and you shall have half."

I turned my back on him, and saw him no more at Genoa.

When I got back to the inn I found M. de Grimaldi giving Rosalie a lesson in Italian.

"She has given me an exquisite dinner," said he, "you must be very happy with her."

In spite of his honest face, M. Grimaldi was in love with her, but I thought I had nothing to fear. Before he went she invited him to come to the rehearsal next day.

When the actors came I noticed amongst them a young man whose face I did not know, and on my enquiring Rossi told me he was the prompter.

"I won't have any prompter; send him about his business."

"We can't get on without him."

"You'll have to; I will be the prompter."

The prompter was dismissed, but the three actresses began to complain.

"If we knew our parts as well as the *pater noster* we should be certain to come to a dead stop if the prompter isn't in his box."

"Very good," said I to the actress, who was to play Lindane, "I will occupy the box myself, but I shall see your drawers."

"You would have some difficulty in doing that," said the first actor, "she doesn't wear any."

"So much the better."

"You know nothing about it," said the actress.

These remarks put us all in high spirits, and the ministers of Thalia ended by promising that they would dispense with a prompter. I was pleased with the way the piece was read, and they said they would be letter-perfect in three days. But something happened.

On the day fixed for the rehearsal they came without

the Lindane and Murray. They were not well, but Rossi said they would not fail us eventually. I took the part of Murray, and asked Rosalie to be the Lindane.

"I don't read Italian well enough," she whispered, "and I don't wish to have the actors laughing at me; but Véronique could do it."

"Ask if she will read the part."

However, Véronique said that she could repeat it by heart.

"All the better," said I to her, laughing internally, as I thought of Soleure, for I saw that I should thus be obliged to make love to the girl to whom I had not spoken for the fortnight she had been with us. I had not even had a good look at her face. I was so afraid of Rosalie (whom I loved better every day) taking fright.

What I had feared happened. When I took Véronique's hand, and said, *"Si, bella Lindana, debbe adorarvi!"* everybody clapped, because I gave the words their proper expression; but glancing at Rosalie I saw a shadow on her face, and I was angry at not having controlled myself better. Nevertheless, I could not help feeling amazed at the way Véronique played the part. When I told her that I adored her she blushed up to her eyes; she could not have played the love-sick girl better.

We fixed a day for the dress-rehearsal at the theatre, and the company announced the first night a week in advance to excite public curiosity. The bills ran:

"We shall give Voltaire's *Ecossaise,* translated by an anonymous author: no prompter will be present."

I cannot give the reader any idea of the trouble I had to quiet Rosalie. She refused to be comforted; wept incessantly, and touched my heart by gentle reproaches.

"You love Véronique," said she, "and you only translated that piece to have an opportunity of declaring
your love."

I succeeded in convicing her that she wronged me,
and at last after I had lavished caresses on her she suffered herself to be calmed. Next morning she begged
pardon for her jealousy, and to cure it insisted on my
speaking constantly to Véronique. Her heroism went
farther. She got up before me and sent me my coffee by
Véronique, who was as astonished as I was.

At heart Rosalie was a great creature, capable of noble
resolves, but like all women she gave way to sudden
emotions. From that day she gave me no more signs of
jealousy, and treated her maid with more kindness than
ever. Véronique was an intelligent and well-mannered
girl, and if my heart had not been already occupied she
would have reigned there.

The first night of the play I took Rosalie to a box, and
she would have Véronique with her. M. de Grimaldi
did not leave her for a moment. The play was praised
to the skies; the large theatre was full of the best people
in Genoa. The actors surpassed themselves, though
they had no prompter, and were loudly applauded. The
piece ran five nights and was performed to full houses.
Rossi, hoping perhaps that I would make him a present of another play, asked my leave to give my lady
a superb pelisse of lynx-fur, which pleased her immensely.

I would have done anything to spare my sweetheart
the least anxiety, and yet from my want of thought I
contrived to vex her. I should never have forgiven
myself if Providence had not ordained that I should be
the cause of her final happiness.

"I have reason to suspect," she said one day, "that I

am with child, and I am enchanted at the thought of giving you a dear pledge of my love."

"If it comes at such a time it will be mine, and I assure you I shall love it dearly."

"And if it comes two or three weeks sooner you will not be sure that you are the parent?"

"Not quite sure; but I shall love it just as well, and look upon it as my child as well as yours."

"I am sure you must be the father. It is impossible the child can be Petri's, who only knew me once, and then very imperfectly, whilst you and I have lived in tender love for so long a time."

She wept hot tears.

"Calm yourself, dearest, I implore you! You are right; it cannot be Petri's child. You know I love you, and I cannot doubt that you are with child by me and by me alone. If you give me a baby as pretty as yourself, it will be mine indeed. Calm yourself."

"How can I be calm when you can have such a suspicion?"

We said no more about it; but in spite of my tenderness, my caresses, and all the trifling cares which bear witness to love, she was often sad and thoughtful. How many times I reproached myself bitterly for having let out my silly calculations.

A few days later she gave me a sealed letter, saying,——

"The servant has given me this letter when you were away. I am offended by his doing so, and I want you to avenge me."

I called the man, and said,——

"Where did you get this letter?"

"From a young man, who is unknown to me. He gave me a crown, and begged me to give the letter to the lady without your seeing me, and he promised to give me two crowns more if I brought him a reply to-morrow. I did not think I was doing wrong, sir, as the lady was at perfect liberty to tell you."

"That's all very well, but you must go, as the lady, who gave me the letter unopened, as you can see for yourself, is offended with you."

I called Le Duc, who paid the man and sent him away. I opened the letter, and found it to be from Petri. Rosalie left my side, not wishing to read the contents. The letter ran as follows:

"I have seen you, my dear Rosalie. It was just as you were coming out of the theatre, escorted by the Marquis de Grimaldi, who is my godfather. I have not deceived you; I was still intending to come and marry you at Marseilles next spring, as I promised. I love you faithfully, and if you are still my good Rosalie I am ready to marry you here in the presence of my kinfolk. If you have done wrong I promise never to speak of it, for I know that it was I who led you astray. Tell me, I entreat you, whether I may speak to the Marquis de Grimaldi with regard to you. I am ready to receive you from the hands of the gentleman with whom you are living, provided you are not his wife. Be sure, if you are still free, that you can only recover your honour by marrying your seducer."

"This letter comes from an honourable man who is worthy of Rosalie," I thought to myself, "and that's more than I shall be, unless I marry her myself. But Rosalie must decide."

I called her to me, gave her the letter, and begged her to read it attentively. She did so, and gave it me back, asking me if I advised her to accept Petri's offer.

"If you do dear Rosalie, I shall die of grief; but if I

do not yield you, my honour bids me marry you, and that I am quite ready to do."

At this the charming girl threw herself on my breast, crying in the voice of true love, "I love you and you alone, darling; but it is not true that your honour bids you marry me. Ours is a marriage of the heart; our love is mutual, and that is enough for my happiness."

"Dear Rosalie, I adore you, but I am the best judge of my own honour. If Petri is a well-to-do man and a man who would make you happy, I must either give you up or take you myself."

"No, no; there is no hurry to decide. If you love me I am happy, for I love you and none other. I shall not answer the letter, and I don't want to hear anything more of Petri."

"You may be sure that I will say no more of him, but I am sure that the marquis will have a hand in it."

"I daresay, but he won't speak to me twice on the subject."

After this treaty—a more sincere one than the Powers of Europe usually make—I resolved to leave Genoa as soon as I got some letters for Florence and Rome. In the meanwhile all was peace and love between myself and Rosalie. She had not the slightest shadow of jealousy in her soul, and M. de Grimaldi was the sole witness of our happiness.

Five or six days later I went to see the marquis at his casino at St. Pierre d'Arena, and he accosted me by saying that he was happy to see me as he had an important matter he wished to discuss with me. I guessed what it would be, but begged him to explain himself. He then spoke as follows:

"A worthy merchant of the town brought his nephew, a young man named Petri, to see me two days ago. He told me that the young man is my godson, and he asked me to protect him. I answered that as his godfather I owed him my protection, and I promised to do what I could.

"He left my godson to talk it over with me, and he informed me that he knew your mistress before you did at Marseilles, that he had promised to marry her next spring, that he had seen her in my company, and that having followed us he found out that she lived with you. He was told that she was your wife, but not believing it, wrote her a letter saying that he was ready to marry her; but this letter fell into your hands, and he has had no reply to it.

"He could not make up his mind to lose a hope which made his happiness, so he resolved to ascertain, through my good offices, whether Rosalie would accept his proposition. He flatters himself that on his informing me of his prosperous condition, I can tell you that he is a likely man to make his wife happy. I told him that I knew you, and would speak to you on the matter, and afterwards inform him of the result of our interview.

"I have made enquires into his condition, and find that he has already amassed a considerable sum of money. His credit, morals, and reputation, are all excellent; besides, he is his uncle's sole heir, and the uncle passes for a man very comfortably off. And now, my dear M. Casanova, tell me what answer I am to make."

"Tell him that Rosalie is much obliged to him, and begs him to forget her. We are going away in three or four days. Rosalie loves me, and I her, and I am ready to marry her whenver she likes."

"That's plain speaking; but I should have thought a man like you would prefer freedom to a woman, however beautiful, to whom you would be bound by indissoluble ties. Will you allow me to speak to Rosalie myself about it?"

"You need not ask my leave; speak to her, but in your own person and not as representing my opinions. I adore her, and would not have her think that I could cherish the thought of separating from her."

"If you don't want me to meddle in the matter, tell me so frankly."

"On the contrary, I wish you to see for yourself that I am not the tyrant of the woman I adore."

"I will talk to her to-night."

I did not come home till supper-time, that the marquis might say what he had to say in perfect freedom. The noble Genoese supped with us, and the conversation turned on indifferent subjects. After he had gone, my sweetheart told me what had passed between them. He had spoken to her in almost the same words that he had addressed to me, and our replies were nearly identical, though she had requested the marquis to say no more about his godson, to which request he had assented.

We thought the matter settled, and busied ourselves with preparations for our departure; but three or four days after, the marquis (who we imagined had forgotten all about his godson) came and asked us to dine with him at St. Pierre d'Arena, where Rosalie had never been.

"I want you to see my beautiful garden before you go," said M. Grimaldi to her; "it will be one more pleasant recollection of your stay for me."

We went to see him at noon the next day. He was with an elderly man and woman, to whom he introduced us. He introduced me by name, and Rosalie as a person who belonged to me.

We proceeded to walk in the garden, where the two old people got Rosalie between them, and overwhelmed her

with politeness and complimentary remarks. She, who
was happy and in high spirits, answered in Italian, and
delighted them by her intelligence, and the grace which
she gave to her mistakes in grammar.

The servants came to tell us that dinner was ready,
and what was my astonishment on entering the room to
see the table laid for six. I did not want much insight
now to see through the marquis's trick, but it was too
late. We sat down, and just then a young man came in.

"You are a little late," said the marquis; and then,
without waiting for his apology, he introduced him to me
as M. Petri, his godson, and nephew to his other guests,
and he made him sit down at his left hand, Rosalie being
on his right. I sat opposite to her, and seeing that she
turned as pale as death the blood rushed to my face;
I was terribly enraged. This small despot's plot seemed
disgraceful to me; it was a scandalous insult to Rosalie
and myself—an insult which should be washed away in
blood. I was tempted to stab him at his table, but in
spite of my agitation I constrained myself. What could
I do? Take Rosalie's arm, and leave the room with her?
I thought it over, but foreseeing the consequences I
could not summon up courage.

I have never spent so terrible an hour as at that fatal
dinner. Neither Rosalie nor myself ate a morsel, and
the marquis who helped all the guests was discreet
enough not to see that we left one course after another
untouched. Throughout dinner he only spoke to Petri
and his uncle, giving them opportunities for saying how
large a trade they did. At dessert the marquis told the
young man that he had better go and look after his
affairs, and after kissing his hand he withdrew with a
bow to which nobody replied.

Petri was about twenty-four, of a moderate height,

with ordinary but yet good-natured and honest features; respectful in his manner, and sensible though not witty in what he said. After all was said and done, I thought him worthy of Rosalie, but I shuddered at the thought that if she became his wife she was lost to me forever. After he had gone, the marquis said he was sorry he had not known him before as he might be of use to him in his business.

"However, we will see to that in the future," said he, meaningly, "I mean to make his fortune."

At this the uncle and aunt, who no doubt knew what to say, began to laud and extol their nephew, and ended by saying that as they had no children they were delighted that Petri, who would be their heir, was to have his excellency's patronage.

"We are longing," they added, "to see the girl from Marseilles he is going to marry. We should welcome her as a beloved daughter."

Rosalie whispered to me that she could bear it no longer, and begged me to take her away. We rose, and after we had saluted the company with cold dignity we left the room. The marquis was visibly disconcerted. As he escorted us to the door he stammered out compliments, for the want of something to say, telling Rosalie that he should not have the honour of seeing her that evening, but that he hoped to call on her the next day.

When we were by ourselves we seemed to breathe again, and spoke to one another to relieve ourselves of the oppression which weighed on our minds.

Rosalie thought, as well as I, that the marquis had played us a shameful trick, and she told me I ought to write him a note, begging him not to give himself the trouble of calling on us again.

"I will find some means of vengeance," said I; "but

I don't think it would be a good plan to write to him. We will hasten our preparations for leaving, and receive him to-morrow with that cold politeness which bears witness to indignation. Above all, we will not make the slightest reference to his godson."

"If Petri really loves me," said she, "I pity him. I think he is a good fellow, and I don't feel angry with him for being present at dinner, as he may possibly be unaware that his presence was likely to give me offence. But I still shudder when I think of it: I thought I should have died when our eyes met! Throughout dinner he could not see my eyes, as I kept them nearly shut, and indeed he could hardly see me. Did he look at me while he was talking?"

"No, he only looked at me. I am as sorry for him as you are, for, as you say, he looks an honest fellow."

"Well, it's over now, and I hope I shall make a good supper. Did you notice what the aunt said? I am sure she was in the plot. She thought she would gain me over by saying she was ready to treat me like her own child. She was a decent-looking woman, too."

We made a good supper, and a pleasant night inclined us to forget the insult the marquis had put upon us. When we woke up in the morning we laughed at it. The marquis came to see us in the evening, and greeting me with an air of mingled confusion and vexation, he said that he knew he had done wrong in surprising me as he had, but that he was ready to do anything in his power by way of atonement, and to give whatever satisfaction I liked.

Rosalie did not give me time to answer. "If you really feel," said she, "that you have insulted us, that is enough; we are amply avenged. But all the same, sir, we shall be on our guard against you for the future, though that will be for a short while, as we are just leaving."

With this proud reply she made him a low bow and left the room.

When he was left alone with me M. Grimaldi addressed me as follows:

"I take a great interest in your mistress's welfare; and as I feel sure that she cannot long be happy in her present uncertain position, while I am sure that she would make my godson an excellent wife, I was determined that both of you should make his acquaintance, for Rosalie herself knows very little of him. I confess that the means I employed were dishonourable, but you will pardon the means for the sake of the excellent end I had in view. I hope you will have a pleasant journey, and that you may live for a long time in uninterrupted happiness with your charming mistress. I hope you will write to me, and always reckon on my standing your friend, and doing everything in my power for you. Before I go, I will tell you something which will give you an idea of the excellent disposition of young Petri, to whose happiness Rosalie seems essential.

"He only told me the following, after I had absolutely refused to take charge of a letter he had written to Rosalie, despairing of being able to send it any other way. After assuring me that Rosalie had loved him, and that consequently she could not have any fixed aversion for him, he added that if the fear of being with child was the reason why she would not marry him he would agree to put off the marriage till after the child was born, provided that she would agree to stay in Genoa in hiding, her presence to be unknown to all save himself. He offers to pay all the expenses of her stay. He made a remarkably wise reflection when we were talking it over.

" 'If she gave birth to a child too soon after our marriage,' said he, 'both her honour and mine would suffer hurt; she might also lose the liking of my relations, and if Rosalie is to be my wife I want her to be happy in everything.' "

At this Rosalie, who had no doubt been listening at the door after the manner of her sex, burst into the room, and astonished me by the following speech:

"If M. Petri did not tell you that it was possible that I might be with child by him, he is a right honest man, but now I tell you so myself. I do not think it likely, but still it is possible. Tell him, sir, that I will remain at Genoa until the child is born, in the case of my being pregnant, of which I have no certain knowledge, or until I am quite sure that I am not with child. If I do have a child the truth will be made known. In the case of there being no doubt of M. Petri's being the parent, I am ready to marry him; but if he sees for himself that the child is not his I hope he will be reasonable enough to let me alone for the future. As to the expenses and my lodging at Genoa, tell him that he need not trouble himself about either."

I was petrified. I saw the consequence of my own imprudent words, and my heart seemed broken. The marquis asked me if this decision was given with my authority, and I replied that as my sweetheart's will was mine he might take her words for law. He went away in high glee, for he foresaw that all would go well with his plans when once he was able to exert his influence on Rosalie. The absent always fare ill.

"You want to leave me, then, Rosalie?" said I, when we were alone.

"Yes, dearest, but it will not be for long."

"I think we shall never see each other again."

"Why not, dearest? You have only to remain faithful to me. Listen to me. Your honour and my own make it imperative that I should convince Petri that I am not with child by him, and you that I am with child by you."

"I never doubted it, dear Rosalie."

"Yes, dear, you doubted it once and that is enough. Our parting will cost me many a bitter tear, but these pangs are necessary to my future happiness. I hope you will write to me, and after the child is born it will be for you to decide on how I shall rejoin you. If I am not pregnant I will rejoin you in a couple of months at latest."

"Though I may grieve at your resolve I will not oppose it, for I promised I would never cross you. I suppose you will go into a convent; and the marquis must find you a suitable one, and protect you like a father. Shall I speak to him on the subject? I will leave you as much money as you will want."

"That will not be much. As for M. de Grimaldi, he is bound in honour to procure me an asylum. I don't think it will be necessary for you to speak to him about it."

She was right, and I could not help admiring the truly astonishing tact of this girl.

In the morning I heard that the self-styled Ivanoff had made his escape an hour before the police were to arrest him at the suit of the banker, who had found out that one of the bills he had presented was forged. He had escaped on foot, leaving all his baggage behind him.

Next day the marquis came to tell Rosalie that his godson had no objection to make to her plan. He added that the young man hoped she would become his wife, whether the child proved to be his or not.

"He may hope as much as he likes," said Rosalie, with a smile.

"He also hopes that you will allow him to call on you now and then. I have spoken to my kinswoman, the mother-superior of —— convent. You are to have two rooms, and a very good sort of woman is to keep you company, wait on you, and nurse you when the time comes. I have paid the amount you are to pay every month for your board. Every morning I will send you a confidential man, who will see your companion and will bring me your orders. And I myself will come and see you at the grating as often as you please."

It was then my sad duty, which the laws of politeness enjoined, to thank the marquis for his trouble.

" 'Tis to you, my lord," said I, "I entrust Rosalie. I am placing her, I am sure, in good hands. I will go on my way as soon as she is in the convent; I hope you will write a letter to the mother-superior for her to take."

"I will write it directly," said he.

And as Rosalie had told him before that she would pay for everything herself, he gave her a written copy of the agreement he had made.

"I have resolved," said Rosalie to the marquis, "to go into the convent to-morrow, and I shall be very glad to have a short visit from you the day after."

"I will be there," said the marquis, "and you may be sure that I will do all in my power to make your stay agreeable."

The night was a sad one for both of us. Love scarcely made a pause amidst our alternate complaints and consolations. We swore to be faithful for ever, and our oaths were sincere, as ardent lovers' oaths always are. But they are as nought unless they are sealed by destiny, and that no mortal mind may know.

Rosalie, whose eyes were red and wet with tears, spent most of the morning in packing up with Véronique, who cried too. I could not look at her, as I felt angry with myself for thinking how pretty she was. Rosalie would only take two hundred sequins, telling me that if she wanted more she could easily let me know.

She told Véronique to look after me well for the two or three days I should spend at Genoa, made me a mute curtsy, and went out with Costa to get a sedan-chair. Two hours after, a servant of the marquis's came to fetch her belongings, and I was thus left alone and full of grief till the marquis came and asked me to give him supper, advising that Véronique should be asked in to keep us company.

"That's a rare girl," said he, "you really don't know her, and you ought to know her better."

Although I was rather surprised, I did not stop to consider what the motives of the crafty Genoese might be, and I went and asked Véronique to come in. She replied politely that she would do so, adding that she knew how great an honour I did her.

I should have been the blindest of men if I had not seen that the clever marquis had succeeded in his well-laid plans, and that he had duped me as if I had been the merest freshman. Although I hoped with all my heart that I should get Rosalie back again, I had good reasons for suspecting that all the marquis's wit would be employed to seduce her, and I could not help thinking that he would succeed. Nevertheless, in the position I was in, I could only keep my fears to myself and let him do his utmost.

He was nearly sixty, a thorough disciple of Epicurus, a heavy player, rich, eloquent, a master of state-craft, highly popular at Genoa, and well acquainted with the hearts of men, and still more so with the hearts of women. He had spent a good deal of time at Venice to be more at liberty, and to enjoy the pleasures of life at his ease. He had never married, and when asked the reason would reply that he knew too well that women would be either tyrants or slaves, and that he did not want to be a tyrant to any woman, nor to be under any woman's orders. He found some way of returning to his beloved Venice, in spite of the law forbidding any noble who has filled the office of doge to leave his native soil. Though he behaved to me in a very friendly manner he knew how to maintain an air of superiority which imposed on me. Nothing else could have given him the courage to ask me to dinner when Petri was to be present. I felt that I had been tricked, and I thought myself in duty bound to make him esteem me by my behaviour for the future. It was gratitude on his part which made him smooth the way to my conquest of Véronique, who doubtless struck him as a fit and proper person to console me for the loss of Rosalie.

I did not take any part in the conversation at supper, but the marquis drew out Véronique, and she shone. It was easy for me to see that she had more wit and knowledge of the world than Rosalie, but in my then state of mind this grieved rather than rejoiced me. M. de Grimaldi seemed sorry to see me melancholy, and forced me, as it were, to join in the conversation. As he was reproaching me in a friendly manner for my silence, Véronique said with a pleasing smile that I had a good reason to be silent after the declaration of love I had made to her, and which she had received so ill. I was astonished at this, and said that I did not remember having ever made her such a declaration; but she made me laugh in spite of myself, when she said that her name that day was Lindane.

"Ah, that's in a play," said I, "in real life the man who declares his love in words is a simpleton; 'tis with deeds the true lover shews his love."

"Very true, but your lady was frightened all the same."

"No, no, Véronique; she is very fond of you."

"I know she is; but I have seen her jealous of me."

"If so, she was quite wrong."

This dialogue, which pleased me little, fell sweetly on the marquis's ears; he told me that he was going to call on Rosalie next morning, and that if I liked to give him a supper, he would come and tell me about her in the evening. Of course I told him that he would be welcome.

After Véronique had lighted me to my room, she asked me to let my servants wait on me, as if she did so now that my lady was gone, people might talk about her.

"You are right," said I, "kindly send Le Duc to me."

Next morning I had a letter from Geneva. It came from my Epicurean syndic, who had presented M. de Voltaire with my translation of his play, with an exceedingly polite letter from me, in which I begged his pardon for having taken the liberty of travestying his fine French prose in Italian. The syndic told me plainly that M. de Voltaire had pronounced my translation to be a bad one.

My self-esteem was so wounded by this, and by his impoliteness in not answering my letter, with which he could certainly find no fault, whatever his criticism of my translation might be, that I became the sworn enemy of the great Voltaire. I have censured him in all the works I have published, thinking that in wronging him

I was avenging myself, to such an extent did passion blind me. At the present time I feel that even if my works survive, these feeble stings of mine can hurt nobody but myself. Posterity will class me amongst the Zoiluses whose own impotence made them attack this great man to whom civilization and human happiness owe so much. The only crime that can truthfully be alleged against Voltaire is his attacks on religion. If he had been a true philosopher he would never have spoken on such matters, for, even if his attacks were based on truth, religion is necessary to morality, without which there can be no happiness.

CHAPTER V

*I Fall in Love With Véronique—Her Sister—Plot Against
Plot—My Victory—Mutual Disappointment*

I HAVE never liked eating by myself, and thus I have
never turned hermit, though I once thought of turning monk; but a monk without renouncing all the
pleasures of life lives well in a kind of holy idleness.
This dislike to loneliness made me give orders that the
table should be laid for two, and indeed, after supping
with the marquis and myself, Véronique had some right
to expect as much, to say nothing of those rights which
her wit and beauty gave her.

I only saw Costa, and asked him what had become
of Le Duc. He said he was ill. "Then go behind the
lady's chair," said I. He obeyed, but smiled as he did
so. Pride is a universal failing, and though a servant's
pride is the silliest of all it is often pushed to the greatest extremes.

I thought Véronique prettier than before. Her behaviour, now free and now reserved, as the occasion
demanded, shewed me that she was no new hand, and
that she could have played the part of a princess in the
best society. Nevertheless (so strange a thing is the
heart of man), I was sorry to find I liked her, and my
only consolation was that her mother would come and
take her away before the day was over. I had adored
Rosalie, and my heart still bled at the thought of our
parting.

The girl's mother came while we were still at table. She was astounded at the honour I shewed her daughter, and she overwhelmed me with thanks.

"You owe me no gratitude," said I to her; "your daughter is clever, good, and beautiful."

"Thank the gentleman for his compliment," said the mother, "for you are really stupid, wanton, and ugly;" and then she added, "But how could you have the face to sit at table with the gentleman in a dirty chemise?"

"I should blush, mother, if I thought you were right; but I put a clean one on only two hours ago."

"Madam," said I to the mother, "the chemise cannot look white beside your daughter's whiter skin."

This made the mother laugh, and pleased the girl immensely. When the mother told her that she was come to take her back, Véronique said, with a sly smile,——

"Perhaps the gentleman won't be pleased at my leaving him twenty-four hours before he goes away."

"On the contrary," said I, "I should be very vexed."

"Well, then, she can stay, sir," said the mother; "but for decency's sake I must send her younger sister to sleep with her."

"If you please," I rejoined. And with that I left them.

The thought of Véronique troubled me, as I knew I was taken with her, and what I had to dread was a calculated resistance.

The mother came into my room where I was writing, and wished me a pleasant journey, telling me for the second time that she was going to send her daughter Annette. The girl came in the evening, accompanied by a servant, and after lowering her *mezzaro,* and kissing my hand respectfully, she ran gaily to kiss her sister.

I wanted to see what she was like, and called for candles; and on their being brought I found she was a blonde of a kind I had never before seen. Her hair, eyebrows, and eyelashes were the colour of pale gold, fairer almost than her skin, which was extremely delicate. She was very short-sighted, but her large pale blue eyes were wonderfully beautiful. She had the smallest mouth imaginable, but her teeth, though regular, were not so white as her skin. But for this defect Annette might have passed for a perfect beauty.

Her shortness of sight made too brilliant a light painful to her, but as she stood before me she seemed to like me looking at her. My gaze fed hungrily on the two little half-spheres, which were not yet ripe, but so white as to make me guess how ravishing the rest of her body must be. Véronique did not shew her breasts so freely. One could see that she was superbly shaped, but everything was carefully hidden from the gaze. She made her sister sit down beside her and work, but when I saw that she was obliged to hold the stuff close to her face I told her that she should spare her eyes, for that night at all events, and with that she obediently put the work down.

The marquis came as usual, and like myself he thought Annette, whom he had never seen before, an astonishing miniature beauty. Taking advantage of his age and high rank, the voluptuous old man dared to pass his hand over her breast, and she, who was too respectful to cross my lord, let him do it without making the slightest objection. She was a compound of innocence and coquetry.

The woman who shewing little succeeds in making a man want to see more, has accomplished three-fourths of the task of making him fall in love with her; for is love anything else than a kind of curiosity? I think not; and what makes me certain is that when the curiosity is satisfied the love disappears. Love, however, is the strongest kind of curiosity in existence, and I was already curious about Annette.

M. Grimaldi told Véronique that Rosalie wished her to stay with me till I left Genoa, and she was as much astonished at this as I was.

"Be kind enough to tell her," said I to the marquis, "that Véronique has anticipated her wishes and has got her sister Annette to stay with her."

"Two are always better than one, my dear fellow," replied the crafty Genoese.

After these remarks we left the two sisters together and went into my room, where he said,——

"Your Rosalie is contented, and you ought to congratulate yourself on having made her happy, as I am sure she will be. The only thing that vexes me is that you can't go and see her yourself with any decency."

"You are in love with her, my lord."

"I confess that I am, but I am an old man, and it vexes me."

"That's no matter, she will love you tenderly; and if Petri ever becomes her husband, I am sure she will never be anything more than a good friend to him. Write to me at Florence and tell me how she receives him."

"Stay here for another three days; the two beauties there will make the time seem short."

"It's exactly for that reason that I want to go to-morrow. I am afraid of Véronique."

"I shouldn't have thought that you would have allowed any woman to frighten you."

"I am afraid she has cast her fatal nets around me, and when the time comes she will be strictly moral. Rosalie is my only love."

"Well, here's a letter from her."

I went apart to read the letter, the sight of which made my heart beat violently; it ran as follows:

"Dearest,—I see you have placed me in the hands of one who will care for me like a father. This is a new kindness which I owe to the goodness of your heart. I will write to you at whatever address you send me. If you like Véronique, my darling, do not fear any jealousy from me; I should be wrong to entertain such a feeling in my present position. I expect that if you make much of her she will not be able to resist, and I shall be glad to hear that she is lessening your sadness. I hope you will write me a few lines before you go."

I went up to the marquis and told him to read it. He seemed greatly moved.

"Yes," said he, "the dear girl will find in me her friend and father, and if she marries my godson and he does not treat her as he ought, he will not possess her long. I shall remember her in my will, and thus when I am dead my care will still continue. But what do you think of her advice as to Véronique? I don't expect she is exactly a vestal virgin, though I have never heard anything against her."

I had ordered that the table should be laid for four, so Annette sat down without our having to ask her. Le Duc appeared on the scene, and I told him that if he were ill he might go to bed.

"I am quite well," said he.

"I am glad to hear it; but don't trouble now, you shall wait on me when I am at Leghorn."

I saw that Véronique was delighted at my sending him away, and I resolved then and there to lay siege to her heart. I began by talking to her in a very meaning

manner all supper-time, while the marquis entertained
Annette. I asked him if he thought I could get a felucca
next day to take me to Lerici.

"Yes," said he, "whenever you like and with as many
oarsmen as you please; but I hope you will put off your
departure for two or three days."

"No," I replied, ogling Véronique, "the delay might
cost me too dear."

The sly puss answered with a smile that shewed she
understood my meaning.

When we rose from the table I amused myself with
Annette, and the marquis with Véronique. After a
quarter of an hour he came and said to me,——

"Certain persons have asked me to beg you to stay a
few days longer, or at least to sup here to-morrow night."

"Very good. We will talk of the few days more at
supper to-morrow."

"Victory!" said the marquis; and Véronique seemed
very grateful to me for granting her request. When our
guest was gone, I asked my new housekeeper if I might
send Costa to bed.

"As my sister is with me, there can be no ground for
any suspicion."

"I am delighted that you consent; now I am going
to talk to you."

She proceeded to do my hair, but she gave no answer
to my soft speeches. When I was on the point of getting
into bed she wished me good night, and I tried to kiss her
by way of return. She repulsed me and ran to the door,
much to my surprise. She was going to leave the room,
when I addressed her in a voice of grave politeness.

"I beg you will stay; I want to speak to you; come
and sit by me. Why should you refuse me a pleasure
which after all is a mere mark of friendship?"

"Because, things being as they are, we could not remain friends, neither could we be lovers."

"Lovers! why not, we are perfectly free."

"I am not free; I am bound by certain prejudices which do not trouble you."

"I should have thought you were superior to prejudices."

"There are some prejudices which a woman ought to respect. The superiority you mention is a pitiful thing; always the dupe of itself. What would become of me, I shoud like to know, if I abandoned myself to the feelings I have for you?"

"I was waiting for you to say that, dear Véronique. What you feel for me is not love. If it were so, you would feel as I do, and you would soon break the bonds of prejudice."

"I confess that my head is not quite turned yet, but still I feel that I shall grieve at your departure."

"If so, that is no fault of mine. But tell me what I can do for you during my short stay here."

"Nothing; we do not know one another well enough."

"I understand you, but I would have you know that I do not intend to marry any woman who is not my friend."

"You mean you will not marry her till you have ceased to be her lover?"

"Exactly."

"You would like to finish where I would begin."

"You may be happy some day, but you play for high stakes."

"Well, well, it's a case of win all or lose all."

"That's as may be. But without further argument it seems to me that we could safely enjoy our love, and pass many happy moments undisturbed by prejudice."

"Possibly, but one gets burnt fingers at that game, and I shudder at the very thought of it. No, no; leave me alone, there is my sister who will wonder why I am in your arms."

"Very good; I see I was mistaken, and Rosalie too."

"Why what did she think about me?"

"She wrote and told me that she thought you would be kind."

"I hope she mayn't have to repent for having been too kind herself."

"Good bye, Véronique."

I felt vexed at having made the trial, for in these matters one always feels angry at failure. I decided I would leave her and her precepts, true or false, alone; but when I awoke in the morning and saw her coming to my bed with a pleasant smile on her face, I suddenly changed my mind. I had slept upon my anger and I was in love again. I thought she had repented, and that I should be victorious when I attacked her again. I put on a smile myself and breakfasted gaily with her and her sister. I behaved in the same way at dinner; and the general high spirits which M. de Grimaldi found prevailing in the evening, made him think, doubtless, that we were getting on well, and he congratulated us. Véronique behaved exactly as if the marquis had guessed the truth, and I felt sure of having her after supper, and in the ecstasy of the thought I promised to stay for four days longer.

"Bravo, Véronique!" said the marquis, "that's the way. You are intended by nature to rule your lovers with an absolute sway."

I thought she would say something to diminish the marquis's certainty that there was an agreement between us, but she did nothing of the sort, seeming to enjoy her

triumph which made her appear more beautiful than
ever; whilst I looked at her with the submissive gaze of
a captive who glories in his chain. I took her behaviour
as an omen of my approaching conquest, and did not
speak to M. de Grimaldi alone lest he might ask me
questions which I should not care to answer. He told
us before he went away that he was engaged on the
morrow, and so could not come to see us till the day
after.

As soon as we were alone Véronique said to me, "You
see how I let people believe what they please; I had
rather be thought kind, as you call it, than ridiculous, as
an honest girl is termed now-a-days. Is it not so?"

"No, dear Véronique, I will never call you ridiculous,
but I shall think you hate me if you make me pass
another night in torture. You have inflamed me."

"Oh, pray be quiet! For pity's sake leave me alone!
I will not inflame you any more. Oh! Oh!"

I had enraged her by thrusting a daring hand into the
very door of the sanctuary. She repulsed me and fled.
Three or four minutes later her sister came to undress
me. I told her gently to go to bed as I had to write for
three or four hours; but not caring that she should come
on a bootless errand I opened a box and gave her a
watch. She took it modestly, saying,——

"This is for my sister, I suppose?"

"No, dear Annette, it's for you."

She gave a skip of delight, and I could not prevent
her kissing my hand.

I proceeded to write Rosalie a letter of four pages. I
felt worried and displeased with myself and everyone
else. I tore up my letter without reading it over, and
making an effort to calm myself I wrote her another
letter more subdued than the first, in which I said noth-

ing of Véronique, but informed my fair recluse that I
was going on the day following.

I did not go to bed till very late, feeling out of temper
with the world. I considered that I had failed in my
duty to Véronique, whether she loved me or not, for I
loved her and I was a man of honour. I had a bad night,
and when I awoke it was noon, and on ringing Costa and
Annette appeared. The absence of Véronique shewed
how I had offended her. When Costa had left the room
I asked Annette after her sister, and she said that she
was working. I wrote her a note, in which I begged her
pardon, promising that I would never offend her again,
and begging her to forget everything and to be just the
same as before. I was taking my coffee when she came
into my room with an expression of mortification which
grieved me excessively.

"Forget everything, I beg, and I will trouble you no
more. Give me my buckles, as I am going for a country
walk, and I shall not be in till suppertime. I shall
doubtless get an excellent appetite, and as you have
nothing more to fear you need not trouble to send me
Annette again."

I dressed myself in haste, and left the town by the first
road that came in my way, and I walked fast for two
hours with the intention of tiring myself, and of thus
readjusting the balance between mind and body. I have
always found that severe exercise and fresh air are the
best cure for any mental perturbation.

I had walked for more than three leagues when hunger
and weariness made me stop at a village inn, where I had
an omelette cooked. I ate it hungrily with brown bread
and wine, which seemed to me delicious though it was
rather sharp.

I felt too tired to walk back to Genoa, so I asked for

a carriage; but there was no such thing to be had. The inn-keeper provided me with a sorry nag and a man to guide me. Darkness was coming on, and we had more than six miles to do. Fine rain began to fall when I started, and continued all the way, so that I got home by eight o'clock wet to the skin, shivering with cold, dead tired, and in a sore plight from the rough saddle, against which my satin breeches were no protection. Costa helped me to change my clothes, and as he went out Annette came in.

"Where is your sister?"

"She is in bed with a bad headache. She gave me a letter for you; here it is."

"I have been obliged to go to bed on account of a severe headache to which I am subject. I feel better already, and I shall be able to wait on you to-morrow. I tell you as much, because I do not wish you to think that my illnes is feigned. I am sure that your repentance for having humiliated me is sincere, and I hope in your turn that you will forgive me or pity me, if my way of thinking prevents me from conforming to yours."

"Annette dear, go and ask your sister if she would like us to sup in her room."

She soon came back telling me that Véronique was obliged, but begged me to let her sleep.

I supped with Annette, and was glad to see that, though she only drank water, her appetite was better than mine. My passion for her sister prevented me thinking of her, but I felt that Annette would otherwise have taken my fancy. When we were taking dessert, I conceived the idea of making her drunk to get her talk of her sister, so I gave her a glass of Lunel muscat.

"I only drink water, sir."

"Don't you like wine?"

"Yes, but as I am not used to it I am afraid of its getting into my head."

"Then you can go to bed; you will sleep all the better."

She drank the first glass, which she enjoyed immensely, then a second, and then a third. Her little brains were in some confusion when she had finished the third glass. I made her talk about her sister, and in perfect faith she told me all the good imaginable.

"Then you are very fond of Véronique?" said I.

"Oh, yes! I love her with all my heart, but she will not let me caress her."

"No doubt she is afraid of your ceasing to love her. But do you think she ought to make me suffer so?"

"No, but if you love her you ought to forgive her."

Annette was still quite reasonable. I made her drink a fourth glass of muscat, but an instant after she told me that she could not see anything, and we rose from the table. Annette began to please me a little too much, but I determined not to make any attempts upon her for fear of finding her too submissive. A little resistance sharpens the appetite, while favours granted with too much ease lose a great deal of their charm. Annette was only fourteen, she had a soft heart, no knowledge of the world or her own rights, and she would not have resisted my embraces for fear of being rude. That sort of thing would only please a rich and voluptuous Turk.

I begged her to do my hair, intending to dismiss her directly after, but when she had finished I asked her to give me the ointment.

"What do you want it for?"

"For the blisters that cursed saddle on which I rode six miles gave me."

"Does the ointment do them good?"

"Certainly; it takes away the smart, and by to-morrow I shall be cured, but you must send Costa to me, as I cannot put it on myself."

"Can't I do it?"

"Yes, but I am afraid that would be an abuse of your kindness."

"I guess why; but as I am short-sighted, how shall I see the blisters?"

"If you want to do it for me, I will place myself so that it will be easier for you. Stay, put the candle on this table."

"There you are, but don't let Costa put it on again to-morrow, or he will guess that I or my sister did it to-night."

"You will do me the same service, then, to-morrow?"

"I or my sister, for she will get up early."

"Your sister! No, my dear; she would be afraid of giving me too much pleasure by touching me so near."

"And I am only afraid of hurting you. Is that right? Good heavens! what a state your skin is in!"

"You have not finished yet."

"I am so short-sighted; turn round."

"With pleasure. Here I am."

The little wanton could not resist laughing at what she saw, doubtless, for the first time. She was obliged to touch it to continue rubbing the ointment in, and I saw that she liked it, as she touched it when she had no need, and not being able to stand it any longer I took hold of her hand and made her stop her work in favour of a pleasanter employment.

When she had finished I burst out laughing to hear her ask, in the most serious way, the pot of ointment still in her left hand,——

"Did I do it right!"

"Oh, admirably, dear Annette! You are an angel, and I am sure you know what pleasure you gave me. Can you come and spend an hour with me?"

"Wait a bit."

She went out and shut the door, and I waited for her to return; but my patience being exhausted I opened the door slightly, and saw her undressing and getting into bed with her sister. I went back to my room and to bed again, without losing all hope. I was not disappointed, for in five minutes back she came, clad in her chemise and walking on tip-toe.

"Come to my arms, my love; it is very cold."

"Here I am. My sister is asleep and suspects nothing; and even if she awoke the bed is so large that she would not notice my absence."

"You are a divine creature, and I love you with all my heart."

"So much the better. I give myself up to you; do what you like with me, on the condition that you think of my sister no more."

"That will not cost me much. I promise that I will not think of her."

I found Annette a perfect neophyte, and though I saw no blood on the altar of love next morning I did not suspect her on that account. I have often seen such cases, and I know by experience that the effusion of blood or its absence proves nothing. As a general rule a girl cannot be convicted of having had a lover unless she be with child.

I spent two hours of delight with this pretty baby, for she was so small, so delicate, and so daintily shaped all over, that I can find no better name for her. Her docility did not detract from the piquancy of the pleasure, for she was voluptuously inclined.

When I rose in the morning she came to my room with Véronique, and I was glad to see that while the younger sister was radiant with happiness the elder looked pleasant and as if she desired to make herself agreeable. I asked her how she was, and she told me that diet and sleep had completely cured her. "I have always found them the best remedy for a headache." Annette had also cured me of the curiosity I had felt about her. I congratulated myself on my achievement.

I was in such high spirits at supper that M. de Grimaldi thought I had won everything from Véronique, and I let him think so. I promised to dine with him the next day, and I kept my word. After dinner I gave him a long letter for Rosalie, whom I did not expect to see again except as Madame Petri, though I took care not to let the marquis know what I thought.

In the evening I supped with the two sisters, and I made myself equally agreeable to both of them. When Véronique was alone with me, putting my hair into curl-papers, she said that she loved me much more now that I behaved discreetly.

"My discretion," I replied, "only means that I have given up the hope of winning you. I know how to take my part."

"Your love was not very great, then?"

"It sprang up quickly, and you, Véronique, could have made it increase to a gigantic size."

She said nothing, but bit her lip, wished me good night and left the room. I went to bed expecting a visit from Annette, but I waited in vain. When I rang the next morning the dear girl appeared looking rather sad. I asked her the reason.

"Because my sister is ill, and spent the whole night in writing," said she.

Thus I learnt the reason of her not having paid me a visit.

"Do you know what she was writing about?"

"Oh, no! She does not tell me that kind of thing, but here is a letter for you."

I read through the long and well-composed letter, but as it bore marks of craft and dissimulation it made me laugh. After several remarks of no consequence she said that she had repulsed me because she loved me so much and that she was afraid that if she satisfied my fancy she might lose me.

"I will be wholly yours," she added, "if you will give me the position which Rosalie enjoyed. I will travel in your company, but you must give me a document, which M. de Grimaldi will sign as a witness, in which you must engage to marry me in a year, and to give me a portion of fifty thousand francs; and if at the end of a year you do not wish to marry me, that sum to be at my absolute disposal."

She stipulated also that if she became a mother in the course of a year the child should be hers in the event of our separating. On these conditions she would become my mistress, and would have for me all possible love and kindness.

This proposal, cleverly conceived, but foolishly communicated to me, shewed me that Véronique had not the talent of duping others. I saw directly that M. de Grimaldi had nothing to do with it, and I felt sure that he would laugh when I told him the story.

Annette soon came back with the chocolate, and told me that her sister hoped I would answer her letter.

"Yes, dear," said I, "I will answer her when I get up."

I took my chocolate, put on my dressing-gown, and went to Véronique's room. I found her sitting up in bed in a negligent attire that might have attracted me if her letter had not deprived her of my good opinion. I sat on the bed, gave her back the letter, and said,——

"Why write, when we can talk the matter over?"

"Because one is often more at ease in writing than in speaking."

"In diplomacy and business that will pass, but not in love. Love makes no conditions. Let us have no documents, no safeguards, but give yourself up to me as Rosalie did, and begin to-night without my promising anything. If you trust in love, you will make him your prisoner. That way will honour us and our pleasures, and if you like I will consult M. de Grimaldi on the subject. As to your plan, if it does not injure your honour, it does small justice to your common sense, and no one but a fool would agree to it. You could not possibly love the man to whom you make such a proposal, and as to M. de Grimaldi, far from having anything to do with it, I am sure he would be indignant at the very idea."

This discourse did not put Véronique out of countenance. She said she did not love me well enough to give herself to me unconditionally; to which I replied that I was not sufficienty taken with her charms to buy them at the price she fixed, and so I left her.

I called Costa, and told him to go and warn the master of the felucca that I was going the next day, and with this idea I went to bid good-bye to the marquis, who informed me that he had just been taking Petri to see Rosalie, who had received him well enough. I told him I was glad to hear it, and said that I commended to him the care of her happiness, but such commendations were thrown away.

It is one of the most curious circumstances of my history, that in one year two women whom I sincerely loved and whom I might have married were taken from me by two old men, whose affections I had fostered without wishing to do so. Happily these gentlemen made my mistresses' fortunes, but on the other hand they did me a still greater service in relieving me of a tie which I should have found very troublesome in course of time. No doubt they both saw that my fortune, though great in outward show, rested on no solid basis, which, as the reader will see, was unhappily too true. I should be happy if I thought that my errors or rather follies would serve as a warning to the readers of these Memoirs.

I spent the day in watching the care with which Véronique and Annette packed up my trunks, for I would not let my two servants help in any way. Véronique was neither sad nor gay. She looked as if she had made up her mind, and as if there had never been any differences between us. I was very glad, for as I no longer cared for her I should have been annoyed to find that she still cared for me.

We supped in our usual manner, discussing only commonplace topics, but just as I was going to bed Annette shook my hand in a way that told me to prepare for a visit from her. I admired the natural acuteness of young girls, who take their degrees in the art of love with so much ease and at such an early age. Annette, almost a child, knew more than a young man of twenty. I decided on giving her fifty sequins without letting Véronique see me, as I did not intend to be so liberal towards her. I took a roll of ducats and gave them to her as soon as she came.

She lay down beside me, and after a moment devoted to love she said that Véronique was asleep, adding,——

"I heard all you said to my sister, and I am sure you love her."

"If I did, dear Annette, I should not have made my proposal in such plain terms."

"I should like to believe that, but what would you have done if she had accepted your offer? You would be in one bed by this, I suppose?"

"I was more than certain, dearest, that her pride would hinder her receiving me."

We had reached this point in our conversation when we were surprised by the sudden appearance of Véronique with a lighted candle, and wearing only her chemise. She laughed at her sister to encourage her, and I joined in the laughter, keeping a firm hold on the little one for fear of her escaping. Véronique looked ravishing in her scanty attire, and as she laughed I could not be angry with her. However, I said,——

"You have interrupted our enjoyment, and hurt your sister's feelings; perhaps you will despise her for the future?"

"On the contrary, I shall always love her."

"Her feelings overcame her, and she surrendered to me without making any terms."

"She has more sense than I."

"Do you mean that?"

"I do, really."

"I am astonished and delighted to hear it; but as it is so, kiss your sister."

At this invitation Véronique put down the candle, and covered Annette's beautiful body with kisses. The scene made me feel very happy.

"Come, Véronique," said I, "you will die of cold; come and lie down."

I made room for her, and soon there were three of us under the same sheet. I was in an ecstasy at this group, worthy of Aretin's pencil.

"Dearest ones," said I, "you have played me a pretty trick; was it premeditated? And was Véronique false this morning, or is she false now?"

"We did not premeditate anything, I was true this morning, and I am true now. I feel that I and my plan were very silly, and I hope you will forgive me, since I have repented and have had my punishment. Now I think I am in my right senses, as I have yielded to the feelings with which you inspired me when I saw you first, and against which I have fought too long."

"What you say pleases me extremely."

"Well, forgive me and finish my punishment by shewing that you are not angry with me."

"How am I to do that?"

"By telling me that you are vexed no longer, and by continuing to give my sister proofs of your love."

"I swear to you that so far from being angry with you I am very fond of you; but would you like us to be fond in your presence?"

"Yes, if you don't mind me."

Feeling excited by voluptuous emotions, I saw that my part could no longer be a passive one.

"What do you say," said I to my blonde, "will you allow your heroic sister to remain a mere looker-on at our sweet struggles? Are you not generous enough to let me make her an actress in the drama?"

"No; I confess I do not feel as if I could be so generous to-night, but next night, if you will play the same part, we will change. Véronique shall act and I will look on."

"That would do beautifully," said Véronique, with some vexation in her manner, "if the gentleman was not going to-morrow morning."

"I will stay, dear Véronique, if only to prove how much I love you,"

I could not have wished for plainer speech on her part, and I should have liked to shew her how grateful I felt on the spot; but that would have been at Annette's expense, as I had no right to make any alteration in the piece of which she was the author and had a right to expect all the profits. Whenever I recall this pleasant scene I feel my heart beat with voluptuous pleasure, and even now, with the hand of old age upon me, I can not recall it without delight.

Véronique resigned herself to the passive part which her younger sister imposed on her, and turning aside she leant her head on her hand, disclosing a breast which would have excited the coldest of men, and bade me begin my attack on Annette. It was no hard task she laid upon me, for I was all on fire, and I was certain of pleasing her as long as she looked at me. As Annette was short-sighted, she could not distinguish in the heat of the action which way I was looking, and I succeeded in getting my right hand free, without her noticing me, and I was thus enabled to communicate a pleasure as real though not as acute as that enjoyed by her sister. When the coverlet was disarranged, Véronique took the trouble to replace it, and thus offered me, as if by accident, a new spectacle. She saw how I enjoyed the sight of her charms, and her eye brightened. At last, full of unsatisfied desire, she shewed me all the treasures which nature had given her, just as I had finished with Annette for the fourth time. She might well think that I was only rehearsing for the following night, and her fancy must have painted her coming joys in the brightest colours. Such at all events were my thoughts, but the fates determined otherwise. I was in the middle of the seventh act, always slower and more pleasant for the actress than the first two or three, when Costa came knocking loudly at my door, calling out that the felucca was ready. I was vexed at this untoward incident, got up in a rage, and after telling him to pay the master for the day, as I was not going till the morror, I went back to bed, no longer, however, in a state to continue the work I begun. My two sweethearts were delighted with me, but we all wanted rest, though the piece should not have finished with an interruption. I wanted to get some amusement out of the interval, and proposed an ablution, which made Annette laugh and which Véronique pronounced to be absolutely necessary. I found it a delicious *hors d'œuvre* to the banquet I had enjoyed. The two sisters rendered each other various services, standing in the most lascivious postures, and I found my situation as looker-on an enviable one.

When the washing and the laughter it gave rise to were over, we returned to the stage where the last act should have been performed. I longed to begin again, and I am sure I should have succeeded if I had been well backed up by my partner; but Annette, who was young and tired out with the toils of the night, forgot her part, and yielded to sleep as she had yielded to love. Véronique began to laugh when she saw her asleep, and I had to do the same, when I saw that she was as still as a corpse.

"What a pity!" said Véronique's eyes; but she said it with her eyes alone, while I was waiting for these words to issue from her lips. We were both of us wrong: she for not speaking, and I for waiting for her to speak. It was a favourable moment, but we let it pass by, and love punished us. I had, it is true, another reason for abstaining. I wished to reserve myself for the night. Véronique went to her own bed to quiet her excited feelings, and I stayed in bed with my sleeping beauty till noon, when I wished her good morning by a fresh assault which was completed neither on her side nor on mine to the best of my belief.

The day was spent in talking about ourselves, and determined to eat only one meal, we did not sit down to table till night began to fall. We spent two hours in the consumption of delicate dishes, and in defying Bacchus to make us feel his power. We rose as we saw Annette falling asleep, but we were not much annoyed at the thought that she would not see the pleasures we promised each other. I thought that I should have enough to do to contemplate the charms of the one nymph without looking at Annette's beauties. We went to bed, our arms interlaced, our bodies tight together, and lip pressed on lip, but that was all. Véronique saw what prevented me going any further, and she was too polite and modest to complain. She dissembled her feelings and continued to caress me, while I was in a frenzy of rage. I had never had such a misfortune, unless as the result of complete exhaustion, or from a strong mental impression capable of destroying my natural faculties. Let my readers imagine what I suffered; in the flower of my age, with a strong constitution, holding the body of a woman I had ardently desired in my arms, while she tenderly caressed me, and yet I could do nothing for her. I was in despair; one cannot offer a greater insult to a woman.

At last we had to accept the facts and speak reasonably, and I was the first to bewail my misfortune.

"You tired yourself too much yesterday," said she, "and you were not sufficiently temperate at supper. Do not let it trouble you, dearest, I am sure you love me. Do not try to force nature, you will only weaken yourself more. I think a gentle sleep would restore your

manly powers better than anything. I can't sleep myself, but don't mind me. Sleep, we will make love together afterwards."

After those excellent and reasonble suggestions, Véronique turned her back to me and I followed her example,
but in vain did I endeavour to obtain a refreshing slumber; nature which would not give me the power of making her, the loveliest creature, happy, envied me the
power of repose as well. My amorous ardour and my
rage forbade all thoughts of rest, and my excited passions
conspired against that which would enable them to satisfy their desires. Nature punished me for having dis-
trusted her, and because I had taken stimulants fit only
for the weak. If I had fasted, I should have done great
things, but now there was a conflict between the stimulants and nature, and by my desire for enjoyment I had
deprived myself of the power to enjoy. Thus nature,
wise like its Divine Author, punishes the ignorance and
presumption of poor weak mortals.

Throughout this terrible and sleepless night my mind
roamed abroad, and amidst the reproaches with which
I overwhelmed myself I found a certain satisfaction in
the thought that they were not wholly undeserved. This
is the sole enjoyment I still have when I meditate on my
past life and its varied adventures. I feel that no misfortune has befallen me save by my own fault, whilst I
attribute to natural causes the blessings, of which I have
enjoyed many. I think I should go mad if in my solilo-
quies I came across any misfortune which I could not
trace to my own fault, for I should not know where to
place the reason, and that would degrade me to the rank
of creatures governed by instinct alone. I feel that I am
somewhat more than a beast. A beast, in truth, is a

foolish neighbour of mine, who tries to argue that the brutes reason better than we do.

"I will grant," I said, "that they reason better than you, but I can go no farther; and I think every reasonable man would say as much."

This reply has made me an enemy, although he admits the first part of the thesis.

Happier than I, Véronique slept for three hours; but she was disagreeably surprised on my telling her that I had not been able to close an eye, and on finding me in the same state of impotence as before. She began to get angry when I tried to convince her rather too forcibly that my misfortune was not due to my want of will, and then she blamed herself as the cause of my impotence; and mortified by the idea, she endeavoured to destroy the spell by all the means which passion suggested, and which I had hitherto thought infallible; but her efforts and mine were all thrown away. My despair was as great as hers when at last, wearied, ashamed, and degraded in her own eyes, she discontinued her efforts, her eyes full of tears. She went away without a word, and left me alone for the two or three hours which had still to elapse before the dawn appeared.

At day-break Costa came and told me that the sea being rough and a contrary wind blowing, the felucca would be in danger of perishing.

"We will go as soon as the weather improves," said I; "in the mean time light me a fire."

I arose, and proceeded to write down the sad history of the night. This occupation soothed me, and feeling inclined to sleep I lay down again and slept for eight hours. When I awoke I felt better, but still rather sad. The two sisters were delighted to see me in good health, but I thought I saw on Véronique's features an unpleasant expression of contempt. However, I had deserved it, and I did not take the trouble of changing her opinion, though if she had been more caressing she might easily have put me in a state to repair the involuntary wrongs I had done her in the night. Before we sat down to table I gave her a present of a hundred sequins, which made her look a little more cheerful. I gave an equal present to my dear Annette, who had not expected anything, thinking herself amply recompensed by my first gift and by the pleasure I had afforded her.

At midnight the master of the felucca came to tell me that the wind had changed, and I took leave of the sisters. Véronique shed tears, but I knew to what to attribute them. Annette kissed me affectionately; thus each played her own part. I sailed for Lerici, where I arrived the next day, and then posted to Leghorn. Before I speak of this town I think I shall interest my readers by narrating a circumstance not unworthy of these Memoirs.

CHAPTER VI

A Clever Cheat—Passano—Pisa—Corilla—My Opinion of Squinting Eyes—Florence—I See Thérèse Again—My Son—Corticelli

I WAS standing at some distance from my carriage into which they were putting four horses, when a man accosted me and asked me if I would pay in advance or at the next stage. Without troubling to look at him I said I would pay in advance, and gave him a coin requesting him to bring me the change.

"Directly, sir," said he, and with that he went into the inn.

A few minutes after, just as I was going to look after my change, the post-master came up and asked me to pay for the stage.

"I have paid already, and I am waiting for my change. Did I not give the money to you?"

"Certainly not, sir."

"Whom did I give it to, then?"

"I really can't say; but you will be able to recognize the man, doubtless."

"It must have been you or one of your people."

I was speaking loud, and all the men came about me.

"These are all the men in my employ," said the master, and he asked if any of them had received the money from me.

They all denied the fact with an air of sincerity which left no room for suspicion. I cursed and swore, but they let me curse and swear as much as I liked. At last I discovered that there was no help for it, and I paid a second time, laughing at the clever rascal who had taken me in so thoroughly. Such are the lessons of life; always full of new experiences, and yet one never knows enough. From that day I have always taken care not to pay for posting except to the proper persons.

In no country are knaves so cunning as in Italy, Greece ancient and modern excepted.

When I got to the best inn at Leghorn they told me that there was a theatre, and my luck made me go and see the play. I was recognized by an actor who accosted me, and introduced me to one of his comrades, a self-styled poet, and a great enemy of the Abbé Chiari, whom I did not like, as he had written a biting satire against me, and I had never succeeded in avenging myself on him. I asked them to come and sup with me—a windfall which these people are not given to refusing. The pretended poet was a Genoese, and called himself Giacomo Passano. He informed me that he had written three hundred sonnets against the abbé, who would burst with rage if they were ever printed. As I could not restrain a smile at the good opinion the poet had of his works, he offered to read me a few sonnets. He had the manuscript about him, and I could not escape the penance. He read a dozen or so, which I thought mediocre, and a mediocre sonnet is necessarily a bad sonnet, as this form of poetry demands sublimity; and thus amongst the myriads of sonnets to which Italy gives birth very few can be called good.

If I had given myself time to examine the man's features, I should, no doubt, have found him to be a rogue; but I was blinded by passion, and the idea of three hundred sonnets against the Abbé Chiari fascinated me.

I cast my eyes over the title of the manuscript, and read, *"La Chiareide di Ascanio Pogomas."*

"That's an anagram of my Christian name and my surname; is it not a happy combination?"

This folly made me smile again. Each of the sonnets was a dull diatribe ending with *"l'abbate Chiari è un coglione."* He did not prove that he was one, but he said so over and over again, making use of the poet's privilege to exaggerate and lie. What he wanted to do was to annoy the abbé, who was by no means what Passano called him, but on the contrary, a wit and a poet; and if he had been acquainted with the requirements of the stage he would have written better plays than Goldoni, as he had a greater command of language.

I told Passano, for civility's sake, that he ought to get his *Chiareide* printed.

"I would do so," said he, "if I could find a publisher, for I am not rich enough to pay the expenses, and the publishers are a pack of ignorant beggars. Besides, the press is not free, and the censor would not let the epithet I give to my hero pass. If I could go to Switzerland I am sure it could be managed; but I must have six sequins to walk to Switzerland, and I have not got them."

"And when you got to Switzerland, where there are no theatres, what would you do for a living?"

"I would paint in miniature. Look at those."

He gave me a number of small ivory tablets, representing obscene subjects, badly drawn and badly painted.

"I will give you an introduction to a gentleman at Berne," I said; and after supper I gave him a letter and six sequins. He wanted to force some of his productions on me, but I would not have them. I was foolish enough to give him a letter to pretty Sara's father, and I told him to write to me at Rome, under cover of the banker Belloni.

I set out from Leghorn the next day and went to Pisa, where I stopped two days. There I made the acquaintance of an Englishman, of whom I bought a travelling carriage. He took me to see Corilla, the celebrated poetess. She received me with great politeness, and was kind enough to improvise on several subjects which I suggested. I was enchanted, not so much with her grace and beauty, as by her wit and perfect elocution. How sweet a language sounds when it is spoken well and the expressions are well chosen. A language badly spoken is intolerable even from a pretty mouth, and I have always admired the wisdom of the Greeks who made their nurses teach the children from the cradle to speak correctly and pleasantly. We are far from following their good example; witness the fearful accents one hears in what is called, often incorrectly, good society.

Corilla was *straba*, like Venus as painted by the ancients—why, I cannot think, for however fair a squint-eyed woman may be otherwise, I always look upon her face as distorted. I am sure that if Venus had been in truth a goddess, she would have made the eccentric Greek, who first dared to paint her cross-eyed, feel the weight of her anger. I was told that when Corilla sang, she had only to fix her squinting eyes on a man and the conquest was complete; but, praised be God! she did not fix them on me.

At Florence I lodged at the "Hotel Carrajo," kept by Dr. Vannini, who delighted to confess himself an unworthy member of the Academy Della Crusca. I took a suite of rooms which looked out on the bank of the Arno. I also took a carriage and a footman, whom, as well as a coachman, I clad in blue and red livery. This was M. de Bragadin's livery, and I thought I might use his colours, not with the intention of deceiving anyone, but merely to cut a dash.

The morning after my arrival I put on my great coat to escape observation, and proceeded to walk about Florence. In the evening I went to the theatre to see the famous harlequin, Rossi, but I considered his reputation was greater than he deserved. I passed the same judgment on the boasted Florentine elocution; I did not care for it at all. I enjoyed seeing Pertici; having become old, and not being able to sing any more, he acted, and, strange to say, acted well; for, as a rule, all singers, men and women, trust to their voice and care nothing for acting, so that an ordinary cold entirely disables them for the time being.

Next day I called on the banker, Sasso Sassi, on whom I had a good letter of credit, and after an excellent dinner I dressed and went to the opera *in via della Pergola,* taking a stage box, not so much for the music, of which I was never much of an admirer, as because I wanted to look at the actress.

The reader may guess my delight and surprise when I recognised in the prima donna Thérèse, the false Bellino, whom I had left at Rimini in the year 1744; that charming Thérèse whom I should certainly have married if M. de Gages had not put me under arrest. I had not seen her for seventeen years, but she looked as beautiful and ravishing as ever as she came forward on the stage. It seemed impossible. I could not believe my eyes, thinking the resemblance must be a coincidence, when, after singing an air, she fixed her eyes on mine and kept them there. I could no longer doubt that it was she;

she plainly recognized me. As she left the stage she stopped at the wings and made a sign to me with her fan to come and speak to her.

I went out with a beating heart, though I could not explain my perturbation, for I did not feel guilty in any way towards Thérèse, save in that I had not answered the last letter she had written me from Naples, thirteen years ago. I went round the theatre, feeling a greater curiosity as to the results of our interview than to know what had befallen her during the seventeen years which seemed an age to me.

I came to the stage-door, and I saw Thérèse standing at the top of the stair. She told the door-keeper to let me pass; I went up and we stood face to face. Dumb with surprise I took her hand and pressed it against my heart.

"Know from that beating heart," said I, "all that I feel."

"I can't follow your example," said she, "but when I saw you I thought I should have fainted. Unfortunately I am engaged to supper. I shall not shut my eyes all night. I shall expect you at eight o'clock to-morrow morning. Where are you staying?"

"At Dr. Vannini's."

"Under what name?"

"My own."

"How long have you been here?"

"Since yesterday."

"Are you stopping long in Florence?"

"As long as you like."

"Are you married?"

"No."

"Cursed be that supper! What an event! You must

leave me now, I have to go on. Good-bye till seven o'clock to-morrow."

She had said eight at first, but an hour sooner was no harm. I returned to the theatre, and recollected that I had neither asked her name or address, but I could find out all that easily. She was playing Mandane, and her singing and acting were admirable. I asked a well-dressed young man beside me what that admirable actress's name was.

"You have only come to Florence to-day, sir?"

"I arrived yesterday."

"Ah! well, then it's excusable. That actress has the same name as I have. She is my wife, and I am Cirillo Palesi, at your service."

I bowed and was silent with surprise. I dared not ask where she lived, lest he might think my curiosity impertinent. Thérèse married to this handsome young man, of whom, of all others, I had made enquiries about her! It was like a scene in a play.

I could bear it no longer. I longed to be alone and to ponder over this strange adventure at my ease, and to think about my visit to Thérèse at seven o'clock the next morning. I felt the most intense curiosity to see what the husband would do when he recognized me, and he was certain to do so, for he had looked at me attentively as he spoke. I felt that my old flame for Thérèse was rekindled in my heart, and I did not know whether I was glad or sorry at her being married.

I left the opera-house and told my footman to call my carriage.

"You can't have it till nine o'clock, sir; it was so cold the coachman sent the horses back to the stable."

"We will return on foot, then."

"You will catch a cold."

"What is the prima donna's name?"

"When she came here, she called herself Lanti, but for the last two months she has been Madame Palesi. She married a handsome young man with no property and no profession, but she is rich, so he takes his ease and does nothing."

"Where does she live?"

"At the end of this street. There's her house, sir; she lodges on the first floor."

This was all I wanted to know, so I said no more, but took note of the various turnings, that I might be able to find my way alone the next day. I ate a light supper, and told Le Duc to call me at six o'clock.

"But it is not light till seven."

"I know that."

"Very good."

At the dawn of day, I was at the door of the woman I had loved so passionately. I went to the first floor, rang the bell, and an old woman came out and asked me if I were M. Casanova. I told her that I was, whereupon she said that the lady had informed her I was not coming till eight.

"She said seven."

"Well, well, it's of no consequence. Kindly walk in here. I will go and awake her."

In five minutes, the young husband in his night-cap and dressing-gown came in, and said that his wife would not be long. Then looking at me attentively with an astounded stare, he said,——

"Are you not the gentleman who asked me my wife's name last night?"

"You are right, I did. I have not seen your wife for many years, but I thought I recognized her. My good fortune made me enquire of her husband, and the friendship which formerly attached me to her will henceforth attach me to you."

As I uttered this pretty compliment Thérèse, as fair as love, rushed into the room with open arms. I took her to my bosom in a transport of delight, and thus we remained for two minutes, two friends, two lovers, happy to see one another after a long and sad parting. We kissed each other again and again, and then bidding her husband sit down she drew me to a couch and gave full course to her tears. I wept too, and my tears were happy ones. At last we wiped our eyes, and glanced towards the husband whom we had completely forgotten. He stood in an attitude of complete astonishment, and we burst out laughing. There was something so comic in his surprise that it would have taxed all the talents of the poet and the caricaturist to depict his expression of amazement. Thérèse, who knew how to manage him, cried in a pathetic an affectionate voice,——

"My dear Palesi, you see before you my father—nay, more than a father, for this is my generous friend to whom I owe all. Oh, happy moment! for which my heart has longed for these ten years past."

At the word "father" the unhappy husband fixed his gaze on me, but I restrained my laughter with considerable difficulty. Although Thérèse was young for her age, she was only two years younger than I; but friendship gives a new meaning to the sweet name of father.

"Yes, sir," said I, "your Thérèse is my daughter, my sister, my cherished friend; she is an angel, and this treasure is your wife."

"I did not reply to your last letter," said I, not giving him time to come to himself.

"I know all," she replied. "You fell in love with a nun. You were imprisoned under the Leads, and I heard of your almost miraculous flight at Vienna. I had a false presentiment that I should see you in that town. Afterwards I heard of you in Paris and Holland, but after you left Paris nobody could tell me any more about you. You will hear some fine tales when I tell you all that has happened to me during the past ten years. Now I am happy. I have my dear Palesi here, who comes from Rome. I married him a couple of months ago. We are very fond of each other, and I hope you will be as much his friend as mine."

At this I arose and embraced the husband, who cut such an extraordinary figure. He met me with open arms, but in some confusion; he was, no doubt, not yet quite satisfied as to the individual who was his wife's father, brother, friend, and perhaps lover, all at once. Thérèse saw this feeling in his eyes, and after I had done she came and kissed him most affectionately, which confused me in my turn, for I felt all my old love for her renewed, and as ardent as it was when Don Sancio Pico introduced me to her at Ancona.

Reassured by my embrace and his wife's caress, M. Palesi asked me if I would take a cup of chocolate with them, which he himself would make. I answered that chocolate was my favourite breakfast-dish, and all the more so when it was made by a friend. He went away to see to it. Our time had come.

As soon as we were alone Thérèse threw herself into my arms, her face shining with such love as no pen can describe.

"Oh, my love! whom I shall love all my life, clasp me to your breast! Let us give each other a hundred embraces on this happy day, but not again, since my fate has made me another's bride. To-morrow we will be like brother and sister; to-day let us be lovers."

She had not finished this speech before my bliss was crowned. Our transports were mutual, and we renewed them again and again during the half hour in which we had no fear of an interruption. Her negligent morning dress and my great coat were highly convenient under the circumstances.

After we had satiated in part our amorous ardour we breathed again and sat down. There was a short pause, and then she said,——

"You must know that I am in love with my husband and determined not to deceive him. What I have just done was a debt I had to pay to the remembrance of my first love. I had to pay it to prove how much I love you; but let us forget it now. You must be contented with the thought of my great affection for you—of which you can have no doubt—and let me still think that you love me; but henceforth do not let us be alone together, as I should give way, and that would vex me. What makes you look so sad?"

"I find you bound, while I am free. I thought we had met never to part again; you had kindled the old fires. I am the same to you as I was at Ancona. I have proved as much, and you can guess how sad I feel at your decree that I am to enjoy you no more. I find that you are not only married but in love with your husband. Alas! I have come too late, but if I had not stayed at Genoa I should not have been more fortunate. You shall know all in due time, and in the meanwhile I will be guided by you in everything. I suppose your husband knows nothing of our connection, and my best plan will be to be reserved, will it not?"

"Yes, dearest, for he knows nothing of my affairs, and

I am glad to say he shews no curiosity respecting them. Like everybody else, he knows I made my fortune at Naples; I told him I went there when I was ten years old. That was an innocent lie which hurts nobody; and in my position I find that inconvenient truths have to give way to lies. I give myself out as only twenty-four, how do you think I look?"

"You look as if you were telling the truth, though I know you must be thirty-two."

"You mean thirty-one, for when I knew you I couldn't have been more than fourteen."

"I thought you were fifteen at least."

"Well, I might admit that between ourselves; but tell me if I look more than twenty-four."

"I swear to you you don't look as old, but at Naples. . . ."

"At Naples some people might be able to contradict me, but nobody would mind them. But I am waiting for what ought to be the sweetest moment of your life."

"What is that, pray?"

"Allow me to keep my own counsel, I want to enjoy your surprise. How are you off? If you want money, I can give you back all you gave me, and with compound interest. All I have belongs to me; my husband is not master of anything. I have fifty thousand ducats at Naples, and an equal sum in diamonds. Tell me how much you want—quick! the chocolate is coming."

Such a woman was Thérèse. I was deeply moved, and was about to throw my arms about her neck without answering when the chocolate came. Her husband was followed by a girl of exquisite beauty, who carried three cups of chocolate on a silver-gilt dish. While we drank it Palesi amused us by telling us with much humour how surprised he was when he recognized the man who made him rise at such an early hour as the same who had asked him his wife's name the night before. Thérèse and I laughed till our sides ached, the story was told so wittily and pleasantly. This Roman displeased me less than I expected; his jealousy seemed only put on for form's sake.

"At ten o'clock," said Thérèse, "I have a rehearsal here of the new opera. You can stay and listen if you like. I hope you will dine with us every day, and it will give me great pleasure if you will look upon my house as yours."

"To-day," said I, "I will stay with you till after supper, and then I will leave you with your fortunate husband."

As I pronounced these words M. Palesi embraced me with effusion, as if to thank me for not objecting to his enjoying his rights as a husband.

He was between the ages of twenty and twenty-two, of a fair complexion, and well-made, but too pretty for a man. I did not wonder at Thérèse being in love with him, for I knew too well the power of a handsome face; but I thought that she had made a mistake in marrying him, for a husband acquires certain rights which may become troublesome.

Thérèse's pretty maid came to tell me that my carriage was at the door.

"Will you allow me," said I to her, "to have my footman in?"

"Rascal," said I, as soon as he came in, "who told you to come here with my carriage?"

"Nobody, sir, but I know my duty."

"Who told you that I was here?"

"I guessed as much."

"Go and fetch Le Duc, and come back with him."

When they arrived I told Le Duc to pay the impertiment fellow three days' wages, to strip him of his livery, and to ask Dr. Vannini to get me a servant of the same build, not gifted with the faculty of divination, but who knew how to obey his master's orders. The rascal was much perturbed at the result of his officiousness, and asked Thérèse to plead for him; but, like a sensible woman, she told him that his master was the best judge of the value of his services.

At ten o'clock all the actors and actresses arrived, bringing with them a mob of amateurs who crowded the hall. Thérèse received their greetings graciously, and I could see she enjoyed a great reputation. The rehearsal lasted three hours, and wearied me extremely. To relieve my boredom I talked to Palesi, whom I liked for not asking me any particulars of my acquaintance with his wife. I saw that he knew how to behave in the position in which he was placed.

A girl from Parma, named Redegonde, who played a man's part and sang very well, stayed to dinner. Thérèse had also asked a young Bolognese, named Corticelli. I was struck with the budding charms of this pretty dancer, but as I was just then full of Thérèse, I did not pay much attention to her. Soon after we sat down I saw a plump abbé coming in with measured steps. He looked to me a regular Tartuffe, after nothing but Thérèse. He came up to her as soon as he saw her, and going on one knee in the Portuguese fashion, kissed her hand tenderly and respectfully. Thérèse received him with smiling courtesy and put him at her right hand; I was at their left. His voice, manner, and all about him told me that I had known him, and in fact I soon recognized him as the Abbé Gama, whom I had left at Rome seventeen years before with Cardinal Acquaviva; but I pretended not to recognize him, and indeed he had aged greatly. This gallant priest had eyes for no one but Thérèse, and he was too busy with saying a thousand soft nothings to her to take notice of anybody else in the company. I hoped that in his turn he would either not recognize me or pretend not to do so, so I was continuing my trifling talk with the Corticelli, when Thérèse told me that the abbé wanted to know whether I did not recollect him. I looked at his face attentively, and with the air of a man who is trying to recollect something, and then I rose and asked if he were not the Abbé Gama, with whose acquaintance I was honoured.

"The same," said he, rising, and placing his arms round my neck he kissed me again and again. This was in perfect agreement with his crafty character; the reader will not have forgotten the portrait of him contained in the first volume of these Memoirs.

After the ice had been thus broken it will be imagined that we had a long conversation. He spoke of Barbaruccia, of the fair Marchioness G——, of Cardinal S—— C——, and told me how he had passed from the Spanish to the Portuguese service, in which he still continued. I was enjoying his talk about numerous subjects which had interested me in my early youth, when an unexpected sight absorbed all my thinking faculties. A young man of fifteen or sixteen, as well grown as Italians usually are at that age, came into the room, saluted the company with easy grace, and kissed Thérèse. I was the only person who did not know him, but I was not the only one who looked surprised. The daring Thérèse introduced him to me with perfect coolness with the words:

"That is my brother."

I greeted him as warmly as I could, but my manner

was slightly confused, as I had not had time to recover my composure. This so-called brother of Thérèse was my living image, though his complexion was rather clearer than mine. I saw at once that he was my son; nature had never been so indiscreet as in the amazing likeness between us. This, then, was the surprise of which Thérèse had spoken; she had devised the pleasure of seeing me at once astounded and delighted, for she knew that my heart would be touched at the thought of having left her such a pledge of our mutual love. I had not the slighest foreknowledge in the matter, for Thérèse had never alluded to her being with child in her letters. I thought, however, that she should not have brought about this meeting in the presence of a third party, for everyone has eyes in their head, and anyone with eyes must have seen that the young man was either my son or my brother. I glanced at her, but she avoided meeting my eye, while the pretended brother was looking at me so attentively that he did not hear what was said to him. As to the others, they did nothing but look first at me and then at him, and if they came to the conclusion that he was my son they would be obliged to suppose that I had been the lover of Thérèse's mother, if she were really his sister, for taking into consideration the age she looked and gave herself out to be she could not possibly be his mother. It was equally impossible that I could be Thérèse's father, as I did not look any older than she did.

My son spoke the Neapolitan dialect perfectly, but he also spoke Italian very well, and in whatever he said I was glad to recognize taste, good sense, and intelligence. He was well-informed, though he had been brought up at Naples, and his manners were very distinguished. His mother made him sit between us at table.

"His favourite amusement," she said to me, "is music. You must hear him on the clavier, and though I am eight years older I shall not be surprised if you pronounce him the better performer."

Only a woman's delicate instinct could have suggested this remark; men hardly ever approach women in this respect.

Whether from natural impulses or self-esteem, I rose from the table so delighted with my son that I embraced him with the utmost tenderness, and was applauded by the company. I asked everybody to dine with me the next day, and my invitation was joyfully accepted; but the Corticelli said, with the utmost simplicity,——

"May I come, too?"

"Certainly; you too."

After dinner the Abbé Gama asked me to breakfast with him, or to have him to breakfast the next morning, as he was longing for a good talk with me.

"Come and breakfast with me," said I, "I shall be delighted to see you."

When the guests had gone Don Cesarino, as the pretended brother of Thérèse was called, asked me if I would walk with him. I kissed him, and replied that my carriage was at his service, and that he and his brother-in-law could drive in it, but that I had resolved not to leave his sister that day. Palesi seemed quite satisfied with the arrangement, and they both went away.

When we were alone, I gave Thérèse an ardent embrace, and congratulated her on having such a brother.

"My dear, he is the fruit of our amours; he is your son. He makes me happy, and is happy himself, and indeed he has everything to make him so."

"And I, too, am happy, dear Thérèse. You must have seen that I recognized him at once."

"But do you want to give him a brother? How ardent you are!"

"Remember, beloved one, that to-morrow we are to be friends, and nothing more."

By this my efforts were crowned with success, but the thought that it was the last time was a bitter drop in the cup of happiness.

When we had regained our composure, Thérèse said,——

"The duke who took me from Rimini brought up our child; as soon as I knew that I was pregnant I confided my secret to him. No one knew of my delivery, and the child was sent to nurse at Sorrento, and the duke had him baptized under the name of Cæsar Philip Lanti. He remained at Sorento till he was nine, and then he was boarded with a worthy man, who superintended his education and taught him music. From his earliest childhood he has known me as his sister, and you cannot think how happy I was when I saw him growing so like you. I have always considered him as a sure pledge of our final union. I was ever thinking what would happen when we met, for I knew that he would have the same influence over you as he has over me. I was sure you would marry me and make him legitimate."

"And you have rendered all this, which would have made me happy, an impossibility."

"The fates decided so; we will say no more about it. On the death of the duke I left Naples, leaving Cesarino at the same boarding school, under the protection of the Prince de la Riccia, who has always looked upon him as a brother. Your son, though he does not know it, possesses the sum of twenty thousand ducats, of which I receive the interest, but you may imagine that I let him want for nothing. My only regret is that I cannot tell him I am his mother, as I think he would love me still more if he knew that he owed his being to me. You cannot think how glad I was to see your surprise to-day, and how soon you got to love him."

"He is wonderfully like me."

"That delights me. People must think that you were my mother's lover. My husband thinks that our friendship is due to the connection between you and my mother. He told me yesterday that Cesarino might be my brother on the mother's side, but not on my father's; as he had seen his father in the theatre, but that he could not possibly be my father, too. If I have children by Palesi all I have will go to them, but if not Cesarino will be my heir. My property is well secured, even if the Prince de Riccia were to die."

"Come," said she, drawing me in the direction of her bed-room.

She opened a large box which contained her jewels and diamonds, and shares to the amount of fifty thousand ducats. Besides that she had a large amount of plate, and her talents which assured her the first place in all the Italian theatres.

"Do you know whether our dear Cesarino has been in love yet?" said I.

"I don't think so, but I fancy my pretty maid is in love with him. I shall keep my eyes open."

"You mustn't be too strict."

"No, but it isn't a good thing for a young man to engage too soon in that pleasure which makes one neglect everything else."

"Let me have him, I will teach him how to live."

"Ask all, but leave me my son. You must know that I never kiss him for fear of my giving way to excessive emotion. I wish you knew how good and pure he is, and how well he loves me; I could not refuse him anything.

What will people say in Venice when they see Casanova again, who escaped from The Leads and has become twenty years younger?"

"You are going to Venice, then, for the *Ascensa?*"

. ."Yes, and you are going to Rome?"

"And to Naples, to see my friend the Duke de Matalone."

"I know him well. He has already had a son by the daughter of the Duke de Bovino, whom he married. She must be a charming woman to have made a man of him, for all Naples knew that he was impotent."

"Probably, she only knew the secret of making him a father."

"Well, it is possible."

We spent the time by talking with interest on various topics till Cesarino and the husband came back. The dear child finished his conquest of me at supper; he had a merry random wit, and all the Neapolitan vivacity. He sat down at the clavier, and after playing several pieces with the utmost skill he began to sing Neapolitan songs which made us all laugh. Thérèse only looked at him and me, but now and again she embraced her husband, saying, that in love alone lies happiness.

I thought then, and I think now, that this day was one of the happiest I have ever spent.

CHAPTER VII

The Corticelli—The Jew Manager Beaten—The False
Charles Ivanoff and the Trick He Played Me—I Am
Ordered to Leave Tuscany—I Arrive at Rome—My
Brother Jean

A T NINE o'clock the next morning, the Abbé Gama
was announced. The first thing he did was to shed
tears of joy (as he said) at seeing me so well and prosperous after so many years. The reader will guess that
the abbé addressed me in the most flattering terms, and
perhaps he may know that one may be clever, experienced in the ways of the world, and even distrustful of
flattery, but yet one's self-love, ever on the watch, listens
to the flatterer, and thinks him pleasant. This polite
and pleasant abbé, who had become extremely crafty
from having lived all his days amongst the high digni-
taries at the court of the *Servus Servorum Dei* (the best
school of strategy), was not altogether an ill-disposed
man, but both his disposition and his profession conspired to make him inquisitive; in fine, such as I have
depicted him in the first volume of these Memoirs. He
wanted to hear my adventures, and did not wait for me
to ask him to tell his story. He told me at great length
the various incidents in his life for the seventeen years
in which we had not seen one another. He had left the
service of the King of Spain for that of the King of
Portugal, he was secretary of embassy to the Commander
Almada, and he had been obliged to leave Rome because

167

the Pope Rezzonico would not allow the King of Portugal to punish certain worthy Jesuit assassins, who had only broken his arm as it happened, but who had none the less meant to take his life. Thus, Gama was staying in Italy corresponding with Almada and the famous Carvalho, waiting for the dispute to be finished before he returned to Rome. In point of fact this was the only substantial incident in the abbé's story, but he worked in so many episodes of no consequence that it lasted for an hour. No doubt he wished me to shew my gratitude by telling him all my adventures without reserve; but the upshot of it was that we both shewed ourselves true diplomatists, he in lengthening his story, I in shortening mine, while I could not help feeling some enjoyment in bulking the curiosity of my cassocked friend.

"What are you going to do in Rome?" said he, indifferently.

"I am going to beg the Pope to use his influence in my favour with the State Inquisitors at Venice."

It was not the truth, but one lie is as good as another, and if I had said I was only going for amusement's sake he would not have believed me. To tell the truth to an unbelieving man is to prostitute, to murder it. He then begged me to enter into a correspondence with him, and as that bound me to nothing I agreed to do so.

"I can give you a mark of my friendship," said he, "by introducing you to the Marquis de Botta-Adamo, Governor of Tuscany; he is supposed to be a friend of the regent's."

I accepted his offer gratefully, and he began to sound me about Thérèse, but found my lips as tightly closed as the lid of a miser's coffer. I told him she was a child when I made the acquaintance of her family at Bologna,

and that the resemblance between her brother and myself was a mere accident—a freak of nature. He happened to catch sight of a well-written manuscript on the
table, and asked me if that superb writing was my secretary's. Costa, who was present, answered in Spanish
that he wrote it. Gama overwhelmed him with compliments, and begged me to send Costa to him to copy some
letters. I guessed that he wanted to pump him about
me, and said that I needed his services all the day.

"Well, well, said the abbé, "another time will do." I
gave him no answer. Such is the character of the
curious.

I am not referring to that curiosity which depends on
the occult sciences, and endeavours to pry into the future
—the daughter of ignorance and superstition, its victims
are either foolish or ignorant. But the Abbé Gama was
neither; he was naturally curious, and his employment
made him still more so, for he was paid to find out
everything. He was a diplomatist; if he had been a little
lower down in the social scale he would have been treated
as a spy.

He left me to pay some calls, promising to be back by
dinner-time.

Dr. Vannini brought me another servant, of the same
height as the first, and engaged that he should obey orders and guess nothing. I thanked the academician and
inn-keeper, and ordered him to get me a sumptuous dinner.

The Corticelli was the first to arrive, bringing with her
her brother, an effeminate-looking young man, who
played the violin moderately well, and her mother, who
informed me that she never allowed her daughter to
dine out without herself and her son.

"Then you can take her back again this instant," said

I, "or take this ducat to dine somewhere else, as I don't want your company or your son's."

She took the ducat, saying that she was sure she was leaving her daughter in good hands.

"You may be sure of that," said I, "so be off."

The daughter made such witty observations on the above dialogue that I could not help laughing, and I began to be in love with her. She was only thirteen, and was so small that she looked ten. She was well-made, lively, witty, and fairer than is usual with Italian women, but to this day I cannot conceive how I fell in love with her.

The young wanton begged me to protect her against the manager of the opera, who was a Jew. In the agreement she had made with him he had engaged to let her dance a *pas de deux* in the second opera, and he had not kept his word. She begged me to compel the Jew to fulfil his engagement, and I promised to do so.

The next guest was Redegonde, who came from Parma. She was a tall, handsome woman, and Costa told me she was the sister of my new footman. After I had talked with her for two or three minutes I found her remarks well worthy of attention.

Then came the Abbé Gama, who congratulated me on being seated between two pretty girls. I made him take my place, and he began to entertain them as if to the manner born; and though the girls were laughing at him, he was not in the least disconcerted. He thought he was amusing them, and on watching his expression I saw that his self-esteem prevented him seeing that he was making a fool of himself; but I did not guess that I might make the same mistake at his age.

Wretched is the old man who will not recognize his old age; wretched unless he learn that the sex whom he seduced so often when he was young will despise him now if he still attempts to gain their favour.

My fair Thérèse, with her husband and my son, was the last to arrive. I kissed Thérèse and then my son, and sat down between them, whispering to Thérèse that such a dear mysterious trinity must not be parted; at which Thérèse smiled sweetly. The abbé sat down between Redegonde and the Corticelli, and amused us all the time by his agreeable conversation.

I laughed internally when I observed how respectfully my new footman changed his sister's plate, who appeared vain of honours to which her brother could lay no claim. She was not kind; she whispered to me, so that he could not hear,——

"He is a good fellow, but unfortunately he is rather stupid."

I had put in my pocket a superb gold snuff-box, richly enamelled and adorned with a perfect likeness of myself. I had had it made at Paris, with the intention of giving it to Madame d'Urfé, and I had not done so because the painter had made me too young. I had filled it with some excellent Havana snuff which M. de Chavigny had given me, and of which Thérèse was very fond; I was waiting for her to ask me for a pinch before I drew it out of my pocket.

The Abbé Gama, who had some exceedingly good snuff in an Origonela box, sent a pinch to Thérèse, and she sent him her snuff in a tortoise-shell box encrusted with gold in arabesques—an exquisite piece of workmanship. Gama criticised Thérèse's snuff, while I said that I found it delicious but that I thought I had some better myself. I took out my snuff-box, and opening it offered her a pinch. She did not notice the portrait, but she agreed that my snuff was vastly superior to hers.

"Well, would you like to make an exchange?" said I.

"Certainly, give me some paper."

"That is not requisite; we will exchange the snuff and the snuff-boxes."

So saying, I put Thérèse's box in my pocket and gave her mine shut. When she saw the portrait, she gave a cry which puzzled everybody, and her first motion was to kiss the portrait.

"Look," said she to Cesarino, "here is your portrait."

Cesarino looked at it in astonishment, and the box passed from hand to hand. Everybody said that it was my portrait, taken ten years ago, and that it might pass for a likeness of Cesarino. Thérèse got quite excited, and swearing that she would never let the box out of her hands again, she went up to her son and kissed him several times. While this was going on I watched the Abbé Gama, and I could see that he was making internal comments of his own on this affecting scene.

The worthy abbé went away towards the evening, telling me that he would expect me to breakfast next morning.

I spent the rest of the day in making love to Redegonde, and Thérèse, who saw that I was pleased with the girl, advised me to declare myself, and promised that she would ask her to the house as often as I liked. But Thérèse did not know her.

Next morning Gama told me that he had informed Marshal Botta that I would come and see him, and he would present me at four o'clock. Then the worthy abbé, always the slave of his curiosity, reproached me in a friendly manner for not having told him anything about my fortune.

"I did not think it was worth mentioning, but as you are interested in the subject I may tell you that my means are small, but that I have friends whose purses are always open to me."

"If you have true friends you are a rich man, but true friends are scarce."

I left the Abbé Gama, my head full of Redegonde, whom I preferred to the young Corticelli, and I went to pay her a visit; but what a reception! She received me in a room in which were present her mother, her uncle, and three or four dirty, untidy little monkeys: these were her brothers.

"Haven't you a better room to receive your friends in?" said I.

"I have no friends, so I don't want a room."

"Get it, my dear, and you will find the friends come fast enough. This is all very well for you to welcome your relations in, but not persons like myself who come to do homage to your charms and your talents."

"Sir," said the mother, "my daughter has but few talents, and thinks nothing of her charms, which are small."

"You are extremely modest, and I appreciate your feelings; but everybody does not see your daughter with the same eyes, and she pleased me greatly."

"That is an honour for her, and we are duly sensible of it, but not so as to be over-proud. My daughter will see you as often as you please, but here, and in no other place."

"But I am afraid of being in the way here."

"An honest man is never in the way."

I felt ashamed, for nothing so confounds a libertine as modesty in the mouth of poverty; and not knowing what to answer I took my leave.

I told Thérèse of my unfortunate visit, and we both laughed at it; it was the best thing we could do.

"I shall be glad to see you at the opera," said she, "and you can get into my dressing-room if you give the door-keeper a small piece of money."

The Abbé Gama came as he promised, to take me to Marshal Botta, a man of high talents whom the affair of Genoa had already rendered famous. He was in command of the Austrian army when the people, growing angry at the sight of the foreigners, who had only come to put them under the Austrian yoke, rose in revolt and made them leave the town. This patriotic riot saved the Republic. I found him in the midst of a crowd of ladies and gentlemen, whom he left to welcome me. He talked about Venice in a way that shewed he understood the country thoroughly, and I conversed to him on France, and, I believe, satisfied him. In his turn he spoke of the Court of Russia, at which he was staying when Elizabeth Petrovna, who was still reigning at the period in question, so easily mounted the throne of her father, Peter the Great. "It is only in Russia," said he, "that poison enters into politics."

At the time when the opera began the marshal left the room, and everybody went away. On my way the abbé assured me, as a matter of course, that I had pleased the governor, and I afterwards went to the theatre, and obtained admission to Thérèse's dressing-room for a tester. I found her in the hands of her pretty chamber-maid, and she advised me to go to Redegonde's dressing-room, as she played a man's part, and might, perhaps, allow me to assist in her toilette.

I followed her advice, but the mother would not let me come in, as her daughter was just going to dress. I assured her that I would turn my back all the time she was dressing, and on this condition she let me in, and made me sit down at a table on which stood a mirror, which enabled me to see all Redegonde's most secret parts to advantage; above all, when she lifted her legs to put on her breeches, either most awkwardly or most cleverly, according to her intentions. She did not lose anything by what she shewed, however, for I was so pleased, that to possess her charms I would have signed any conditions she cared to impose upon me.

"Redegonde must know," I said to myself, "that I could see everything in the glass;" and the idea inflamed me. I did not turn round till the mother gave me leave, and I then admired my charmer as a young man of five feet one, whose shape left nothing to be desired.

Redegonde went out, and I followed her to the wings.

"My dear," said I, "I am going to talk plainly to you. You have inflamed my passions and I shall die if you do not make me happy."

"You do not say that you will die if you chance to make me unhappy."

"I could not say so, because I cannot conceive such a thing as possible. Do not trifle with me, dear Redegonde, you must be aware that I saw all in the mirror, and I cannot think that you are so cruel as to arouse my passions and then leave me to despair."

"What could you have seen? I don't know what you are talking about."

"May be, but know that I have seen all your charms. What shall I do to possess you?"

"To possess me? I don't understand you, sir; I'm an honest girl."

"I dare say; but you wouldn't be any less honest after making me happy. Dear Redegonde, do not let me languish for you, but tell me my fate now this instant."

"I do not know what to tell you, but you can come and see me whenever you like."

"When shall I find you alone?"

"Alone! I am never alone."

"Well, well, that's of no consequence; if only your mother is present, that comes to the same thing. If she is sensible, she will pretend not to see anything, and I will give you a hundred ducats each time."

"You are either a madman, or you do not know what sort of people we are."

With these words she went on, and I proceeded to tell Thérèse what had passed.

"Begin," said she, "by offering the hundred ducats to the mother, and if she refuses, have no more to do with them, and go elsewhere."

I returned to the dressing-room, where I found the mother alone, and without any ceremony spoke as follows:

"Good evening, madam, I am a stranger here; I am only staying a week, and I am in love with your daughter. If you like to be obliging, bring her to sup with me. I will give you a hundred sequins each time, so you see my purse is in your power."

"Whom do you think you are talking to, sir? I am astonished at your impudence. Ask the townsfolk what sort of character I bear, and whether my daughter is an honest girl or not! and you will not make such proposals again."

"Good-bye, madam."

"Good-bye, sir."

As I went out I met Redegonde, and I told her word for word the conversation I had had with her mother. She burst out laughing.

"Have I done well or ill?" said I.

"Well enough, but if you love me come and see me."

"See you after what your mother said?"

"Well, why not, who knows of it?"

"Who knows? You don't know me, Redegonde. I do not care to indulge myself in idle hopes, and I thought I had spoken to you plainly enough."

Feeling angry, and vowing to have no more to do with this strange girl, I supped with Thérèse, and spent three delightful hours with her. I had a great deal of writing to do the next day and kept in doors, and in the evening I had a visit from the young Corticelli, her mother and brother. She begged me to keep my promise regarding the manager of the theatre, who would not let her dance the *pas de deux* stipulated for in the agreement.

"Come and breakfast with me to-morrow morning," said I, "and I will speak to the Israelite in your presence —at least I will do so if he comes."

"I love you very much," said the young wanton, "can't I stop a little longer here."

"You may stop as long as you like, but as I have got some letters to finish, I must ask you to excuse my entertaining you."

"Oh! just as you please."

I told Costa to give her some supper.

I finished my letters and felt inclined for a little amusement, so I made the girl sit by me and proceeded to toy with her, but in such a way that her mother could make no objection. All at once the brother came up and tried to join in the sport, much to my astonishment.

"Get along with you," said I, "you are not a girl."

At this the young scoundrel proceeded to shew me his sex, but in such an indecent fashion that his sister, who was sitting on my knee, burst out laughing and took refuge with her mother, who was sitting at the other end of the room in gratitude for the good supper I had given her. I rose from my chair, and after giving the impudent pederast a box on the ear I asked the mother with what intentions she had brought the young rascal to my house. By way of reply the infamous woman said,——

"He's a pretty lad, isn't he?"

I gave him a ducat for the blow I had given him, and told the mother to begone, as she disgusted me. The pathic took my ducat, kissed my hand, and they all departed.

I went to bed feeling amused at the incident, and wondering at the wickedness of a mother who would prostitute her own son to the basest of vices.

Next morning I sent and asked the Jew to call on me. The Corticelli came with her mother, and the Jew soon after, just as we were going to breakfast.

I proceeded to explain the grievance of the young dancer, and I read the agreement he had made with her, telling him politely that I could easily force him to fulfil it. The Jew put in several excuses, of which the Corticelli demonstrated the futility. At last the son of Judah was forced to give in, and promised to speak to the ballet-master the same day, in order that she might dance the *pas* with the actor she named.

"And that, I hope, will please your excellency," he added, with a low bow, which is not often a proof of sincerity, especially among Jews.

When my guests had taken leave I went to the Abbé Gama, to dine with Marshal Botta who had asked us to dinner. I made the acquaintance there of Sir —— Mann, the English ambassador, who was the idol of Florence, very rich, of the most pleasing manners although an Englishman; full of wit, taste, and a great lover of the fine arts. He invited me to come next day and see his house and garden. In this home he had made—furniture, pictures, choice books—all shewed the man of genius. He called on me, asked me to dinner, and had the politeness to include Thérèse, her husband, and Cesarino in the invitation. After dinner my son sat down at the clavier and delighted the company by his exquisite playing. While we were talking of likenesses, Sir —— Mann shewed us some miniatures of great beauty.

Before leaving, Thérèse told me that she had been thinking seriously of me.

"In what respect?" I asked.

"I have told Redegonde that I am going to call for her, that I will keep her to supper, and have her taken home. You must see that this last condition is properly carried out. Come to supper too, and have your carriage in waiting. I leave the rest to you. You will only be a few minutes with her, but that's something; and the first step leads far."

"An excellent plan. I will sup with you, and my carriage shall be ready. I will tell you all about it to-morrow."

I went to the house at nine o'clock, and was welcomed as an unexpected guest. I told Redegonde that I was glad to meet her, and she replied that she had not hoped to have the pleasure of seeing me. Redegonde was the only one who had any appetite; she ate capitally, and laughed merrily at the stories I told her.

After supper Thérèse asked her if she would like to have a sedan-chair sent for, or if she would prefer to be taken back in my carriage.

"If the gentleman will be so kind," said she, "I need not send for a chair."

I thought this reply of such favourable omen that I no longer doubted of my success. After she had wished the others good night, she took my arm, pressing it as she did so; we went down the stairs, and she got into the carriage. I got in after her, and on attempting to sit down I found the place taken.

"Who is that?" I cried.

Redegonde burst out laughing, and informed me it was her mother.

I was done; I could not summon up courage to pass it off as a jest. Such a shock makes a man stupid; for a moment it numbs all the mental faculties, and wounded self-esteem only gives place to anger.

I sat down on the front seat and coldly asked the mother why she had not come up to supper with us. When the carriage stopped at their door, she asked me to come in, but I told her I would rather not. I felt that for a little more I would have boxed her ears, and the man at the house door looked very like a cut-throat.

I felt enraged and excited physically as well as mentally, and though I had never been to see the Corticelli, told the coachman to drive there immediately, as I felt sure of finding her well disposed. Everybody was gone to bed. I knocked at the door till I got an answer, I gave my name, and I was let in, everything being in total darkness. The mother told me she would light a candle, and that if she had expected me she would have waited up in spite of the cold. I felt as if I were in the middle of an iceberg. I heard the girl laughing, and going up to the bed and passing my hand over it I came across some plain tokens of the masculine gender. I had got hold of her brother. In the meanwhile the mother had got a candle, and I saw the girl with the bedclothes up to her chin, for, like her brother, she was as naked as my hand. Although no Puritan, I was shocked.

"Why do you allow this horrible union?" I said to the mother.

"What harm is there? They are brother and sister."

"That's just what makes it a criminal matter."

"Everything is perfectly innocent."

"Possibly; but it's not a good plan."

The pathic escaped from the bed and crept into his mother's, while the little wanton told me there was really no harm, as they only loved each other as brother and sister, and that if I wanted her to sleep by herself all I had to do was to get her a new bed. This speech, delivered with arch simplicity, in her Bolognese jargon, made me laugh with all my heart, for in the violence of her gesticulations she had disclosed half her charms, and I saw nothing worth looking at. In spite of that, it was doubtless decreed that I should fall in love with her skin, for that was all she had.

If I had been alone I should have brought matters to a crisis on the spot, but I had a distaste to the presence of her mother and her scoundrelly brother. I was afraid lest some unpleasant scenes might follow. I gave her ten ducats to buy a bed, said good night, and left the house. I returned to my lodging, cursing the too scrupulous mothers of the opera girls.

I passed the whole of the next morning with Sir —— Mann, in his gallery, which contained some exquisite paintings, sculptures, mosaics, and engraved gems. On leaving him, I called on Thérèse and informed her of my misadventure of the night before. She laughed heartily at my story, and I laughed too, in spite of a feeling of anger due to my wounded self-esteem.

"You must console yourself," said she; "you will not find much difficulty in filling the place in your affections."

"Ah! why are you married?"

"Well, it's done; and there's no helping it. But listen

to me. As you can't do without someone, take up with the Corticelli; she's as good as any other woman, and won't keep you waiting long."

On my return to my lodging, I found the Abbé Gama, whom I had invited to dinner, and he asked me if I would accept a post to represent Portugal at the approaching European Congress at Augsburg. He told me that if I did the work well, I could get anything I liked at Lisbon.

"I am ready to do my best," said I; "you have only to write to me, and I will tell you where to direct your letters." This proposal made me long to become a diplomatist.

In the evening I went to the opera-house and spoke to the ballet-master, the dancer who was to take part in the *pas de deux*, and to the Jew, who told me that my *protégée* should be satisfied in two or three days, and that she should perform her favourite *pas* for the rest of the carnival. I saw the Corticelli, who told me she had got her bed, and asked me to come to supper. I accepted the invitation, and when the opera was over I went to her house.

Her mother, feeling sure that I would pay the bill, had ordered an excellent supper for four, and several flasks of the best Florence wine. Besides that, she gave me a bottle of the wine called Oleatico, which I found excellent. The three Corticellis unaccustomed to good fare and wine, ate like a troop, and began to get intoxicated. The mother and son went to bed without ceremony, and the little wanton invited me to follow their example. I should have liked to do so, but I did not dare. It was very cold and there was no fire in the room, there was only one blanket on the bed, and I might have caught a bad cold, and I was too fond of my good health to expose myself to such a danger. I therefore satisfied my-

self by taking her on my knee, and after a few preliminaries she abandoned herself to my transports, endeavouring to persuade me that I had got her maidenhead. I pretended to believe her, though I cared very little whether it were so or not.

I left her after I had repeated the dose three or four times, and gave her fifty sequins, telling her to get a good wadded coverlet and a large brazier, as I wanted to sleep with her the next night.

Next morning I received an extremely interesting letter from Grenoble. M. de Valenglard informed me that the fair Mdlle. Roman, feeling convinced that her horoscope would never come true unless she went to Paris, had gone to the capital with her aunt.

Her destiny was a strange one; it depended on the liking I had taken to her and my aversion to marriage, for it lay in my power to have married the handsomest woman in France, and in that case it is not likely that she would have become the mistress of Louis XV. What strange whim could have made me indicate in her horoscope the necessity of her journeying to Paris; for even if there were such a science as astrology I was no astrologer; in fine, her destiny depended on my absurd fancy. And in history, what a number of extraodinary events would never have happened if they had not been predicted!

In the evening I went to the theatre, and found my Corticelli clad in a pretty cloak, while the other girls looked at me contemptuously, for they were enraged at the place being taken; while the proud favourite caressed me with an air of triumph which became her to admiration.

In the evening I found a good supper awaiting me, a large brazier on the hearth, and a warm coverlet on the bed. The mother shewed me all the things her daughter had bought, and complained that she had not got any clothes for her brother. I made her happy by giving her a few louis.

When I went to bed I did not find my mistress in any amorous transports, but in a wanton and merry mood. She made me laugh, and as she let me do as I liked I was satisfied. I gave her a watch when I left her, and promised to sup with her on the following night. She was to have danced the *pas de deux,* and I went to see her do it, but to my astonishment she only danced with the other girls.

When I went to supper I found her in despair. She wept and said that I must avenge her on the Jew, who had excused himself by putting the fault on somebody else, but that he was a liar. I promised everything to quiet her, and after spending several hours in her company I returned home, determined to give the Jew a bad quarter of an hour. Next morning I sent Costa to ask him to call on me, but the rascal sent back word that he was not coming, and if the Corticelli did not like his theatre she might try another.

I was indignant, but I knew that I must dissemble, so I only laughed. Nevertheless, I had pronounced his doom, for an Italian never forgets to avenge himself on his enemy; he knows it is the pleasure of the gods.

As soon as Costa had left the room, I called Le Duc and told him the story, saying that if I did not take vengeance I should be dishonoured, and that it was only he who could procure the scoundrel a good thrashing for daring to insult me.

"But you know, Le Duc, the affair must be kept secret."

"I only want twenty-four hours to give you an answer."

I knew what he meant, and I was satisfied.

Next morning Le Duc told me he had spent the previous day in learning the Jew's abode and habits, without asking anybody any questions.

"To-day I will not let him go out of my sight. I shall find out at what hour he returns home, and to-morrow you shall know the results."

"Be discreet," said I, "and don't let anybody into your plans."

"Not I."

Next day, he told me that if the Jew came home at the same time and by the same way as before, he would have a thrashing before he got to bed.

"Whom have you chosen for this expedition?"

"Myself. These affairs ought to be kept secret, and a secret oughtn't to be known to more than two people. I am sure that everything will turn out well, but when you are satisfied that the ass's hide has been well tanned, will there be anything to be picked up?"

"Twenty-five sequins."

"That will do nicely. When I have done the trick I shall put on my great coat again and return by the back door. If necessary Costa himself will be able to swear that I did not leave the house, and that therefore I cannot have committed the assault. However, I shall put my pistols in my pocket in case of accidents, and if anybody tries to arrest me I shall know how to defend myself."

Next morning he came coolly into my room while Costa was putting on my dressing-gown, and when we were alone he said,——

"The thing's done. Instead of the Jew's running away when he received the first blow he threw himself on to the ground. Then I tanned his skin for him nicely, but on hearing some people coming up I ran off. I don't know whether I did for him, but I gave him two sturdy blows on the head. I should be sorry if he were killed, as then he could not see about the dance."

This jest did not arouse my mirth; the matter promised to be too serious.

Thérèse had asked me to dine with the Abbé Gama and M. Sassi, a worthy man, if one may prostitute the name of man to describe a being whom cruelty has separated from the rest of humanity; he was the first *castrato* of the opera. Of course the Jew's mishap was discussed.

"I am sorry for him," said I, "though he is a rascally fellow."

"I am not at all sorry for him myself," said Sassi, "he's a knave. I daresay that everybody will be putting down his wooden baptism to my account."

"No," said the abbé, "people say that M. Casanova did the deed for good reasons of his own."

"It will be difficult to pitch on the right man," I answered, "the rascal has pushed so many worthy people to extremities that he must have a great many thrashings owing him."

The conversation then passed to other topics, and we had a very pleasant dinner.

In a few days the Jew left his bed with a large plaster on his nose, and although I was generally regarded as the author of his misfortune the matter was gradually allowed to drop, as there were only vague suspicions to go upon. But the Corticelli, in an ecstasy of joy, was stupid enough to talk as if she were sure it was I who had avenged her, and she got into a rage when I would not admit the deed; but, as may be guessed, I was not foolish enough to do so, as her imprudence might have been a hanging matter for me.

I was well enough amused at Florence, and had no thoughts of leaving, when one day Vannini gave me a letter which someone had left for me. I opened it in his presence, and found it contained a bill of exchange for two hundred Florentine crowns on Sasso Sassi. Vannini looked at it and told me it was a good one. I went into my room to read the letter, and I was astonished to find it signed "Charles Ivanoff." He dated it from Pistoia, and told me that in his poverty and misfortune he had appealed to an Englishman who was leaving Florence for Lucca, and had generously given him a bill of exchange for two hundred crowns, which he had written in his presence. It was made payable to bearer.

"I daren't cash it in Florence," said he, "as I am afraid of being arrested for my unfortunate affair at Genoa. I entreat you, then, to have pity on me, to get the bill cashed, and to bring me the money here, that I may pay my landlord and go."

It looked like a very simple matter, but I might get into trouble, for the note might be forged; and even if it were not I should be declaring myself a friend or a correspondent, at all events, of a man who had been posted. In this dilemma I took the part of taking the bill of exchange to him in person. I went to the posting establishment, hired two horses, and drove to Pistoia. The landlord himself took me to the rascal's room, and left me alone with him. I did not stay more than three minutes, and all I said was that as Sassi knew me I did not wish him to think that there was any kind of connection between us.

"I advise you," I said, "to give the bill to your land-lord, who will cash it at M. Sassi's and bring you your change."

"I will follow your advice," he said, and I therewith returned to Florence.

I thought no more of it, but in two days' time I received a visit from M. Sassi and the landlord of the inn at Pistoia. The banker shewed me the bill of exchange, and said that the person who had given it me had deceived me, as it was not in the writing of the Englishman whose name it bore, and that even if it were, the Englishman not having any money with Sassi could not draw a bill of exchange.

"The inn-keeper here," said he, "discounted the bill, the Russian has gone off, and when I told him that it was a forgery he said that he knew Charles Ivanoff had it of you, and that thus he had made no difficulty in cashing it; but now he wants you to return him two hundred crowns."

"Then he will be disappointed!"

I told all the circumstances of the affair to Sassi; I shewed him the rascal's letter; I made Dr. Vannini, who had given it me, come up, and he said he was ready to swear that he had seen me take the bill of exchange out of the letter, that he had examined it, and had thought it good.

On this the banker told the inn-keeper that he had no business to ask me to pay him the money; but he persisted in his demand, and dared to say that I was an accomplice of the Russian's.

In my indignation I ran for my cane, but the banker held me by the arm, and the impertinent fellow made his escape without a thrashing.

"You had a right to be angry," said M. Sassi, "but you must not take any notice of what the poor fellow says in his blind rage."

He shook me by the hand and went out.

Next day the chief of police, called the auditor at Florence, sent me a note begging me to call on him. There was no room for hesitation, for as a stranger I felt that I might look on this invitation as an intimation. He received me very politely, but he said I should have to repay the landlord his two hundred crowns, as he would not have discounted the bill if he had not seen me bring it. I replied that as a judge he could not condemn me unless he thought me the Russian's accomplice, but instead of answering he repeated that I would have to pay.

"Sir," I replied, "I will not pay."

He rang the bell and bowed, and I left him, walking towards the banker's, to whom I imparted the conversation I had had from the auditor. He was extremely astonished, and at my request called on him to try and make him listen to reason. As we parted I told him that I was dining with the Abeé Gama.

When I saw the abbé I told him what had happened, and he uttered a loud exclamation of astonishment.

"I foresee," he said, "that the auditor will not let go his hold, and if M. Sassi does not succeed with him I advise you to speak to Marshal Botta."

"I don't think that will be necessary; the auditor can't force me to pay."

"He can do worse."

"What can he do?"

"He can make you leave Florence."

"Well, I shall be astonished if he uses his power in this

case, but rather than pay I will leave the town. Let us go to the marshal."

We called on him at four o'clock, and we found the banker there, who had told him the whole story.

"I am sorry to tell you," said M. Sassi, "that I could do nothing with the auditor, and if you want to remain in Florence you will have to pay."

"I will leave as soon as I receive the order," said I; "and as soon as I reach another state I will print the history of this shameful perversion of justice."

"It's an incredible, a monstrous sentence" said the marshal, "and I am sorry I cannot interfere. You are quite right," he added, "to leave the place rather than pay."

Early the next morning a police official brought me a letter from the auditor, informing me that as he could not, from the nature of the case, oblige me to pay, he was forced to warn me to leave Florence in three days, and Tuscany in seven. This, he added, he did in virtue of his office; but whenever the Grand Duke, to whom I might appeal, had quashed his judgment I might return.

I took a piece of paper and wrote upon it, "Your judgment is an iniquitous one, but it shall be obeyed to the letter."

At that moment I gave orders to pack up and have all in readiness for my departure. I spent three days of respite in amusing myself with Thérèse. I also saw the worthy Sir —— Mann, and I promised the Corticelli to fetch her in Lent, and spend some time with her in Bologna. The Abbé Gama did not leave my side for three days, and shewed himself my true friend. It was a kind of triumph for me; on every side I heard regrets at my departure, and curses of the auditor. The Marquis Botta seemed to approve my conduct by giving me a dinner, the table being laid for thirty, and the company being composed of the most distinguished people in Florence. This was a delicate attention on his part, of which I was very sensible.

I consecrated the last day to Thérèse, but I could not find any opportunity to ask her for a last consoling embrace, which she would not have refused me under the circumstances, and which I should still fondly remember. We promised to write often to one another, and we embraced each other in a way to make her husband's heart ache. Next day I started on my journey, and got to Rome in thirty-six hours.

It was midnight when I passed under the Porta del Popolo, for one may enter the Eternal City at any time. I was then taken to the custom-house, which is always open, and my mails were examined. The only thing they are strict about at Rome is books, as if they feared the light. I had about thirty volumes, all more or less against the Papacy, religion, or the virtues inculcated thereby. I had resolved to surrender them without any dispute, as I felt tired and wanted to go to bed, but the clerk told me politely to count them and leave them in his charge for the night, and he would bring them to my hotel in the morning. I did so, and he kept his word. He was well enough pleased when he touched the two sequins with which I rewarded him.

I put up at the Ville de Paris, in the Piazza di Spagna. It is the best inn in the town. All the world, I found, was drowned in sleep, but when they let me in they asked me to wait on the ground floor while a fire was lighted in my room. All the seats were covered with dresses, petticoats, and chemises, and I heard a small feminine voice begging me to sit on her bed. I approached and saw a laughing mouth, and two black eyes shining like carbuncles.

"What splendid eyes!" said I, "let me kiss them."

By way of reply she hid her head under the coverlet, and I slid a hasty hand under the sheets; but finding her quite naked, I drew it back and begged pardon. She put out her head again, and I thought I read gratitude for my moderation in her eyes.

"Who are you, my angel?"

"I am Thérèse, the inn-keeper's daughter, and this is my sister." There was another girl beside her, whom I had not seen, as her head was under the bolster.

"How old are you?"

"Nearly seventeen."

"I hope I shall see you in my room to-morrow morning."

"Have you any ladies with you?"

"No."

"That's a pity, as we never go to the gentlemen's rooms."

"Lower the coverlet a little; I can't hear what you say."

"It's too cold."

"Dear Thérèse, your eyes make me feel as if I were in flames."

She put back her head at this, and I grew daring, and after sundry experiments I was more than ever charmed with her. I caressed her in a somewhat lively manner, and drew back my hand, again apologizing for my daring, and when she let me see her face I thought I saw delight rather than anger in her eyes and on her cheeks, and I felt hopeful with regard to her. I was just going to begin again, for I felt on fire, when a handsome chamber-maid came to tell me that my room was ready and my fire lighted.

"Farewell till to-morrow," said I to Thérèse, but she only answered by turning on her side to go to sleep.

I went to bed after ordering dinner for one o'clock, and I slept till noon, dreaming of Thérèse. When I woke up, Costa told me that he had found out where my brother lived, and had left a note at the house. This was my brother Jean, then about thirty, and a pupil of the famous Raphael Mengs. This painter was then deprived of his pension on account of a war which obliged the King of Poland to live at Warsaw, as the Prussians occupied the whole electorate of Saxe. I had not seen my brother for ten years, and I kept our meeting as a holiday. I was sitting down to table when he came, and we embraced each other with transport. We spent an hour in telling, he his small adventures, and I my grand ones, and he told me that I should not stay at the hotel, which was too dear, but come and live at the Chevalier Mengs's house, which contained an empty room, where I could stay at a much cheaper rate.

"As to your table, there is a restaurant in the house where one can get a capital meal."

"Your advice is excellent," said I, "but I have not the courage to follow it, as I am in love with my landlord's daughter;" and I told him what had happened the night before.

"That's a mere nothing," said he, laughing; "you can cultivate her acquaintance without staying in the house."

I let myself be persuaded, and I promised to come to him the following day; and then we proceeded to take a walk about Rome.

I had many interesting memories of my last visit, and I wanted to renew my acquaintance with those who had interested me at that happy age when such impressions

are so durable because they touch the heart rather than
the mind; but I had to make up my mind to a good
many disappointments, considering the space of time
that had elapsed since I had been in Rome.

I went to the Minerva to find Donna Cecilia; she was
no more in this world. I found out where her daughter
Angelica lived, and I went to see her, but she gave me a
poor reception, and said that she really scarcely remembered me.

"I can say the same," I replied, "for you are not the
Angelica I used to know. Good-bye, madam!"

The lapse of time had not improved her personal
appearance. I found out also where the printer's son,
who had married Barbaruccia, lived, but I put off the
pleasure of seeing him till another time, and also my visit
to the Reverend Father Georgi, who was a man of great
repute in Rome. Gaspar Vivaldi had gone into the
country.

My brother took me to Madame Cherubini. I found
her mansion to be a splendid one, and the lady welcomed
me in the Roman manner. I thought her pleasant and
her daughters still more so, but I thought the crowd of
lovers too large and too miscellaneous. There was too
much luxury and ceremony, and the girls, one of whom
was as fair as Love himself, were too polite to everybody.
An interesting question was put to me, to which I answered in such a manner as to elicit another question,
but to no purpose. I saw that the rank of my brother,
who had introduced me, prevented my being thought a
person of any consequence, and on hearing an abbé say,
"He's Casanova's brother," I turned to him and said,——

"That's not correct; you should say Casanova's my
brother."

"That comes to the same thing."

"Not at all, my dear abbé."

I said these words in a tone which commanded attention, and another abbé said,——

"The gentleman is quite right; it does *not* come to the same thing."

The first abbé made no reply to this. The one who had taken my part, and was my friend from that moment, was the famous Winckelmann, who was unhappily assassinated at Trieste twelve years afterwards.

While I was talking to him, Cardinal Alexander Albani arrived. Winckelmann presented me to his eminence, who was nearly blind. He talked to me a great deal, without saying anything worth listening to. As soon as he heard that I was the Casanova who had escaped from The Leads, he said in a somewhat rude tone that he wondered I had the hardihood to come to Rome, where on the slightest hint from the State Inquisitors at Venice an *ordine santissimo* would re-consign me to my prison. I was annoyed by this unseemly remark, and replied in a dignified voice,——

"It is not my hardihood in coming to Rome that your eminence should wonder at, but a man of any sense would wonder at the Inquisitors if they had the hardihood to issue an *ordine santissimo* against me; for they would be perplexed to allege any crime in me as a pretext for thus infamously depriving me of my liberty."

This reply silenced his eminence. He was ashamed at having taken me for a fool, and to see that I thought him one. Shortly after I left and never set foot in that house again.

The Abbé Winckelmann went out with my brother and myself, and as he came with me to my hotel he did me the honour of staying to supper. Winckelmann was the second volume of the celebrated Abbé de Voisenon. He called for me next day, and we went to Villa Albani to see the Chevalier Mengs, who was then living there and painting a ceiling.

My landlord Roland (who knew my brother) paid me a visit at supper. Roland came from Avignon and was fond of good living. I told him I was sorry to be leaving him to stay with my brother, because I had fallen in love with his daughter Thérèse, although I had only spoken to her for a few minutes, and had only seen her head.

"You saw her in bed, I will bet."

"Exactly, and I should very much like to see the rest of her. Would you be so kind as to ask her to step up for a few minutes?"

"With all my heart."

She came upstairs, seeming only too glad to obey her father's summons. She had a lithe, graceful figure, her eyes were of surpassing brilliancy, her features exquisite, her mouth charming; but taken altogether I did not like her so well as before. In return, my poor brother became enamoured of her to such an extent that he ended by becoming her slave. He married her next year, and two years afterwards he took her to Dresden. I saw her five years later with a pretty baby; but after ten years of married life she died of consumption.

I found Mengs at the Villa Albani; he was an indefatigable worker, and extremely original in his conceptions. He welcomed me, and said he was glad to be able to lodge me at his house in Rome, and that he hoped to return home himself in a few days, with his whole family. I was astonished with the Villa Albani. It had been built by Cardinal Alexander, and had been wholly constructed from antique materials to satisfy the cardinal's love for classic art; not only the statues and the vases, but the columns, the pedestals— in fact, everything was Greek. He was a Greek himself, and had a perfect knowledge of antique work, and had contrived to spend comparatively little money compared with the masterpiece he had produced. If a sovereign monarch had had a villa like the cardinal's built, it would have cost him fifty million francs, but the cardinal made a much cheaper bargain.

As he could not get any ancient ceilings, he was obliged to have them painted, and Mengs was undoubtedly the greatest and the most laborious painter of his age. It is a great pity that death carried him off in the midst of his career, as otherwise he would have enriched the stores of art with numerous masterpieces. My brother never did anything to justify his title of pupil of this great artist. When I come to my visit to Spain in 1767, I shall have some more to say about Mengs.

As soon as I was settled with my brother I hired a carriage, a coachman, and a footman, whom I put into fancy livery, and I called on Monsignor Cornaro, auditor of the rota, with the intention of making my way into good society, but fearing lest he as a Venetian might get compromised, he introduced me to Cardinal Passionei, who spoke of me to the sovereign pontiff.

Before I pass on to anything else, I will inform my readers of what took place on the occasion of my second visit to this old cardinal, a great enemy of the Jesuits, a wit, and man of letters.

CHAPTER VIII

Cardinal Passionei—The Pope—Mariuccia—I Arrive At Naples

CARDINAL PASSIONEI received me in a large hall where he was writing. He begged me to wait till he had finished, but he could not ask me to take a seat as he occupied the only chair that his vast room contained.

When he had put down his pen, he rose, came to me, and after informing me that he would tell the Holy Father of my visit, he added,——

"My brother Cornaro might have made a better choice, as he knows the Pope does not like me."

"He thought it better to choose the man who is esteemed than the man who is merely liked."

"I don't know whether the Pope esteems me, but I am sure he knows I don't esteem him. I both liked and esteemed him before he was pope, and I concurred in his election, but since he has worn the tiara it's a different matter; he has shewn himself too much of a *coglione*."

"The conclave ought to have chosen your eminence."

"No, no; I'm a root-and-branch reformer, and my hand would not have been stayed for fear of the vengeance of the guilty, and God alone knows what would have come of that. The only cardinal fit to be pope was Tamburini; but it can't be helped now. I hear people coming; good-bye, come again to-morrow."

What a delightful thing to have heard a cardinal call

198

the Pope a fool, and name Tamburini as a fit person. I
did not lose a moment in noting this pleasant circumstance down: it was too precious a morsel to let slip.
But who was Tamburini? I had never heard of him.
I asked Winckelmann, who dined with me.

"He's a man deserving of respect for his virtues, his
character, his firmness, and his farseeing intelligence.
He has never disguised his opinion of the Jesuits, whom
he styles the fathers of deceits, intrigues, and lies;
and that's what made Passionei mention him. I think,
with him, that Tamburini would be a great and good
pope."

I will here note down what I heard at Rome nine
years later from the mouth of a tool of the Jesuits. The
Cardinal Tamburini was at the last gasp, and the conversation turned upon him, when somebody else
said,——

"This Benedictine cardinal is an impious fellow after
all; he is on his death-bed, and he has asked for the
viaticum, without wishing to purify his soul by confession."

I did not make any remark, but feeling as if I should
like to know the truth of the matter I asked somebody
about it next day, my informant being a person who
must have known the truth, and could not have had any
motive for disguising the real facts of the case. He told
me that the cardinal had said mass three days before,
and that if he had not asked for a confessor it was doubtless because he had nothing to confess.

Unfortunate are they that love the truth, and do not
seek it out at its source. I hope the reader will pardon
this digression, which is not without interest.

Next day I went to see Cardinal Passionei, who told
me I was quite right to come early, as he wanted to

learn all about my escape from The Leads, of which he had heard some wonderful tales told.

"I shall be delighted to satisfy your eminence, but the story is a long one."

"All the better; they say you tell it well."

"But, my lord, am I to sit down on the floor?"

"No, no; your dress is too good for that."

He rang his bell, and having told one of his gentlemen to send up a seat, a servant brought in a stool. A seat without a back and without arms! It made me quite angry. I cut my story short, told it badly, and had finished in a quarter of an hour.

"I write better than you speak," said he.

"My lord, I never speak well except when I am at my ease."

"But you are not afraid of me?"

"No, my lord, a true man and a philosopher can never make me afraid; but this stool of yours. . . ."

"You like to be at your ease, above all things."

"Take this, it is the funeral oration of Prince Eugène; I make you a present of it. I hope you will approve of my Latinity. You can kiss the Pope's feet to-morrow at ten o'clock."

When I got home, as I reflected on the character of this strange cardinal—a wit, haughty, vain, and boastful, I resolved to make him a fine present. It was the *Pandectarum liber unicus* which M. de F—— had given me at Berne, and which I did not know what to do with. It was a folio well printed on fine paper, choicely bound, and in perfect preservation. As chief librarian the present should be a valuable one to him, all the more as he had a large private library, of which my friend the Abbé Winckelmann was librarian. I therefore wrote a short Latin letter, which I enclosed in another to Winckelmann, whom I begged to present my offering to his eminence. I thought it was as valuable as his funeral oration at any rate, and I hoped that he would give me a more comfortable chair for the future.

Next morning, at the time appointed, I went to Monte Cavallo, which ought to be called Monte Cavalli, as it gets its name from two fine statues of horses standing on a pedestal in the midst of the square, where the Holy Father's palace is situated.

I had no real need of being presented to the Pope by anyone, as any Christian is at liberty to go in when he sees the door open. Besides I had known His Holiness when he was Bishop of Padua; but I had preferred to claim the honor of being introduced by a cardinal.

After saluting the Head of the Faithful, and kissing the holy cross embroidered on his holy slipper, the Pope put his right hand on my left shoulder, and said he remembered that I always forsook the assembly at Padua, when he intoned the Rosary.

"Holy Father, I have much worse sins than that on my conscience, so I come prostrate at your foot to receive your absolution."

He then gave me his benediction, and asked me very graciously what he could do for me.

"I beg Your Holiness to plead for me, that I may be able to return to Venice."

"We will speak of it to the ambassador, and then we will speak again to you on the matter."

"Do you often go and see Cardinal Passionei?"

"I have been three times. He gave me his funeral oration on Prince Eugène, and in return I sent him the Pandects."

"Has he accepted them?"

"I think so, Holy Father."

"If he has, he will send Winckelmann to pay you for them."

"That would be treating me like a bookseller; I will not receive any payment."

"Then he will return the volume of the Pandects; we are sure of it, he always does so."

"If his eminence returns me the Pandects, I will return him his funeral oration."

At this the Pope laughed till his sides shook.

"We shall be pleased to hear the end of the story without anyone being informed of our innocent curiosity."

With these words, a long benediction delivered with much unction informed me that my audience was at an end.

As I was leaving His Holiness's palace, I was accosted by an old abbé, who asked me respectfully if I were not the M. Casanova who had escaped from The Leads.

"Yes," said I, "I am the man."

"Heaven be praised, worthy sir, that I see you again in such good estate!"

"But whom have I the honour of addressing?"

"Don't you recollect me? I am Momolo, formerly gondolier at Venice."

"Have you entered holy orders, then?"

"Not at all, but here everyone wears the cassock. I am the first *scopatore* (sweeper) of His Holiness the Pope."

"I congratulate you on your appointment, but you musn't mind me laughing."

"Laugh as much as you like. My wife and daughters laugh when I put on the cassock and bands, and I laugh myself, but here the dress gains one respect. Come and see us."

"Where do you live?"

"Behind the Trinity of Monti; here's my address."

"I will come to-night."

I went home delighted with this meeting, and determined to enjoy the evening with my Venetian boatman. I got my brother to come with me, and I told him how the Pope had received me.

The Abbé Winckelmann came in the afternoon and informed me that I was fortunate enough to be high in favour with his cardinal, and that the book I had sent him was very valuable; it was a rare work, and in much better condition than the Vatican copy.

"I am commissioned to pay you for it."

"I have told his eminence that it was a present."

"He never accepts books as presents, and he wants yours for his own library; and as he is librarian of the Vatican Library he is afraid lest people might say unpleasant things."

"That's very well, but I am not a bookseller; and as this book only cost me the trouble of accepting it, I am determined only to sell it at the same price. Pray ask the cardinal to honour me by accepting it."

"He is sure to send it back to you."

"He can if he likes, but I will send back his funeral oration, as I am not going to be under an obligation to anyone who refuses to take a present from me."

Next morning the eccentric cardinal returned me my Pandects, and I immediately returned his funeral oration, with a letter in which I pronounced it a masterpiece of composition, though I had barely glanced over it in reality. My brother told me I was wrong, but I did not trouble what he said, not caring to guide myself by his rulings.

In the evening my brother and I went to the *scopatore*

santissimo, who was expecting me, and had announced me to his family as a prodigy of a man. I introduced my brother, and proceeded to a close scrutiny of the family. I saw an elderly woman, four girls, of whom the eldest was twenty-four, two small boys, and above all universal ugliness. It was not inviting for a man of voluptuous tastes, but I was there, and the best thing was to put a good face on it; so I stayed and enjoyed myself. Besides the general ugliness, the household presented the picture of misery, for the *scopatore santissimo* and his numerous family were obliged to live on two hundred Roman crowns a year, and as there are no perquisites attached to the office of apostolic sweeper, he was compelled to furnish all needs out of this slender sum. In spite of that Momolo was a most generous man. As soon as he saw me seated he told me he should have liked to give me a good supper, but there was only pork chops and a polenta.

"They are very nice," said I; "but will you allow me to send for half a dozen flasks of Orvieto from my lodging?"

"You are master here."

I wrote a note to Costa, telling him to bring the six flasks directly, with a cooked ham. He came in half an hour, and the four girls cried when they saw him, "What a fine fellow!" I saw Costa was delighted with this reception, and said to Momolo,——

"If you like him as well as your girls I will let him stay."

Costa was charmed with such honour being shewn him, and after thanking me went into the kitchen to help the mother with the polenta.

The large table was covered with a clean cloth, and soon after they brought in two huge dishes of polenta and an enormous pan full of chops. We were just going to begin when a knocking on the street door was heard.

" 'Tis Signora Maria and her mother," said one of the boys.

At this announcement I saw the four girls pulling a wry face. "Who asked them?" said one. "What do they want?" said another. "What troublesome people they are!" said a third. "They might have stayed at home," said the fourth. But the good, kindly father said, "My children, they are hungry, and they shall share what Providence has given us."

I was deeply touched with the worthy man's kindness. I saw that true Christian charity is more often to be found in the breasts of the poor than the rich, who are so well provided for that they cannot feel for the wants of others.

While I was making these wholesome reflections the two hungry ones came in. One was a young woman of a modest and pleasant aspect, and the other her mother, who seemed very humble and as if ashamed of their poverty. The daughter saluted the company with that natural grace which is a gift of nature, apologizing in some confusion for her presence, and saying that she would not have taken the liberty to come if she had known there was company. The worthy Momolo was the only one who answered her, and he said, kindly, that she had done quite right to come, and put her a chair between my brother and myself. I looked at her and thought her a perfect beauty.

Then the eating began and there was no more talking. The polenta was excellent, the chops delicious, and the ham perfect, and in less than an hour the board was as bare as if there had been nothing on it; but the Orvieto kept the company in good spirts. They began to talk of the lottery which was to be drawn the day after next, and all the girls mentioned the numbers on which they had risked a few bajocchi.

"If I could be sure of one number," said I, "I would stake something on it."

Mariuccia told me that if I wanted a number she could give me one. I laughed at this offer, but in the gravest way she named me the number 27.

"Is the lottery still open?" I asked the Abbé Momolo.

"Till midnight," he replied, "and if you like I will go and get the number for you."

"Here are fifty crowns," said I, "put twenty-five crowns on 27—this for these five young ladies; and the other twenty-five on 27 coming out the fifth number, and this I will keep for myself."

He went out directly and returned with the two tickets.

My pretty neighbour thanked me and said she was sure of winning, but that she did not think I should succeed as it was not probable that 27 would come out fifth.

"I am sure of it," I answered, "for you are the fifth young lady I saw in this house." This made everybody laugh. Momolo's wife told me I would have done much better if I had given the money to the poor, but her husband told her to be quiet, as she did not know my intent. My brother laughed, and told me I had done a foolish thing. "I do, sometimes," said I, "but we shall see how it turns out, and when one plays one is obliged either to win or lose."

I managed to squeeze my fair neighbour's hand, and she returned the pressure with all her strength. From that time I knew that my fate with Mariuccia was sealed. I left them at midnight, begging the worthy

Momolo to ask me again in two days' time, that we might rejoice together over our gains. On our way home my brother said I had either become as rich as Crœsus or had gone mad. I told him that both suppositions were incorrect, but that Mariuccia was as handsome as an angel, and he agreed.

Next day Mengs returned to Rome, and I supped with him and his family. He had an exceedingly ugly sister, who for all that, was a good and talented woman. She had fallen deeply in love with my brother, and it was easy to see that the flame was not yet extinguished, but whenever she spoke to him, which she did whenever she could get an opportunity, he looked another way.

She was an exquisite painter of miniatures, and a capital hand at catching a likeness. To the best of my belief she is still living at Rome with Maroni her husband. She often used to speak of my brother to me, and one day she said that he must be the most thankless of men or he would not despise her so. I was not curious enough to enquire what claim she had to his gratitude.

Mengs's wife was a good and pretty woman, attentive to her household duties and very submissive to her husband, though she could not have loved him, for he was anything but amiable. He was obstinate and fierce in his manner, and when he dined at home he made a point of not leaving the table before he was drunk; out of his own house he was temperate to the extent of not drinking anything but water. His wife carried her obedience so far as to serve as his model for all the nude figures he painted. I spoke to her one day about this unpleasant obligation, and she said that her confessor had charged her to fulfil it, "for," said he, "if your husband has another woman for a model he will be sure to enjoy her before painting her, and that sin would be laid to your charge."

After supper, Winckelmann, who was as far gone as all the other male guests, played with Mengs's children. There was nothing of the pedant about this philosopher; he loved children and young people, and his cheerful disposition made him delight in all kinds of enjoyment.

Next day, as I was going to pay my court to the Pope, I saw Momolo in the first ante-chamber, and I took care to remind him of the polenta for the evening.

As soon as the Pope saw me, he said,——

"The Venetian ambassador has informed us that if you wish to return to your native land, you must go and present yourself before the secretary of the Tribunal."

"Most Holy Father, I am quite ready to take this step, if Your Holiness will grant me a letter of commendation written with your own hand. Without this powerful protection I should never dream of exposing myself to the risk of being again shut up in a place from which I escaped by a miracle and the help of the Almighty."

"You are gaily dressed; you do not look as if you were going to church."

"True, most Holy Father, but neither am I going to a ball."

"We have heard all about the presents being sent back. Confess that you did so to gratify your pride."

"Yes, but also to lower a pride greater than mine."

The Pope smiled at this reply, and I knelt down and begged him to permit me to present the volume of Pandects to the Vatican Library. By way of reply he gave me his blessing, which signifies, in papal language, "Rise; your request is granted."

"We will send you," said he, "a mark of our *singular affection* for you without your having to pay any fees."

A second blessing bid me begone. I have often felt what a good thing it would be if this kind of dismissal could be employed in general society to send away importunate petitioners, to whom one does not dare say, "Begone."

I was extremely curious to know what the Pope had meant by "a mark of our singular affection." I was afraid that it would be a blessed rosary, with which I should not have known what to do.

When I got home I sent the book by Costa to the Vatican, and then I went to dine with Mengs. While we were eating the soup the winning numbers from the lottery were brought in. My brother glanced at them and looked at me with astonishment. I was not thinking of the subject at that moment, and his gaze surprised me.

"Twenty-seven," he cried, "came out fifth."

"All the better," said I, "we shall have some amusement out of it."

I told the story to Mengs, who said,——

"It's a lucky folly for you this time; but it always is a folly."

He was quite right, and I told him that I agreed with him; but I added that to make a worthy use of the fifteen hundred roman crowns which fortune had given me, I should go and spend fifteen days at Naples.

"I will come too," said the Abbé Alfani. "I will pass for your secretary."

"With all my heart," I answered, "I shall keep you to your word."

I asked Winckelmann to come and eat polenta with the *scopatore santissimo*, and told my brother to shew him the way; and I then called on the Marquis Belloni, my banker, to look into my accounts, and to get a letter of credit on the firm at Naples, who were his agents. I still had two hundred thousand francs: I had jewellery worth thirty thousand francs, and fifty thousand florins at Amsterdam.

I got to Momolo's in the dusk of the evening, and I found Winckelmann and my brother already there; but instead of mirth reigning round the board I saw sad faces on all sides.

"What's the matter with the girls?" I asked Momolo.

"They are vexed that you did not stake for them in the same way as you did for yourself."

"People are never satisfied. If I had staked for them as I did for myself, and the number had come out first instead of fifth, they would have got nothing, and they would have been vexed then. Two days ago they had nothing, and now that they have twenty-seven pounds apiece they ought to be contented."

"That's just what I tell them, but all women are the same."

"And men too, dear countryman, unless they are philosophers. Gold does not spell happiness, and mirth can only be found in hearts devoid of care. Let us say no more about it, but be happy."

Costa placed a basket containing ten packets of sweets upon the table.

"I will distribute them," said I, "when everybody is here."

On this, Momolo's second daughter told me that Mariuccia and her mother were not coming, but that they would send them the sweets.

"Why are they not coming?"

"They had a quarrel yesterday," said the father, "and Mariuccia, who was in the right, went away saying that she would never come here again."

"You ungrateful girls!" said I, to my host's daughters,

"don't you know that it is to her that you owe your winnings, for she gave me the number twenty-seven, which I should never have thought of. Quick! think of some way to make her come, or I will go away and take all the sweets with me."

"You are quite right," said Momolo.

The mortified girls looked at one another and begged their father to fetch her.

"No," said he, "that won't do; you made her say that she would never come here again, and you must make up the quarrel."

They held a short consultation, and then, asking Costa to go with them, they went to fetch her.

In half an hour they returned in triumph, and Costa was quite proud of the part he had taken in the reconciliation. I then distributed the sweets, taking care to give the two best packets to the fair Mary.

A noble polenta was placed upon the board, flanked by two large dishes of pork chops. But Momolo, who knew my tastes, and whom I had made rich in the person of his daughters, added to the feast some delicate dishes and some excellent wine. Mariuccia was simply dressed, but her elegance and beauty and the modesty of her demeanour completely seduced me.

We could only express our mutual flames by squeezing each other's hands; and she did this so feelingly that I could not doubt her love. As we were going out I took care to go downstairs beside her and asked if I could not meet her by herself, to which she replied by making an appointment with me for the next day at eight o'clock at the Trinity of Monti.

Mariuccia was tall and shapely, a perfect picture, as fair as a white rose, and calculated to inspire voluptuous desires. She had beautiful light brown hair, dark blue

eyes, and exquisitely arched eyelids. Her mouth, the
vermilion of her lips, and her ivory teeth were all perfect.
Her well-shaped forehead gave her an air approaching
the majestic. Kindness and gaiety sparkled in her eyes;
while her plump white hands, her rounded finger-tips,
her pink nails, her breast, which the corset seemed
scarcely able to restrain, her dainty feet, and her prominent hips, made her worthy of the chisel of Praxiteles.
She was just on her eighteenth year, and so far had escaped the connoisseurs. By a lucky chance I came
across her in a poor and wretched street, and I was
fortunate enough to insure her happiness.

It may easily be believed that I did not fail to keep
the appointment, and when she was sure I had seen her
she went out of the church. I followed her at a considerable distance: she entered a ruined building, and I
after her. She climbed a flight of steps which seemed to
be built in air, and when she had reached the top she
turned.

"No one will come and look for me here," said she, "so
we can talk freely together."

I sat beside her on a stone, and I then declared my
passionate love for her.

"Tell me," I added, "what I can do to make you
happy; for I wish to possess you, but first to shew my
deserts."

"Make me happy, and I will yield to your desires,
for I love you."

"Tell me what I can do."

"You can draw me out of the poverty and misery
which overwhelm me. I live with my mother, who is a
good woman, but devout to the point of superstition;
she will damn my soul in her efforts to save it. She

finds fault with my keeping myself clean, because I have to touch myself when I wash, and that might give rise to evil desires. If you had given me the money you made me win in the lottery as a simple alms she would have made me refuse it, because you might have had intentions. She allows me to go by myself to mass because our confessor told her she might do so; but I dare not stay away a minute beyond the time, except on feast days, when I am allowed to pray in the church for two or three hours. We can only meet here, but if you wish to soften my lot in life you can do so as follows:

"A fine young man, who is a hairdresser, and bears an excellent character, saw me at Momolo's a fortnight ago, and met me at the church door next day and gave me a letter. He declared himself my lover, and said that if I could bring him a dowry of four hundred crowns, he could open a shop, furnish it, and marry me.

" 'I am poor,' I answered, 'and I have only a hundred crowns in charity tickets, which my confessor keeps for me.' Now I have two hundred crowns, for if I marry, my mother will willingly give me her share of the money you made us gain. You can therefore make me happy by getting me tickets to the amount of two hundred crowns more. Take the tickets to my confessor, who is a very good man and fond of me; he will not say anything to my mother about it."

"I needn't go about seeking for charity tickets, my angel. I will take two hundred piastres to your confessor to-morrow, and you must manage the rest yourself. Tell me his name, and to-morrow I will tell you what I have done, but not here, as the wind and the cold would be the death of me. You can leave me to find out a room where we shall be at our ease, and without any danger of people suspecting that we have spent an hour together. I will meet you at the church to-morrow at the same hour, and when you see me follow me."

Mariuccia told me her confessor's name, and allowed me all the caresses possible in our uncomfortable position. The kisses she gave me in return for mine left no doubt in my mind as to her love for me. As nine o'clock struck I left her, perishing with cold, but burning with desire; my only thought being where to find a room in which I might possess myself of the treasure the next day.

On leaving the ruined palace, instead of returning to the Piazza di Spagna I turned to the left and passed along a narrow and dirty street only inhabited by people of the lowest sort. As I slowly walked along, a woman came out of her house and asked me politely if I were looking for anybody.

"I am looking for a room to let."

"There are none here, sir, but you will find a hundred in the square."

"I know it, but I want the room to be here, not for the sake of the expense, but that I may be sure of being able to spend an hour or so of a morning with a person in whom I am interested. I am ready to pay anything."

" I understand what you mean, and you should have a room in my house if I had one to spare, but a neighbour of mine has one on the ground floor, and if you will wait a moment I will go and speak to her."

"You will oblige me very much."

"Kindly step in here."

I entered a poor room, where all seemed wretchedness, and I saw two children doing their lessons. Soon after, the good woman came back and asked me to follow her. I took several pieces of money from my pocket, and put

them down on the only table which this poor place contained. I must have seemed very generous, for the poor
mother came and kissed my hand with the utmost
gratitude. So pleasant is it to do good, that now when
I have nothing left the remembrance of the happiness I
have given to others at small cost is almost the only
pleasure I enjoy.

I went to a neighbouring house where a woman received me in an empty room, which she told me she
would let cheaply if I would pay three months in advance, and bring in my own furniture.

"What do you ask for the three months' rent?"

"Three Roman crowns."

"If you will see to the furnishing of the room this very
day I will give you twelve crowns."

"Twelve crowns! What furniture do you want?"

" A good clean bed, a small table covered with a clean
cloth, four good chairs, and a large brazier with plenty of
fire in it, for I am nearly perishing of cold here. I shall
only come occasionally in the morning, and I shall leave
by noon at the latest."

"Come at three o'clock, then, to-day, and you will find
everything to your satisfaction."

From there I went to the confessor. He was a French
monk, about sixty, a fine and benevolent-looking man,
who won one's respect and confidence.

"Reverend father," I began, "I saw at the house of
Abbé Momolo, *scopatore santissimo*, a young girl named
Mary, whose confessor you are. I fell in love with her,
and offered her money to try and seduce her. She replied
that instead of trying to lead her into sin I would do
better to get her some charity tickets that she might be
able to marry a young man who loved her, and would
make her happy. I was touched by what she said, but

my passion still remained. I spoke to her again, and said that I would give her two hundred crowns for nothing, and that her mother should keep them.

" 'That would be my ruin,' said she; 'my mother would think the money was the price of sin, and would not accept it. If you are really going to be so generous, take the money to my confessor, and ask him to do what he can for my marriage.'

"Here, then, reverend father, is the sum of money for the good girl; be kind enough to take charge of it, and I will trouble her no more. I am going to Naples the day after to-morrow, and I hope when I come back she will be married."

The good confessor took the hundred sequins and gave me a receipt, telling me that in interesting myself on behalf of Mariuccia I was making happy a most pure and innocent dove, whom he had confessed since she was five years old, and that he had often told her that she might communicate without making her confession because he knew she was incapable of mortal sin.

"Her mother," he added, "is a sainted woman, and as soon as I have enquired into the character of the future husband I will soon bring the marriage about. No one shall ever know from whom this generous gift comes."

After putting this matter in order I dined with the Chevalier Mengs, and I willingly consented to go with the whole family to the Aliberti Theatre that evening. I did not forget, however, to go and inspect the room I had taken. I found all my orders executed, and I gave twelve crowns to the landlady and took the key, telling her to light the fire at seven every morning.

So impatient did I feel for the next day to come that I thought the opera detestable, and the night for me was a sleepless one.

Next morning I went to the church before the time, and when Mariuccia came, feeling sure that she had seen me, I went out. She followed me at a distance, and when I got to the door of the lodging I turned for her to be sure that it was I, and then went in and found the room well warmed. Soon after Mariuccia came in, looking timid, confused, and as if she were doubtful of the path she was treading. I clasped her to my arms, and re-assured her by my tender embraces; and her courage rose when I shewed her the confessor's receipt, and told her that the worthy man had promised to care for her marriage. She kissed my hand in a transport of delight, assuring me that she would never forget my kindness. Then, as I urged her to make me a happy man, she said,——

"We have three hours before us, as I told my mother I was going to give thanks to God for having made me a winner in the lottery."

This reassured me, and I took my time, undressing her by degrees, and unveiling her charms one by one, to my delight, without the slightest attempt at resistance on her part. All the time she kept her eyes fixed on mine, as if to soothe her modesty; but when I beheld and felt all her charms I was in an ecstasy. What a body; What beauties! Nowhere was there the slight-est imperfection. She was like Venus rising from the foam of the sea. I carried her gently to the bed, and while she strove to hide her alabaster breasts and the soft hair which marked the entrance to the sanctuary, I undressed in haste, and consummated the sweetest of sacrifices, without there being the slightest doubt in my mind of the purity of the victim. In the first sacrifice no doubt the young priestess felt some pain, but she assured me out of delicacy that she had not been hurt, and at the second assault she shewed that she shared my flames. I was going to immolate the victim for the third time when the clock struck ten. She began to be restless, and hurriedly put on our clothes. I had to go to Naples, but I assured her that the desire of embracing her once more before her marriage would hasten my return to Rome. I promised to take another hundred crowns to her confessor, advising her to spend the money she had won in the lottery on her trousseau.

"I shall be at Momolo's to-night, dearest, and you must come, too; but we must appear indifferent to each other, though our hearts be full of joy, lest those malicious girls suspect our mutual understanding."

"It is all the more necessary to be cautious," she replied, "as I have noticed that they suspect that we love each other."

Before we parted she thanked me for what I had done for her, and begged me to believe that, her poverty notwithstanding, she had given herself for love alone.

I was the last to leave the house, and I told my landlady that I should be away for ten or twelve days. I then went to the confessor to give him the hundred crowns I had promised my mistress. When the good old Frenchman heard that I had made this fresh sacrifice that Mariuccia might be able to spend her lottery winnings on her clothes, he told me that he would call on the mother that very day and urge her to consent to her daughter's marriage, and also learn where the young man lived. On my return from Naples I heard that he had faithfully carried out his promise.

I was sitting at table with Mengs when a chamberlain of the Holy Father called. When he came in he asked M. Mengs if I lived there, and on that gentleman pointing me out, he gave me, from his holy master, the Cross of the Order of the Golden Spur with the diploma, and a patent under the pontifical seal, which, in my quality as doctor of laws, made me a prothonotary-apostolic *extra urbem.*

I felt that I had been highly honoured, and told the bearer that I would go and thank my new sovereign and ask his blessing the next day. The Chevalier Mengs embraced me as a brother, but I had the advantage over him in not being obliged to pay anything, whereas the great artist had to disburse twenty-five Roman crowns to have his diploma made out. There is a saying at Rome, *Sine effusione sanguinis non fit remissio,* which may be interpreted, *Nothing without money;* and as a matter of fact, one can do anything with money in the Holy City.

Feeling highly flattered at the favour the Holy Father had shewn me, I put on the cross which depended from a broad red ribbon—red being the colour worn by the Knights of St. John of the Lateran, the companions of the palace, *comites palatini,* or count-palatins. About the same time poor Cahusac, author of the opera of Zoroaster, went mad for joy on the receipt of the same order. I was not so bad as that, but I confess, to my shame, that I was so proud of my decoration that I asked Winckelmann whether I should be allowed to have the cross set with diamonds and rubies. He said I could if I liked, and if I wanted such a cross he could get me one cheap. I was delighted, and bought it to make a show at Naples, but I had not the face to wear it in Rome. When I went to thank the Pope I wore the cross in my button-hole out of modesty. Five years afterwards when I was at Warsaw, Czartoryski, a Russian prince-palatine, made me leave it off by saying,——

"What are you doing with that wretched bauble? It's

a drug in the market, and no one but an impostor would wear it now."

The Popes knew this quite well, but they continued to give the cross to ambassadors while they also gave it to their *valets de chambre*. One has to wink at a good many things in Rome.

In the evening Momolo gave me a supper by way of celebrating my new dignity. I recouped him for the expense by holding a bank at faro, at which I was dexterous enough to lose forty crowns to the family, without having the slightest partiality to Mariuccia who won like the rest. She found the opportunity to tell me that her confessor had called on her, that she had told him where her future husband lived, and that the worthy monk had obtained her mother's consent to the hundred crowns being spent on her trousseau.

I noticed that Momolo's second daughter had taken a fancy to Costa, and I told Momolo that I was going to Naples, but that I would leave my man in Rome, and that if I found a marriage had been arranged on my return I would gladly pay the expenses of the wedding.

Costa liked the girl, but he did not marry her then for fear of my claiming the first-fruits. He was a fool of a peculiar kind, though fools of all sorts are common enough. He married her a year later after robbing me, but I shall speak of that again.

Next day, after I had breakfasted and duly embraced my brother, I set out in a nice carriage with the Abbé Alfani, Le Duc preceding me on horseback, and I reached Naples at a time when everybody was in a state of excitement because an eruption of Vesuvius seemed imminent. At the last stage the inn-keeper made me read the will of his father who had died during the eruption of 1754. He said that in the year 1761 God would overwhelm the sinful town of Naples, and the worthy host consequently advised me to return to Rome. Alfani took the thing seriously, and said that we should do well to be warned by so evident an indication of the will of God. The event was predicted, therefore it had to happen. Thus a good many people reason, but as I was not of the number I proceeded on my way.

CHAPTER IX

My Short But Happy Stay at Naples—The Duke de Matalone—My Daughter—Donna Lucrezia—My Departure

I SHALL not, dear reader, attempt the impossible, however much I should like to describe the joy, the happiness, I may say the ecstasy, which I experienced in returning to Naples, of which I had such pleasant memories, and where, eighteen years ago, I had made my first fortune in returning from Mataro. As I had come there for the second time to keep a promise I had made to the Duke de Matalone to come and see him at Naples, I ought to have visited this nobleman at once; but foreseeing that from the time I did so I should have little liberty left me, I began by enquiring after all my old friends.

I walked out early in the morning and called on Belloni's agent. He cashed my letter of credit and gave me as many bank-notes as I liked, promising that nobody should know that we did business together. From the bankers I went to see Antonio Casanova, but they told me he lived near Salerno, on an estate he had bought which gave him the title of marquis. I was vexed, but I had no right to expect to find Naples in the *statu quo* I left it. Polo was dead, and his son lived at St. Lucia with his wife and children; he was a boy when I saw him last, and though I should have much liked to see him again I had no time to do so.

222

It may be imagined that I did not forget the advocate, Castelli, husband of my dear Lucrezia, whom I had loved so well at Rome and Tivoli. I longed to see her face once more, and I thought of the joy with which we should recall old times that I could never forget. But Castelli had been dead for some years, and his widow lived at a distance of twenty miles from Naples. I resolved not to return to Rome without embracing her. As to Lelio Caraffa, he was still alive and residing at the Matalone Palace.

I returned, feeling tired with my researches, dressed with care, and drove to the Matalone Palace, where they told me that the duke was at table. I did not care for that but had my name sent in, and the duke came out and did me the honour of embracing me and *thouing* me, and then presented me to his wife, a daughter of the Duke de Bovino, and to the numerous company at table. I told him I had only come to Naples in fulfillment of the promise I had made him at Paris.

"Then," said he, "you must stay with me;" and, without waiting for my answer, ordered my luggage to be brought from the inn, and my carriage to be placed in his coach-house. I accepted his invitation.

One of the guests, a fine-looking man, on hearing my name announced, said gaily,——

"If you bear my name, you must be one of my father's bastards."

"No," said I, directly, "one of your mother's."

This repartee made everybody laugh, and the gentleman who had addressed me came and embraced me, not in the least offended. The joke was explained to me. His name was Casalnovo, not Casanova, and he was duke and lord of the fief of that name.

"Did you know," said the Duke de Matalone, "that I had a son?"

"I was told so, but did not believe it, but now I must do penance for my incredulity, for I see before me an angel capable of working this miracle."

The duchess blushed, but did not reward my compliment with so much as a glance; but all the company applauded what I had said, as it was notorious that the duke had been impotent before his marriage. The duke sent for his son, I admired him, and told the father that the likeness was perfect. A merry monk, who sat at the right hand of the duchess, said, more truthfully, that there was no likeness at all. He had scarcely uttered the words when the duchess coolly gave him a box on the ear, which the monk received with the best grace imaginable.

I talked away to the best of my ability, and in half an hour's time I had won everybody's good graces, with the exception of the duchess, who remained inflexible. I tried to make her talk for two days without success; so as I did not care much about her I left her to her pride.

As the duke was taking me to my room he noticed my Spaniard, and asked where my secretary was, and when he saw that it was the Abbé Alfani, who had taken the title so as to escape the notice of the Neapolitans, he said,——

"The abbé is very wise, for he has deceived so many people with his false antiques that he might have got into trouble."

He took me to his stables where he had some superb horses, Arabs, English, and Andalusians; and then to his gallery, a very fine one; to his large and choice library;

and at last to his study, where he had a fine collection of prohibited books.

I was reading titles and turning over leaves, when the duke said,——

"Promise to keep the most absolute secrecy on what I am going to shew you."

I promised, without making any difficulty, but I expected a surprise of some sort. He then shewed me a satire which I could not understand, but which was meant to turn the whole Court into ridicule. Never was there a secret so easily kept.

"You must come to the St. Charles Theatre," said he, "and I will present you to the handsomest ladies in Naples, and afterwards you can go when you like, as my box is always open to my friends. I will also introduce you to my mistress, and she, I am sure, will always be glad to see you."

"What! you have a mistress, have you?"

"Yes, but only for form's sake, as I am very fond of my wife. All the same, I am supposed to be deeply in love with her, and even jealous, as I never introduce anyone to her, and do not allow her to receive any visitors."

"But does not your young and handsome duchess object to your keeping a mistress?"

"My wife could not possibly be jealous, as she knows that I am impotent—except, of course, with her."

"I see, but it sems strange; can one be said to have a mistress whom one does not love?"

"I did not say I loved her not; on the contrary, I am very fond of her; she has a keen and pleasant wit, but she interests my head rather than my heart."

"I see; but I suppose she is ugly?"

"Ugly? You shall see her to-night, and you can tell me what you think of her afterwards. She is a handsome and well-educated girl of seventeen."

"Can she speak French?"

"As well as a Frenchwoman."

"I am longing to see her."

When we got to the theatre I was introduced to several ladies, but none of them pleased me. The king, a mere boy, sat in his box in the middle of the theatre, surrounded by his courtiers, richly but tastefully dressed. The pit was full and the boxes also. The latter were ornamented with mirrors, and on that occasion were all illuminated for some reason or other. It was a magnificent scene, but all this glitter and light put the stage into the background.

After we had gazed for some time at the scene, which is almost peculiar to Naples, the duke took me to his private box and introduced me to his friends, who consisted of all the wits in the town.

I have often laughed on hearing philosophers declare that the intelligence of a nation is not so much the result of the climate as of education. Such sages should be sent to Naples and then to St. Petersburg, and be told to reflect, or simply to look before them. If the great Boerhaave had lived at Naples he would have learnt more about the nature of sulphur by observing its effects on vegetables, and still more on animals. In Naples, and Naples alone, water, and nothing but water, will cure diseases which are fatal elsewhere, despite the doctors' efforts.

The duke, who had left me to the wits for a short time, returned and took me to the box of his mistress, who was accompanied by an old lady of respectable appearance. As he went in he said,——

"Leonilda mia, ti presento il cavalier Don Giacomo Casanova, Veneziano, amico mio."

She received me kindly and modestly, and stopped listening to the music to talk to me.

When a woman is pretty, one recognizes her charms instantaneously; if one has to examine her closely, her beauty is doubtful. Leonilda was strikingly beautiful. I smiled and looked at the duke, who had told me that he loved her like a daughter, and that he only kept her for form's sake. He understood the glance, and said,——

"You may believe me."

"It's credible," I replied.

Leonilda no doubt understood what we meant, and said, with a shy smile,——

"Whatever is possible is credible."

"Quite so," said I, "but one may believe, or not believe, according to the various degrees of possibility."

"I think it's easier to believe than to disbelieve. You came to Naples yesterday; that's true and yet incredible."

"Why incredible?"

"Would any man suppose that a stranger would come to Naples at a time when the inhabitants are wishing themselves away?"

"Indeed, I have felt afraid till this moment, but now I feel quite at my ease, since, you being here, St. Januarius will surely protect Naples."

"Why?"

"Because I am sure he loves you; but you are laughing at me."

"It is such a funny idea. I am afraid that if I had a lover like St. Januarius I should not grant him many favours."

"Is he very ugly, then?"

"If his portrait is a good likeness, you can see for yourself by examining his statue."

Gaiety leads to freedom, and freedom to friendship. Mental graces are superior to bodily charms.

Leonilda's frankness inspired my confidence, and I led the conversation to love, on which she talked like a past mistress.

"Love," said she, "unless it leads to the possession of the beloved object, is a mere torment; if bounds are placed to passion, love must die."

"You are right; and the enjoyment of a beautiful object is not a true pleasure unless it be preceded by love."

"No doubt if love precedes it accompanies, but I do not think it necessarily follows, enjoyment."

"True, it often makes love to cease."

"She is a selfish daughter, then, to kill her father; and if after enjoyment love still continue in the heart of one, it is worse than murder, for the party in which love still survives must needs be wretched."

"You are right; and from your strictly logical arguments I conjecture that you would have the senses kept in subjection: that is too hard!"

"I would have nothing to do with that Platonic affection devoid of love, but I leave you to guess what my maxim would be."

"To love and enjoy; to enjoy and love. Turn and turn about."

"You have hit the mark."

With this Leonilda burst out laughing, and the duke kissed her hand. Her governess, not understanding French, was attending to the opera, but I was in flames.

Leonilda was only seventeen, and was as pretty a girl as the heart could desire.

The duke repeated a lively epigram of Lafontaine's on "Enjoyment," which is only found in the first edition of his works. It begins as follows:

> *"La jouissance et les désirs*
> *Sont ce que l'homme a de plus rare;*
> *Mais ce ne sont pas vrais plaisirs*
> *Dès le moment qu'on les sépare."*

I have translated this epigram into Italian and Latin; in the latter language I was almost able to render Lafontaine line for line; but I had to use twenty lines of Italian to translate the first ten lines of the French. Of course this argues nothing as to the superiority of the one language over the other.

In the best society at Naples one addresses a newcomer in the second person singular as a peculiar mark of distinction. This puts both parties at their ease without diminishing their mutual respect for one another.

Leonilda had already turned my first feeling of admiration into something much warmer, and the opera, which lasted for five hours, seemed over in a moment.

After the two ladies had gone the duke said, "Now we must part, unless you are fond of games of chance."

"I don't object to them when I am to play with good hands."

"Then follow me; ten or twelve of my friends will play faro, and then sit down to a cold collation, but I warn you it is a secret, as gaming is forbidden. I will answer for you keeping your own counsel, however."

"You may do so."

He took me to the Duke de Monte Leone's. We went up to the third floor, passed through a dozen rooms, and at last reached the gamester's chamber. A polite-looking banker, with a bank of about four hundred sequins, had the cards in his hands. The duke introduced me as his friend, and made me sit beside him. I was going to draw out my purse, but I was told that debts were not paid for twenty-four hours after they were due. The banker gave me a pack of cards, with a little basket containing a thousand counters. I told the company that I should consider each counter as a Naples ducat. In less than two hours my basket was empty. I stopped playing and proceeded to enjoy my supper. It was arranged in the Neapolitan style, and consisted of an enormous dish of macaroni and ten or twelve different kinds of shellfish which are plentiful on the Neapolitan coasts. When we left I took care not to give the duke time to condole with me on my loss, but began to talk to him about his delicious Leonilda.

Early next day he sent a page to my room to tell me that if I wanted to come with him and kiss the king's hand I must put on my gala dress. I put on a suit of rose-coloured velvet, with gold spangles, and I had the great honour of kissing a small hand, covered with chilblains, belonging to a boy of nine. The Prince de St. Nicander brought up the young king to the best of his ability, but he was naturally a kindly, just, and generous monarch; if he had had more dignity he would have been an ideal king; but he was too unceremonious, and that, I think, is a defect in one destined to rule others.

I had the honour of sitting next the duchess at dinner, and she deigned to say that she had never seen a finer dress. "That's my way," I said, "of distracting attention from my face and figure." She smiled, and her politeness to me during my stay were almost limited to these few words.

When we left the table the duke took me to the apartment occupied by his uncle, Don Lelio, who recognized me directly. I kissed the venerable old man's hand, and begged him to pardon me for the freaks of my youth. "It's eighteen years ago," said he, "since I chose M. Casanova as the companion of your studies." I delighted him by giving him a brief account of my adventures in Rome with Cardinal Acquaviva. As we went out, he begged me to come and see him often.

Towards the evening the duke said,——

"If you go to the Opera Buffa you will please Leonilda."

He gave me the number of her box, and added,——

"I will come for you towards the close, and we will sup together as before."

I had no need to order my horses to be put in, as there was always a carriage ready for me in the courtyard.

When I got to the theatre the opera had begun. I presented myself to Leonilda, who received me with the pleasant words, "Caro Don Giacomo, I am so pleased to see you again."

No doubt she did not like to *thou* me, but the expression of her eyes and the tone of her voice were much better than the *tu* which is often used lavishly at Naples.

The seductive features of this charming girl were not altogether unknown to me, but I could not recollect of what woman she reminded me. Leonilda was certainly a beauty, and something superior to a beauty, if possible. She had splendid light chestnut hair, and her black and brilliant eyes, shaded by thick lashes, seemed to hear and speak at the same time. But what ravished me still more was her expression, and the exquisite appropriateness of the gestures with which she accompanied what she was saying. It seemed as if her tongue could not give speech to the thoughts which crowded her brain. She was naturally quick-witted, and her intellect had been developed by an excellent education.

The conversation turned upon Lafontaine's epigram, of which I had only recited the first ten verses, as the rest is too licentious; and she said,——

"But I suppose it is only a poet's fancy, at which one could but smile."

"Possibly, but I did not care to wound your ears."

"You are very good," said she, using the pleasant *tu*, "but all the same, I am not so thin-skinned, as I have a closet which the duke has had painted over with couples in various amorous attitudes. We go there sometimes, and I assure you that I do not experience the slightest sensation."

"That may be through a defect of temperament, for whenever I see well-painted voluptuous pictures I feel myself on fire. I wonder that while you and the duke look at them, you do not try to put some of them into practice."

"We have only friendship for one another."

"Let him believe it who will."

"I am sure he is a man, but I am unable to say whether he is able to give a woman any real proofs of his love."

"Yet he has a son."

"Yes, he has a child who calls him father; but he himself confesses that he is only able to shew his manly powers with his wife."

"That's all nonsense, for you are made to give birth to amorous desires, and a man who could live with you without being able to possess you ought to cease to live."

"Do you really think so?"

"Dear Leonilda, if I were in the duke's place I would shew you what a man who really loves can do."

"*Caro Don Giacomo,* I am delighted to hear you love me, but you will soon forget me, as you are leaving Naples."

"Cursed be the gaming-table, for without it we might spend some delightful hour together."

"The duke told me that you lost a thousand ducats yesterday evening like a perfect gentleman. You must be very unlucky."

"Not always, but when I play on a day in which I have fallen in love I am sure to lose."

"You will win back your money this evening."

"This is the declaration day; I shall lose again."

"Then don't play."

"People would say I was afraid, or that all my money was gone."

"I hope at all events that you will win sometimes, and that you will tell me of your good luck. Come and see me to-morrow with the duke."

The duke came in at that moment, and asked me if I had liked the opera. Leonilda answered for me,——

"We have been talking about love all the time, so we don't know what has been going on the stage."

"You have done well."

"I trust you will bring M. Casanova to see me to-morrow morning, as I hope he will bring me news that he has won."

"It's my turn to deal this evening, dearest, but whether he wins or loses you shall see him to-morrow. You must give us some breakfast."

"I shall be delighted."

We kissed her hand, and went to the same place as the night before. The company was waiting for the duke. There were twelve members of the club, and they all held the bank in turn. They said that this made the chances more equal; but I laughed at this opinion, as there is nothing more difficult to establish than equality between players.

The Duke de Matalone sat down, drew out his purse and his pocket-book, and put two thousand ducats in the bank, begging pardon of the others for doubling the usual sum in favour of the stranger. The bank never exceeded a thousand ducats.

"Then," said I, "I will hazard two thousand ducats also and not more, for they say at Venice that a prudent player never risks more than he can win. Each of my counters will be equivalent to two ducats." So saying, I took ten notes of a hundred ducats each from my pocket, and gave them to the last evening's banker who had won them from me.

Play began; and though I was prudent, and only risked my money on a single card, in less than three hours my counters were all gone. I stopped playing, though I had still twenty-five thousand ducats; but I had said that I would not risk more than two thousand, and I was ashamed to go back from my word.

Though I have always felt losing my money, no one has ever seen me put out, my natural gaiety was heightened by art on such occasions, and seemed to be more brilliant than ever. I have always found it a great advantage to be able to lose pleasantly.

I made an excellent supper, and my high spirits furnished me with such a fund of amusing conversation that all the table was in a roar. I even succeeded in dissipating the melancholy of the Duke de Matalone, who was in despair at having won such a sum from his friend and guest. He was afraid he had half ruined me, and also that people might say he had only welcomed me for the sake of my money.

As we returned to the palace the conversation was affectionate on his side and jovial on mine, but I could see he was in some trouble, and guessed what was the matter. He wanted to say that I could pay the money I owed him whenever I liked, but was afraid of wounding my feelings; but as soon as he got in he wrote me a friendly note to the effect that if I wanted money his banker would let me have as much as I required. I replied directly that I felt the generosity of his offer, and if I was in need of funds I would avail myself of it.

Early next morning I went to his room, and after an affectionate embrace I told him not to forget that we were going to breakfast with his fair mistress. We both put on great coats and went to Leonilda's pretty house.

We found her sitting up in bed, negligently but decently dressed, with a dimity corset tied with red ribbons. She looked beautiful, and her graceful posture added to her charms. She was reading Crébillon's *Sopha.*. The duke sat down at the bottom of the bed, and I stood staring at her in speechless admiration, endeavouring to recall to my memory where I had seen such another face as hers. It seemed to me that I had loved a woman like her. This was the first time I had seen her without the deceitful glitter of candles. She laughed at my absent-mindedness, and told me to sit down on a chair by her bedside.

The duke told her that I was quite pleased at having lost two thousand ducats to his bank, as the loss made me sure she loved me.

"Caro mio Don Giacomo, I am sorry to hear that! You would have done better not to play, for I should have loved you all the same, and you would have been two thousand ducats better off."

"And I two thousand ducats worse off," said the duke, laughing.

"Never mind, dear Leonilda, I shall win this evening if you grant me some favour to-day. If you do not do so, I shall lose heart, and you will mourn at my grave before long."

"Think, Leonilda, what you can do for my friend."

"I don't see that I can do anything."

The duke told her to dress, that we might go and breakfast in the painted closet. She began at once, and preserved a just mean in what she let us see and what she concealed, and thus set me in flames, though I was already captivated by her face, her wit, and her charming manners. I cast an indiscreet glance towards her beautiful breast, and thus added fuel to the fire. I confess that I only obtained this satisfaction by a species of larceny, but I could not have succeeded if she had not been well disposed towards me. I pretended to have seen nothing.

While dressing she maintained with much ingenuity that a wise girl will be much more chary of her favours towards a man she loves than towards a man she does not love, because she would be afraid to lose the first, whereas she does not care about the second.

"It will not be so with me, charming Leonilda," said I.

"You make a mistake, I am sure."

The pictures with which the closet where we breakfasted was adorned were admirable more from the colouring and the design than from the amorous combats they represented.

"They don't make any impression on me," said the duke, and he shewed us that it was so.

Leonilda looked away, and I felt shocked, but concealed my feelings.

"I am in the same state as you," said I, "but I will not take the trouble of convincing you."

"That can't be," said he; and passing his hand rapidly over me he assured himself that it was so. "It's astonishing," he cried; "you must be as impotent as I am."

"If I wanted to controvert that assertion one glance into Leonilda's eyes would be enough."

"Look at him, dearest Leonilda, that I may be convinced."

Leonilda looked tenderly at me, and her glance produced the result I had expected.

"Give me your hand," said I, to the poor duke, and he did so.

"I was in the wrong," he exclaimed, but when he endeavoured to bring the surprising object to light I resisted. He persisted in his endeavours, and I determined to play on him a trick. I took Leonilda's hand and pressed my lips to it, and just as the duke thought he had triumphed I besprinkled him, and went off into a roar of laughter. He laughed too, and went to get a napkin.

The girl could see nothing of all this, as it went on under the table; and while my burning lips rested on her hand, my eyes were fixed on hers and our breath mingled. This close contact had enabled me to baptise the duke, but when she took in the joke we made a group worthy of the pen of Aretin.

It was a delightful breakfast, though we passed certain bounds which decency ought to have proscribed to us, but Leonilda was wonderfully innocent considering her position. We ended the scene by mutual embraces, and when I took my burning lips from Leonilda's I felt consumed with a fire which I could not conceal.

When we left I told the duke that I would see his mistress no more, unless he would give her up to me, declaring that I would marry her and give her a dower of five thousand ducats.

"Speak to her, and if she consents I will not oppose it. She herself will tell you what property she has."

I then went to dress for dinner. I found the duchess in the midst of a large circle, and she told me kindly that she was very sorry to hear of my losses.

"Fortune is the most fickle of beings, but I don't complain of my loss—nay, when you speak thus I love it, and I even think that you will make me win this evening."

"I hope so, but I am afraid not; you will have to contend against Monte Leone, who is usually very lucky."

In considering the matter after dinner, I determined for the future to play with ready money and not on my word of honour, lest I should at any time be carried away by the excitement of play and induced to stake more than I possessed. I thought, too, that the banker might have his doubts after the two heavy losses I had sustained, and I confess that I was also actuated by the gambler's superstition that by making a change of any kind one changes the luck.

I spent four hours at the theatre in Leonilda's box, where I found her more gay and charming than I had seen her before.

"Dear Leonilda," I said, "the love I feel for you will suffer no delay and no rivals, not even the slightest inconstancy. I have told the duke that I am ready to marry you, and that I will give you a dower of five thousand ducats."

"What did he say?"

"That I must ask you, and that he would offer no opposition."

"Then we should leave Naples together."

"Directly, dearest, and thenceforth death alone would part us."

"We will talk of it to-morrow, dear Don Giacomo, and if I can make you happy I am sure you will do the same by me."

As she spoke these delightful words the duke came in.

"Don Giacomo and I are talking of marrying," said she.

"Marriage, *mia carissima*," he replied, "ought to be well considered beforehand."

"Yes, when one has time; but my dear Giacomo cannot wait, and we shall have plenty of time to think it over afterwards."

"As you are going to marry," said the duke, "you can put off your departure, or return after the wedding."

"I can neither put it off nor return, my dear duke. We have made up our minds, and if we repent we have plenty of time before us."

He laughed and said we would talk it over next day. I gave my future bride a kiss which she returned with ardour, and the duke and I went to the club, where we found the Duke de Monte Leone dealing.

"My lord," said I, "I am unlucky playing on my word of honour, so I hope you will allow me to stake money."

"Just as you please; it comes to the same thing, but don't trouble yourself. I have made a bank of four thousand ducats that you may be able to recoup yourself for your losses."

"Thanks, I promise to break it or to lose as much."

I drew out six thousand ducats, gave two thousand

ducats to the Duke de Matalone, and began to punt at a hundred ducats. After a short time the duke left the table, and I finally succeeded in breaking the bank. I went back to the place by myself, and when I told the duke of my victory the next day, he embraced me with tears of joy, and advised me to stake money for the future.

As the Princess de Vale was giving a great supper, there was no play that evening. This was some respite. We called on Leonilda, and putting off talking of our marriage till the day after we spent the time in viewing the wonders of nature around Naples. In the evening I was introduced by a friend at the princess's supper, and saw all the highest nobility of the place.

Next morning the duke told me that he had some business to do, and that I had better go and see Leonilda, and that he would call for me later on. I went to Leonilda, but as the duke did not put in an appearance we could not settle anything about our marriage. I spent several hours with her, but I was obliged to obey her commands, and could only shew myself amorous in words. Before leaving I repeated that it only rested with her to unite our lives by indissoluble ties, and to leave Naples almost immediately.

When I saw the duke he said,——

"Well, Don Giacomo, you have spent all the morning with my mistress; do you still wish to marry her?"

"More than ever; what do you mean?"

"Nothing; and as you have passed this trial to which I purposely subjected you, we will discuss your union to-morrow, and I hope you will make this charming woman happy, for she will be an excellent wife."

"I agree with you."

When we went to Monte Leone's in the evening, we saw a banker with a good deal of gold before him. The duke told me he was Don Marco Ottoboni. He was a fine-looking man, but he held the cards so closely together in his left hand that I could not see them. This did not inspire me with confidence, so I only punted a ducat at a time. I was persistently unlucky, but I only lost a score of ducats. After five or six deals the banker asked me politely why I staked such small sums against him.

"Because I can't see half the pack," I replied, "and I am afraid of losing."

Some of the company laughed at my answer.

Next night I broke the bank held by the Prince the Cassaro, a pleasant and rich nobleman, who asked me to give him revenge, and invited me to supper at his pretty house at Posilipo, where he lived with a virtuosa of whom he had become amorous at Palermo. He also invited the Duke de Matalone and three or four other gentlemen. This was the only occasion on which I held the bank while I was at Naples, and I staked six thousand ducats after warning the prince that as it was the eve of my departure I should only play for ready money.

He lost ten thousand ducats, and only rose from the table because he had no more money. Everybody left the room, and I should have done the same if the prince's mistress had not owed me a hundred ducats. I continued to deal in the hope that she would get her money back, but seeing that she still lost I put down the cards, and told her that she must pay me at Rome. She was a handsome and agreeable woman, but she did not inspire me with any passions, no doubt because my mind was occupied with another, otherwise I should have drawn a bill on sight, and paid myself without meddling with her purse. It was two o'clock in the morning when I got to bed.

Both Leonilda and myself wished to see Caserta before leaving Naples, and the duke sent us there in a carriage drawn by six mules, which went faster than most horses. Leonilda's governess accompanied us.

The day after, we settled the particulars of our marriage in a conversation which lasted for two hours.

"Leonilda," began the duke, "has a mother, who lives at a short distance from here, on an income of six hundred ducats, which I have given her for life, in return for an estate belonging to her husband; but Leonilda does not depend on her. She gave her up to me seven years ago, and I have given her an annuity of five hundred ducats, which she will bring to you, with all her diamonds and an extensive trousseau. Her mother gave her up to me entirely, and I gave my word of honour to get her a good husband. I have taken peculiar care of her education, and as her mind has developed I have put her on her guard against all prejudices, with the exception of that which bids a woman keep herself intact for her future husband. You may rest assured that you are the first man whom Leonilda (who is a daughter to me) has pressed to her heart."

I begged the duke to get the contract ready, and to add to her dower the sum of five thousand ducats, which I would give him when the deed was signed.

"I will mortgage them," said he, "on a house which is worth double."

Then turning to Leonilda, who was shedding happy tears, he said,——

"I am going to send for your mother, who will be delighted to sign the settlement, and to make the acquaintance of your future husband."

The mother lived at the Marquis Galiani's, a day's journey from Naples. The duke said he would send a carriage for her the next day, and that we could all sup together the day after.

"The law business will be all done by then, and we shall be able to go to the little church at Portici, and the priest will marry you. Then we will take your mother to St. Agatha and dine with her, and you can go your way with her maternal blessing."

This conclusion gave me an involuntary shudder, and Leonilda fell fainting in the duke's arms. He called her dear child, cared for her tenderly, and brought her to herself.

We all had to wipe our eyes, as we were all equally affected.

I considered myself as a married man and under obligation to alter my way of living, and I stopped playing. I had won more than fifteen thousand ducats, and this sum added to what I had before and Leonilda's dowry should have sufficed for an honest livelihood.

Next day, as I was at supper with the duke and Leonilda, she said,——

"What will my mother say to-morrow evening, when she sees you?"

"She will say that you are silly to marry a stranger whom you have only known for a week. Have you told her my name, my nation, my condition, and my age?"

"I wrote to her as follows:

" 'Dear mamma, come directly and sign my marriage contract with a gentleman introduced to me by the duke, with whom I shall be leaving for Rome on Monday next.' "

"My letter ran thus," said the duke:

" 'Come without delay, and sign your daughter's marriage contract, and give her your blessing. She has wisely chosen a husband old enough to be her father; he is a friend of mine.' "

"That's not true," cried Leonilda, rushing to my arms, "she will think you are really old, and I am sorry."

"Is your mother an elderly woman?"

"She's a charming woman," said the duke, "full of wit, and not thirty-eight yet."

"What has she got to do with Galiani?"

"She is an intimate friend of the marchioness's, and she lives with the family but pays for her board."

Next morning, having some business with my banker to attend to, I told the duke that I should not be able to see Leonilda till supper-time. I went there at eight o'clock and I found the three sitting in front of the fire.

"Here he is!" cried the duke.

As soon as the mother saw me she screamed and fell nearly fainting on a chair. I looked at her fixedly for a minute, and exclaimed,——

"Donna Lucrezia! I am fortunate indeed!"

"Let us take breath, my dear friend. Come and sit by me. So you are going to marry my daughter, are you?"

I took a chair and guessed it all. My hair stood on end, and I relapsed into a gloomy silence.

The stupefied astonishment of Leonilda and the duke cannot be described. They could see that Donna Lucrezia and I knew each other, but they could not get any farther. As for myself, as I pondered gloomily and compared Leonilda's age with the period at which I had been intimate with Lucrezia Castelli, I could see that it was quite possible that she might be my daughter; but I told myself that the mother could not be certain of the fact, as at the time she lived with her husband, who was very fond of her and not fifty years of age. I could bear the suspense no longer, so, taking a light and begging Leonilda and the duke to excuse me, I asked Lucrezia to come into the next room with me.

As soon as she was seated, she drew me to her and said,——

"Must I grieve my dear one when I have loved so well? Leonilda is your daughter, I am certain of it. I always looked upon her as your daughter, and my husband knew it, but far from being angry, he used to adore her. I will shew you the register of her birth, and you can calculate for yourself. My husband was at Rome, and did not see me once, and my daughter did not come before her time. You must remember a letter which my mother should have given you, in which I told you I was with child. That was in January, 1744, and in six months my daughter will be seventeen. My late husband gave her the names of Leonilda Giacomina at the baptismal font, and when he played with her he always called her by the latter name. This idea of your marrying her horrifies me, but I cannot oppose it, as I am ashamed to tell the reason. What do you think? Have you still the courage to marry her? You seem to hesitate. Have you taken any earnest of the marriage-bed?"

"No, dear Lucrezia, your daughter is as pure as a lily."

"I breathe again."

"Ah, yes! but my heart is torn asunder."

"I am grieved to see you thus."

"She has no likeness to me."

"That proves nothing; she has taken after me. You are weeping, dearest, you will break my heart."

"Who would not weep in my place? I will send the duke to you; he must know all."

I left Lucrezia, and I begged the duke to go and speak to her. The affectionate Leonilda came and sat on my knee, and asked me what the dreadful mystery was. I was too much affected to be able to answer her; she kissed me, and we began to weep. We remained thus sad and silent till the return of the duke and Donna Lucrezia, who was the only one to keep her head cool.

"Dear Leonilda," said she, "you must be let into the secret of this disagreeable mystery, and your mother is the proper person to enlighten you. Do you remember what name my late husband used to call you when he petted you?"

"He used to call me his charming Giacomina."

"That is M. Casanova's name; it is the name of your father. Go and kiss him; his blood flows in your veins; and if he has been your lover, repent of the crime which was happily quite involuntary."

The scene was a pathetic one, and we were all deeply moved. Leonilda clung to her mother's knees, and in a voice that struggled with sobs exclaimed,——

"I have only felt what an affectionate daughter might feel for a father."

At this point silence fell on us, a silence that was only broken by the sobs of the two women, who held each other tightly embraced; while the duke and I sat as motionless as two posts, our heads bent and our hands crossed, without as much as looking at each other.

Supper was served, and we sat at table for three hours, talking sadly over this dramatic recognition, which had brought more grief than joy; and we departed at midnight full of melancholy, and hoping that we should be calmer on the morrow, and able to take the only step that now remained to us.

As we were going away the duke made several observations on what moral philosophers call prejudices. There is no philosopher who would maintain or even advance the thesis that the union of a father and daughter is horrible naturally, for it is entirely a social prejudice; but it is so widespread, and education has graven it so deeply in our hearts, that only a man whose heart is utterly depraved could despise it. It is the result of a respect for the laws, it keeps the social scheme together; in fact, it is no longer a prejudice, it is a principle.

I went to bed, but as usual, after the violent emotion I had undergone, I could not sleep. The rapid transition from carnal to paternal love cast my physical and mental faculties into such a state of excitement that I could scarcely withstand the fierce struggle that was taking place in my heart.

Towards morning I fell asleep for a short time, and woke up feeling as exhausted as two lovers who have been spending a long and voluptuous winter's night.

When I got up I told the duke that I intended to set out from Naples the next day; and he observed that as everybody knew I was on the eve of my departure, this haste would make people talk.

"Come and have some broth with me," said he; "and from henceforth look upon this marriage project as one of the many pranks in which you have engaged. We will spend the three or four days pleasantly together, and perhaps when we have thought over all this for some time we shall end by thinking it matter for mirth and not sadness. Believe me the mother's as good as the daughter; recollection is often better than hope; console yourself with Lucrezia. I don't think you can see any difference between her present appearance and that of eighteen years ago, for I don't see how she can ever have been handsomer than she is now."

This remonstrance brought me to my senses. I felt that the best thing I could do would be to forget the illusion which had amused me for four or five days, and as my self-esteem was not wounded it ought not to be a difficult task; but yet I was in love and unable to satisfy my love.

Love is not like merchandise, where one can substitute one thing for another when one cannot have what one wants. Love is a sentiment, only the object who has kindled the flame can soothe the heat thereof.

We went to call on my daughter, the duke in his usual mood, but I looking pale, depressed, weary, and like a boy going to receive the rod. I was extremely surprised when I came into the room to find the mother and daughter quite gay, but this helped on my cure. Leonilda threw her arms round my neck, calling me dear papa, and kissing me with all a daughter's freedom. Donna Lucrezia stretched out her hand, addressing me as her dear friend. I regarded her attentively, and I was forced to confess that the eighteen years that had passed away had done little ill to her charms. There was the same sparkling glance, that fresh complexion, those perfect shapes, those beautiful lips—in fine, all that had charmed my youthful eyes.

We mutely caressed each other. Leonilda gave and received the tenderest kisses without seeming to notice what desires she might cause to arise; no doubt she knew that as her father I should have strength to resist, and she was right. One gets used to everything, and I was ashamed to be sad any longer.

I told Donna Lucrezia of the curious welcome her sister had given me in Rome, and she went off into peals of laughter. We reminded each other of the night at Tivoli, and these recollections softened our hearts. From these softened feelings to love is but a short way; but neither place nor time were convenient, so we pretended not to be thinking of it.

After a few moments of silence I told her that if she cared to come to Rome with me to pay a visit to her sister Angélique, I would take her back to Naples at the beginning of Lent. She promised to let me know whether she could come on the following day.

I sat between her and Leonilda at dinner; and as I could no longer think of the daughter, it was natural that my old flame for Lucrezia should rekindle; and whether from the effect of her gaiety and beauty, or from my need of someone to love, or from the excellence of the wine, I found myself in love with her by the dessert, and asked her to take the place which her daughter was to have filled.

"I will marry you," said I, "and we will all of us go to Rome on Monday, for since Leonilda is my daughter I do not like to leave her at Naples."

At this the three guests looked at each other and said nothing. I did not repeat my proposal, but led the conversation to some other topic.

After dinner I felt sleepy and lay down on a bed, and did not wake till eight o'clock, when to my surprise I found that my only companion was Lucrezia, who was writing. She heard me stir, and came up to me and said affectionately,——

"My dear friend, you have slept for five hours; and as I did not like to leave you alone I would not go with the duke and our daughter to the opera."

The memory of former loves awakens when one is near the once beloved object, and desires rapidly become irresistible if the beauty still remain. The lovers feel as if they were once more in possession of a blessing which belongs to them, and of which they have been long deprived by unfortunate incidents. These were our feelings, and without delay, without idle discussion, and above all, without false modesty, we abandoned ourselves to love, the only true source of nature.

In the first interval, I was the first to break the silence; and if a man is anything of a wit, is he the less so at that delicious moment of repose which follows on an amorous victory?

"Once again, then," said I, "I am in this charming land which I entered for the first time to the noise of the drum and the rattle of musket shots."

This remark made her laugh, and recalled past events to her memory. We recollected with delight all the pleasures we had enjoyed at Testaccio, Frascati, and Tivoli. We reminded each other of these events, only to make each other laugh; but with two lovers, what is laughter but a pretext for renewing the sweet sacrifice of the goddess of Cythera?

At the end of the second act, full of the enthusiasm of the fortunate lover, I said,——

"Let us be united for life; we are of the same age, we love each other, our means are sufficient for us, we may hope to live a happy life, and to die at the same moment."

" 'Tis the darling wish of my heart," Lucrezia replied, "but let us stay at Naples and leave Leonilda to the duke. We will see company, find her a worthy husband, and our happiness will be complete."

"I cannot live at Naples, dearest, and you know that your daughter intended to leave with me."

"My daughter! Say our daughter. I see that you are still in love with her, and do not wish to be considered her father."

"Alas, yes! But I am sure that if I live with you my passion for her will be stilled, but otherwise I cannot answer for myself. I shall fly, but flight will not bring me happiness. Leonilda charms me still more by her intelligence than by her beauty. I was sure that she loved me so well that I did not attempt to seduce her, lest thereby I should weaken my hold on her affections; and as I wanted to make her happy I wished to deserve her esteem. I longed to possess her, but in a lawful manner, so that our rights should have been equal. We have created an angel, Lucrezia, and I cannot imagine how the duke . . ."

"The duke is completely impotent. Do you see now how I was able to trust my daughter to his care?"

"Impotent? I always thought so myself, but he has a son."

"His wife might possibly be able to explain that mystery to you, but you may take it for granted that the poor duke will die a virgin in spite of himself; and he knows that as well as anybody."

"Do not let us say any more about it, but allow me to treat you as at Tivoli."

"Not just now, as I hear carriage wheels."

A moment after the door opened, and Leonilda laughed heartily to see her mother in my arms, and threw herself upon us, covering us with kisses. The duke came in a little later, and we supped together very merrily. He thought me the happiest of men when I told him I was going to pass the night honourably with my wife and daughter; and he was right, for I was so at that moment.

As soon as the worthy man left us we went to bed, but here I must draw a veil over the most voluptuous night I have ever spent. If I told all I should wound chaste ears, and, besides, all the colours of the painter and all the phrases of the poet could not do justice to the delirium of pleasure, the ecstasy, and the license which passed during that night, while two wax lights burnt dimly on the table like candles before the shrine of a saint.

We did not leave the stage, which I watered with my blood, till long after the sun had risen. We were scarcely dressed when the duke arrived.

Leonilda gave him a vivid description of our nocturnal labours, but in his unhappy state of impotence he must have been thankful for his absence.

I was determined to start the next day so as to be at Rome for the last week of the carnival and I begged the duke to let me give Leonilda the five thousand ducats which would have been her dower if she had become my bride.

"As she is your daughter," said he, "she can and ought to take this present from her father, if only as a dowry for her future husband."

"Will you accept it, then, my dear Leonilda?"

"Yes, papa dear," she said, embracing me, "on the condition that you will promise to come and see me again as soon as you hear of my marriage."

I promised to do so, and I kept my word.

"As you are going to-morrow," said the duke, "I shall ask all the nobility of Naples to meet you at supper. In the meanwhile I leave you with your daughter; we shall see each other again at supper-time."

He went out and I dined with my wife and daughter in the best of spirits. I spent almost the whole afternoon with Leonilda, keeping within the bounds of decency, less, perhaps, out of respect to morality, than because of my labours of the night before. We did not kiss each other till the moment of parting, and I could see that both mother and daughter were grieved to lose me.

After a careful toilette I went to supper, and found an assembly of a hundred of the very best people in Naples. The duchess was very agreeable, and when I kissed her hand to take leave, she said,——

"I hope, Don Giacomo, that you have had no unpleasantness during your short stay at Naples, and that you will sometimes think of your visit with pleasure."

I answered that I could only recall my visit with delight after the kindness with which she had deigned to treat me that evening; and, in fact, my recollections of Naples were always of the happiest description.

After I had treated the duke's attendants with generosity, the poor nobleman, whom fortune had favoured, and whom nature had deprived of the sweetest of all enjoyments, came with me to the door of my carriage and I went on my way.

CHAPTER X

My Carriage Broken—Mariuccia's Wedding—Flight of Lord Lismore—My Return to Florence, and My Departure with the Corticelli

MY SPANIARD was going on before us on horseback, and I was sleeping profoundly beside Don Ciccio Alfani in my comfortable carriage, drawn by four horses, when a violent shock aroused me. The carriage had been overturned on the highway, at midnight, beyond Francolisa and four miles from St. Agatha.

Alfani was beneath me and uttered piercing shrieks, for he thought he had broken his left arm. Le Duc rode back and told me that the postillions had taken flight, possibly to give notice of our mishap to highwaymen, who are very common in the States of the Church and Naples.

I got out of the carriage easily enough, but poor old Alfani, who was unwieldy with fat, badly hurt, and half dead with fright, could not extricate himself without assistance. It took us a quarter of an hour to get him free. The poor wretch amused me by the blasphemies which he mingled with prayers to his patron saint, St. Francis of Assisi.

I was not without experience of such accidents and was not at all hurt, for one's safety depends a good deal on the position one is in. Don Ciccio had probably hurt his arm by stretching it out just as the accident took place.

I took my sword, my musket, and my horse-pistols

out of the carriage, and I made them and my pockets
pistols ready so as to offer a stiff resistance to the brig-
ands if they came; and I then told Le Duc to take some
money and ride off and see if he could bring some peasants to our assistance.

Don Ciccio groaned over the accident, but I, resolving
to sell my money and my life dearly, made a rampart of
the carriage and four horses, and stood sentry, with my
arms ready.

I then felt prepared for all hazards, and was quite
calm, but my unfortunate companion continued to pour
forth his groans, and prayers, and blasphemies, for all
that goes together at Naples as at Rome. I could do
nothing but compassionate him; but in spite of myself
I could not help laughing, which seemed to vex the poor
abbé, who looked for all the world like a dying dolphin
as he rested motionless against the bank. His distress
may be imagined, when the nearest horse yielded to the
call of nature, and voided over the unfortunate man the
contents of its bladder. There was nothing to be done,
and I could not help roaring with laughter.

Neverthless, a strong northerly wind rendered our
situation an extremely unpleasant one. At the slightest noise I cried, "Who goes there?" threatening to fire
on anyone who dared approach. I spent two hours in
this tragic-comic position, until at last Le Duc rode up
and told me that a band of peasants, all armed and provided with lanterns, were approaching to our assistance.

In less than an hour, the carriage, the horses, and Alfani were seen to. I kept two of the country-folk to serve
as postillions, and I sent the others away well paid for
the interruption of their sleep. I reached St. Agatha at
day-break, and I made the devil's own noise at the door
of the postmaster, calling for an attorney to take down

my statement, and threatening to have the postillions who had overturned and deserted me, hanged.

A wheelwright inspected my coach and pronounced the axle-tree broken, and told me I should have to remain for a day at least.

Don Ciccio, who stood in need of a surgeon's aid, called on the Marquis Galliani without telling me anything about it. However, the marquis hastened to beg me to stay at his home till I could continue my journey. I accepted the invitation with great pleasure, and with this my ill humour, which was really only the result of my desire to make a great fuss like a great man, evaporated.

The marquis ordered my carriage to be taken to his coach-house, took me by the arm, and led me to his house. He was as learned as he was polite, and a perfect Neapolitan—*i.e.*, devoid of all ceremony. He had not the brilliant wit of his brother, whom I had known at Paris as secretary of embassy under the Count Cantillana Montdragon, but he possessed a well-ordered judgment, founded on study and the perusal of ancient and modern classics. Above all, he was a great mathematician, and was then preparing an annotated edition of Vitruvius, which was afterwards published.

The marquis introduced me to his wife, whom I knew as the intimate friend of my dear Lucrezia. There was something saint-like in her expression, and to see her surrounded by her little children was like looking at a picture of the Holy Family.

Don Ciccio was put to bed directly, and a surgeon sent for, who consoled him by saying that it was only a simple luxation, and that he would be well again in a few days.

At noon a carriage stopped at the door, and Lucrezia

got down. She embraced the marchioness, and said to me in the most natural manner, as we shook hands,——

"What happy chance brings you hear, dear Don Giacomo?"

She told her friend that I was a friend of her late husband's, and that she had recently seen me again with great pleasure at the Duke de Matalone's.

After dinner, on finding myself alone with this charming woman, I asked her if it were not possible for us to pass a happy night together, but she shewed me that it was out of the question, and I had to yield. I renewed my offer to marry her.

"Buy a property," said she, "in the kingdom of Naples, and I will spend the remainder of my days with you, without asking a priest to give us his blessing, unless we happen to have children."

I could not deny that Lucrezia spoke very sensibly, and I could easily have bought land in Naples, and lived comfortably on it, but the idea of binding myself down to one place was so contrary to my feelings that I had the good sense to prefer my vagabond life to all the advantages which our union would have given me, and I do not think that Lucrezia altogether disapproved of my resolution.

After supper I took leave of everybody, and I set out at day-break in order to get to Rome by the next day. I had only fifteen stages to do, and the road was excellent.

As we were getting into Carillano, I saw one of the two-wheeled carriages, locally called *mantice*, two horses were being put into it, while my carriage required four. I got out, and on hearing myself called I turned round. I was not a little surprised to find that the occupants of the *mantice* were a young and pretty girl and Signora

Diana, the Prince de Sassaro's mistress, who owed me
three hundred onces. She told me that she was going to
Rome, and that she would be glad if we could make the
journey together.

"I suppose you don't mind stopping for the night at
Piperno?"

"No," said I, "I am afraid that can't be managed; I
don't intend to break my journey."

"But you would get to Rome by to-morrow."

"I know that, but I sleep better in my carriage than in
the bad beds they give you in the inns."

"I dare not travel by night."

"Well, well, madam, I have no doubt we shall see each
other at Rome."

"You are a cruel man. You see I have only a stupid
servant, and a maid who is as timid as I am, besides
it is cold and my carriage is open. I will keep you company in yours."

"I really can't take you in, as all the available space is
taken up by my old secretary, who broke his arm yesterday."

"Shall we dine together at Terracino? We could have
a little talk."

"Certainly."

We made good cheer at this small town, which is the
frontier of the States of the Church. We should not
reach Piperno till far on in the night, and the lady renewed and redoubled her efforts to keep me till day-
break; but though young and pretty she did not take
my fancy; she was too fair and too fat. But her maid,
who was a pretty brunette, with a delicious rounded
form and a sparkling eye, excited all my feelings of
desire. A vague hope of possessing the maid won
me over, and I ended by promising the signora to sup

with her, and not to continue my journey without giving notice to the landlord.

When we got to Piperno, I succeeded in telling the pretty maid that if she would let me have her quietly I would not go any further. She promised to wait for me, and allowed me to take such liberties as are usually the signs of perfect complaisance.

We had our supper, and I wished the ladies good night and escorted them to their room, where I took note of the relative positions of their beds so that there should be no mistake. I left them and came back in a quarter of an hour. Finding the door open I felt sure of success, and I got into bed; but as I found out, it was the signora and not the maid who received me. Evidently the little hussy had told her mistress the story, and the mistress had thought fit to take the maid's place. There was no possibility of my being mistaken, for though I could not see I could feel.

For a moment I was undecided, should I remain in bed and make the best of what I had got, or go on my way to Rome immediately? The latter counsel prevailed. I called Le Duc, gave my orders, and started, enjoying the thought of the confusion of the two women, who must have been in a great rage at the failure of their plans. I saw Signora Diana three or four times at Rome, and we bowed without speaking; if I had thought it likely that she would pay me the four hundred louis she owed me I might have taken the trouble to call on her, but I know that your stage queens are the worst debtors in the world.

My brother, the Chevalier Mengs, and the Abbé Winckelmann were all in good health and spirits. Costa was delighted to see me again. I sent him off directly to His Holiness's *scopatore maggiore* to warn him that

I was coming to take polenta with him, and all he need do was to get a good supper for twelve. I was sure of finding Mariuccia there, for I knew that Momolo had noticed her presence pleased me.

The carnival began the day after my arrival, and I hired a superb landau for the whole week. The Roman landaus seat four people and have a hood which may be lowered at pleasure. In these landaus one drives along the Corso with or without masks from nine to twelve o'clock during the carnival time.

From time immemorial the Corso at Rome has presented a strange and diverting spectacle during the carnival. The horses start from the Piazza del Popolo, and gallop along to the Column of Trajan, between two lines of carriages drawn up beside two narrow pavements which are crowded with maskers and people of all classes. All the windows are decorated. As soon as the horses have passed the carriages begin to move, and the maskers on foot and horseback occupy the middle of the street. The air is full of real and false sweetmeats, pamphlets, pasquinades, and puns. Throughout the mob, composed of the best and worst classes of Rome, liberty reigns supreme, and when twelve o'clock is announced by the third report of the cannon of St. Angelo the Corso begins to clear, and in five minutes you would look in vain for a carriage or a masker. The crowd disperses amongst the neighbouring streets, and fills the opera houses, the theatres, the rope-dancers' exhibitions, and even the puppet-shows. The restaurants and taverns are not left desolate; everywhere you will find crowds of people, for during the carnival the Romans only think of eating, drinking, and enjoying themselves.

I banked my money with M. Belloni and got a letter of credit on Turin, where I expected to find the Abbé

Gama and to receive a commission to represent the Portuguese Court at the Congress of Augsburg, to which all Europe was looking forward, and then I went to inspect my little room, where I hoped to meet Mariuccia the next day. I found everything in good order.

In the evening Momolo and his family received me with joyful exclamations. The eldest daughter said with a smile that she was sure she would please me by sending for Mariuccia.

"You are right," said I, "I shall be delighted to see the fair Mariuccia."

A few minutes after she entered with her puritanical mother, who told me I must not be surprised to see her daughter better dressed, as she was going to be married in a few days. I congratulated her, and Momolo's daughters asked who was the happy man. Mariuccia blushed and said modestly, to one of them,——

"It is somebody whom you know, So and so, he saw me here, and we are going to open a hair-dresser's shop."

"The marriage was arranged by good Father St. Barnabé," added the mother. "He has in his keeping my daughter's dower of four hundred Roman crowns."

"He's a good lad," said Momolo. "I have a high opinion of him; he would have married one of my daughters if I could have given him such a dowry."

At these words the girl in question blushed and lowered her eyes.

"Never mind, my dear," said I, "your turn will come in time."

She took my words as seriously meant, and her face lit up with joy. She thought I had guessed her love for Costa, and her idea was confirmed when I told him to get my landau the next day and take out all Momolo's daughters, well masked, as it would not do for them to be recognized in a carriage I meant to make use of myself. I also bade him hire some handsome costumes from a Jew, and paid the hire-money myself. This put them all in a good humour.

"How about Signora Maria?" said the jealous sister.

"As Signora Maria is going to be married," I replied, "she must not be present at any festivity without her future husband."

The mother applauded this decision of mine, and sly Mariuccia pretended to feel mortified. I turned to Momolo and begged him to ask Mariuccia's future husband to meet me at supper, by which I pleased her mother greatly.

I felt very tired, and having nothing to keep me after seeing Mariuccia, I begged the company to excuse me, and after wishing them a good appetite I left them.

I walked out next morning at an early hour. I had no need of going into the church, which I reached at seven o'clock, for Mariuccia saw me at some distance off and followed me, and we were soon alone together in the little room, which love and voluptuous pleasure had transmuted into a sumptuous place. We would gladly have talked to each other, but as we had only an hour before us, we set to without even taking off our clothes. After the last kiss which ended the third assault, she told me that she was to be married on the eve of Shrove Tuesday, and that all had been arranged by her confessor. She also thanked me for having asked Momolo to invite her intended.

"When shall we see each other again, my angel?"

"On Sunday, the eve of my wedding, we shall be able to spend four hours together."

"Delightful! I promise you that when you leave me

you will be in such a state that the caresses of your husband won't hurt you."

She smiled and departed, and I threw myself on the bed where I rested for a good hour.

As I was going home I met a carriage and four going at a great speed. A footman rode in front of the carriage, and within it I saw a young nobleman. My attention was arrested by the blue ribbon on his breast. I gazed at him, and he called out my name and had the carriage stopped. I was extremely surprised when I found it was Lord O'Callaghan, whom I had known at Paris at his mother's, the Countess of Lismore, who was separated from her husband, and was the kept mistress of M. de St. Aubin, the unworthy successor of the good and virtuous Fénélon in the archbishopric of Cambrai. However, the archbishop owed his promotion to the fact that he was a bastard of the Duc d'Orleans, the French Regent.

Lord O'Callaghan was a fine-looking young man, with wit and talent, but the slave of his unbridled passions and of every species of vice. I knew that if he were lord in name he was not so in fortune, and I was astonished to see him driving such a handsome carriage, and still more so at his blue ribbon. In a few words he told me that he was going to dine with the Pretender, but that he would sup at home. He invited me to come to supper, and I accepted.

After dinner I took a short walk, and then went to enliven myself at the theatre, where I saw Momolo's girls strutting about with Costa; afterwards I went to Lord O'Callaghan, and was pleasantly surprised to meet the poet Poinsinet. He was young, short, ugly, full of poetic fire, a wit, and dramatist. Five or six years later the poor fellow fell into the Guadalquivir and was drowned. He had gone to Madrid in the hope of making his fortune. As I had known him at Paris I addressed him as an old acquaintance.

"What are you doing at Rome? Where's my Lord O'Callaghan?"

"He's in the next room, but as his father is dead his title is now Earl of Lismore. You know he was an adherent of the Pretender's. I left Paris with him, well enough pleased at being able to come to Rome without its costing me anything."

"Then the earl is a rich man now?"

"Not exactly; but he will be, as he is his father's heir, and the old earl left an immense fortune. It is true that it is all confiscated, but that is nothing, as his claims are irresistible."

"In short, he is rich in claims and rich in the future; but how did he get himself made a knight of one of the French king's orders?"

"You're joking. That is the blue ribbon of the Order of St. Michael, of which the late Elector of Cologne was grand master. As you know, my lord plays exquisitely on the violin, and when he was at Bonn he played the Elector a concerto by Tartini. The prince could not find words in which to express the pleasure of my lord's performance, and gave him the ribbon you have seen."

"A fine present, doubtless."

"You don't know what pleasure it gave my lord, for when we go back to Paris everybody will take it for the Order of the Holy Ghost."

We passed into a large room, where we found the earl with the party he had asked to supper. As soon as he saw me he embraced me, called me his dear friend, and named his guests. There were seven or eight girls, all of them pretty, three or four *castrati* who played women's parts in the Roman theatre, and five or six abbés, the husband of every wife and the wives of every husband, who boasted of their wickedness, and challenged the girls to be more shameless than they. The girls were not common courtezans, but past mistresses of music, painting, and vice considered as a fine art. The kind of society may be imagined when I say that I found myself a perfect novice amongst them.

"Where are you going, prince?" said the earl to a respectable-looking man who was making for the door.

"I don't feel well, my lord. I think I must go out."

"What prince is that?" said I.

"The Prince de Chimai. He is a sub-deacon, and is endeavouring to gain permission to marry, lest his family should become extinct."

"I admire his prudence or his delicacy, but I am afraid I should not imitate him."

There were twenty-four of us at table, and it is no exaggeration to say that we emptied a hundred bottles of the choicest wines. Everybody was drunk, with the exception of myself and the poet Poinsinet, who had taken nothing but water. The company rose from table, and then began a foul orgy which I should never have conceived possible, and which no pen could describe, though possibly a seasoned profligate might get some idea of it.

A *castrato* and a girl of almost equal height proposed to strip in an adjoining room, and to lie on their backs, in the same bed with their faces covered. They challenged us all to guess which was which.

We all went in and nobody could pronounce from sight which was male and which was female, so I bet the earl fifty crowns that I would point out the woman.

He accepted the wager, and I guessed correctly, but payment was out of the question.

This first act of the orgy ended with the prostitution of the two individuals, who defied everybody to accomplish the great act. All, with the exception of Poinsinet and myself, made the attempt, but their efforts were in vain.

The second act displayed four or five couples reversed, and here the abbés shone, both in the active and passive parts of this lascivious spectacle. I was the only person respected.

All at once, the earl, who had hitherto remained perfectly motionless, attacked the wretched Poinsinet, who in vain attempted to defend himself. He had to strip like my lord, who was as naked as the others. We stood round in a circle. Suddenly the earl, taking his watch, promised it to the first who succeeded in giving them a sure mark of sensibility. The desire of gaining the prize excited the impure crowd immensely, and the *castrati*, the girls, and the abbés all did their utmost, each one striving to be the first. They had to draw lots. This part interested me most, for throughout this almost incredible scene of debauchery I did not experience the slightest sensation, although under other circumstances any of the girls would have claimed my homage, but all I did was to laugh, especially to see the poor poet in terror of experiencing the lust of the flesh, for the profligate nobleman swore that if he made him lose he would deliver him up to the brutal lust of all the abbés. He escaped, probably through fear of the consequences.

The orgy came to an end when nobody had any further hopes of getting the watch. The secret of the Lesbians was only employed, however, by the abbés and the *castrati*. The girls, wishing to be able to despise those who made use of it, refrained from doing so. I suspect they were actuated by pride rather than shame, as they might possibly have employed it without success.

This vile debauch disgusted me, and yet gave me a better knowledge of myself. I could not help confessing that my life had been endangered, for the only arm I had was my sword, but I should certainly have used it if the earl had tried to treat me like the others, and as he had treated poor Poinsinet. I never understood how it was that he respected me, for he was quite drunk, and in a kind of Bacchic fury.

As I left, I promised to come and see him as often as he pleased, but I promised myself never to set foot in his house again.

Next day, he came to see me in the afternoon, and asked me to walk with him to the Villa Medici.

I complimented him on the immense wealth he had inherited to enable him to live so splendidly, but he laughed and told me that he did not possess fifty piastres, that his father had left nothing but debts, and that he himself already owed three or four thousand crowns.

"I wonder people give you credit, then."

"They give me credit because everybody knows that I have drawn a bill of exchange on Paris to the tune of two hundred thousand francs. But in four or five days the bill will be returned protested, and I am only waiting for that to happen to make my escape."

"If you are certain of its being protested, I advise you to make your escape to-day; for as it is so large a sum it may be taken up before it is due."

"No, I won't do that; I have one hope left. I have written to tell my mother that I shall be undone if she does not furnish the banker, on whom I have drawn the bill, with sufficient funds and if she does that, the bill will be accepted. You know my mother is very fond of me."

"Yes, but I also know that she is far from rich."

"True, but M. de St. Aubin is rich enough, and between you and me I think he is my father. Meanwhile, my creditors are almost as quiet as I am. All those girls you saw yesterday would give me all they have if I asked them, as they are all expecting me to make them a handsome present in the course of the week, but I won't abuse their trust in me. But I am afraid I shall be obliged to cheat the Jew, who wants me to give him three thousand sequins for this ring, as I know it is only worth one thousand."

"He will send the police after you."

"I defy him to do whatever he likes."

The ring was set with a straw-coloured diamond of nine or ten carats. He begged me to keep his secret as we parted. I did not feel any sentiments of pity for this extravagant madman, as I only saw in him a man unfortunate by his own fault, whose fate would probably make him end his days in a prison unless he had the courage to blow his brains out.

I went to Momolo's in the evening, and found the intended husband of my fair Mariuccia there, but not the lady herself. I heard she had sent word to the *scopatore santissimo* that, as her father had come from Palestrina to be present at her wedding, she could not come to supper. I admired her subtlety. A young girl has no need of being instructed in diplomacy, nature and her own heart are her teachers, and she never blunders. At supper I studied the young man, and found him eminently suitable for Mariuccia; he was handsome, modest, and intelligent, and whatever he said was spoken frankly and to the point.

He told me before Momolo's daughter, Tecla, that he would have married her if she had possessed means to enable him to open his shop, and that he had reason to thank God for having met Maria, whose confessor had been such a true spiritual father to her. I asked him where the wedding festivities were to take place, and he told me they were to be at his father's house, on the other side of the Tiber. As his father, who kept a garden, was poor, he had furnished him with ten crowns to defray the expenses.

I wanted to give him the ten crowns, but how was I to do it? It would have betrayed me.

"Is your father's garden a pretty one?" I asked.

"Not exactly pretty, but very well kept. As he owns the land, he has separated a plot which he wants to sell; it would bring in twenty crowns a year, and I should be as happy as a cardinal if I could buy it."

"How much will it cost?"

"It's a heavy price; two hundred crowns."

"Why, that's cheap! Listen to me. I have met your future bride at this house, and I have found her all worthy of happiness. She deserves an honest young fellow like you for a husband. Now what would you do supposing I were to make you a present of two hundred crowns to buy the garden?"

"I should put it to my wife's dowry."

"Then here are the two hundred crowns. I shall give them to Momolo, as I don't know you well enough, though I think you are perfectly to be trusted. The garden is yours, as part of your wife's dowry."

Momolo took the money, and promised to buy the garden the following day, and the young man shedding tears of joy and gratitude fell on his knees and kissed my hand. All the girls wept, as I myself did, for there's a contagion in such happy tears. Nevertheless, they did not all proceed from the same source; some were virtuous and some vicious, and the young man's were the only ones whose source was pure and unalloyed. I lifted him from the 'ground, kissed him, and wished him a happy marriage. He made bold to ask me to his wedding, but I refused, thanking him kindly. I told him that if he wanted to please me, he must come and sup at Momolo's on the eve of his wedding, and I begged the good *scopatore* to ask Mariuccia, her father and mother as well. I was sure of seeing her for the last time on the Sunday morning.

At seven o'clock on the Sunday morning we were in each other's arms, with four hours before us. After the first burst of mutual ardour she told me that all arrangements had been made in her house the evening before, in the presence of her confessor and of Momolo; and that on the receipt for the two hundred crowns being handed in the notary had put the garden into the settlement, and that the good father had made her a present of twenty piastres towards defraying the notary's fees and the wedding expenses.

"Everything is for the best, and I am sure I shall be happy. My intended adores you, but you did wisely not to accept his invitation, for you would have found everything so poor, and besides tongues might have been set wagging to my disadvantage."

"You are quite right, dearest, but what do you intend to do if your husband finds that the door has been opened by someone else, for possibly he expects you to be a maid."

"I expect he will know no more about it than I did the first time you knew me; besides, I do not feel that you have defiled me, and my clean conscience will not allow me to think of the matter; and I am sure that he will not think of it any more than I."

"Yes, but if he does?"

"It would not be delicate on his part, but what should prevent me from replying that I don't know what he means?"

"You are right; that's the best way. But have you told your confessor of our mutual enjoyment?"

"No, for as I did not give myself up to you with any criminal intention, I do not think I have offended God."

"You are an angel, and I admire the clearness of your reasoning. But listen to me; it's possible that you are already with child, or that you may become so this morning; promise to name the child after me."

"I will do so."

The four hours sped rapidly away. After the sixth assault we were wearied though not satiated. We parted with tears, and swore to love each other as brother and sister ever after.

I went home, bathed, slept an hour, rose, dressed, and dined pleasantly with the family. In the evening I took the Mengs family for a drive in my landau, and we then went to the theatre, where the *castrato* who played the prima donna was a great attraction. He was the favourite pathic of Cardinal Borghese, and supped every evening with his eminence.

This *castrato* had a fine voice, but his chief attraction was his beauty. I had seen him in man's clothes in the street, but though a fine-looking fellow, he had not made any impression on me, for one could see at once that he was only half a man, but on the stage in woman's dress the illusion was complete; he was ravishing.

He was enclosed in a carefully-made corset and looked like a nymph; and incredible though it may seem, his breast was as beautiful as any woman's; it was the monster's chiefest charm. However well one knew the fellow's neutral sex, as soon as one looked at his breast one felt all aglow and quite madly amorous of him. To feel nothing one would have to be as cold and impassive as a German. As he walked the boards, waiting for the refrain of the air he was singing, there was something grandly voluptuous about him; and as he glanced towards the boxes, his black eyes, at once tender and modest, ravished the heart. He evidently wished to fan the flame of those who loved him as a man, and probably would not have cared for him if he had been a woman.

Rome the holy, which thus strives to make all men pederasts, denies the fact, and will not believe in the effects of the glamour of her own devising.

I made these reflections aloud, and an ecclesiastic, wishing to blind me to the truth, spoke as follows:

"You are quite right. Why should this *castrato* be allowed to shew his breast, of which the fairest Roman lady might be proud, and yet wish everyone to consider him as a man and not a woman? If the stage is forbidden to the fair sex lest they excite desires, why do they seek out men-monsters made in the form of women, who excite much more criminal desires? They keep on preaching that pederasty is comparatively unknown and entraps only a few, but many clever men endeavour to be entrapped, and end by thinking it so pleasant that they prefer these monsters to the most beautiful women."

"The Pope would be sure of heaven if he put a stop to this scandalous practice."

"I don't agree with you. One could not have a pretty actress to supper without causing a scandal, but such an invitation to a *castrato* makes nobody talk. It is of course known perfectly well that after supper both heads rest on one pillow, but what everybody knows is ignored by all. One may sleep with a man out of mere friendship, it is not so with a woman."

"True, monsignor, appearances are saved, and a sin concealed is half pardoned, as they say in Paris."

"At Rome we say it is pardoned altogether. *Peccato nascosto non offende.*"

His Jesuitical arguments interested me, for I knew that he was an avowed partisan of the forbidden fruit.

In one of the boxes I saw the Marchioness Passarini (whom I had known at Dresden) with Don Antonio Borghese, and I went to pay my addresses to them. The prince, whom I had known at Paris ten years before, recognized me, and asked me to dine with him on the following day. I went, but my lord was not at home. A page told me that my place was laid at table, and that I could dine just as if the prince was there, on which I turned my back on him and went away. On Ash Wednesday he sent his man to ask me to sup with him and the marchioness, who was his mistress, and I sent word that I would not fail to come; but he waited for me in vain. Pride is the daughter of folly, and always keeps its mother's nature.

After the opera I went to Momolo's, where I found Mariuccia, her father, her mother, and her future husband. They were anxiously expecting me. It is not difficult to make people happy when one selects for one's bounty persons who really deserve happiness. I was amidst poor but honest people, and I can truly say that I had a delightful supper. It may be that some of my enjoyment proceeded from a feeling of vanity, for I knew that I was the author of the happiness depicted on the faces of the bride and bridegroom and of the father and mother of Mariuccia; but when vanity causes good deeds it is a virtue. Nevertheless, I owe it to myself to tell my readers that my pleasure was too pure to have in it any admixture of vice.

After supper I made a small bank at faro, making everybody play with counters, as nobody had a penny, and I was so fortunate as to make everyone win a few ducats.

After the game we danced in spite of the prohibition of the Pope, whom no Roman can believe to be infallible, for he forbids dancing and permits games of chance. His successor Ganganelli followed the opposite course, and was no better obeyed. To avoid suspicion I did not give the pair any present, but I gave up my landau to them that they might enjoy the carnival on the Corso, and I told Costa to get them a box at the Capranica Theatre. Momolo asked me to supper on Shrove Tuesday.

I wished to leave Rome on the second day of Lent, and I called on the Holy Father at a time when all Rome was on the Corso. His Holiness welcomed me most graciously, and said he was surprised that I had not gone to see the sights on the Corso like everybody else. I replied that as a lover of pleasure I had chosen the greatest pleasure of all for a Christian—namely, to kneel at the feet of the vicar of Christ on earth. He bowed with a kind of majestic humility, which shewed me how the compliment had pleased him. He kept me for more than an hour, talking about Venice, Padua, and Paris, which latter city the worthy man would not have been sorry to have visited. I again commended myself to his apostolic intercession to enable me to return to my native country, and he replied,——

"Have recourse to God, dear son; His grace will be

more efficacious than my prayers;" and then he blessed me and wished me a prosperous journey.

I saw that the Head of the Church had no great opinion of his own power.

On Shrove Tuesday I dressed myself richly in the costume of Polichinello, and rode along the Corso showering sweetmeats on all the pretty women I saw. Finally I emptied the basket on the daughters of the worthy *scopatore,* whom Costa was taking about in my landau with all the dignity of a pasha.

At night-time I took off my costume and went to Momolo's, where I expected to see dear Mariuccia for the last time. Supper passed off in almost a similar manner to the supper of last Sunday; but there was an interesting novelty for me—namely, the sight of my beloved mistress in her character of bride. Her husband seemed to be much more reserved with respect to me than at our first meeting. I was puzzled by his behaviour, and sat down by Mariuccia and proceeded to question her. She told me all the circumstances which had passed on the first night, and she spoke highly of her husband's good qualities. He was kind, amorous, good-tempered, and delicate. No doubt he must have noticed that the casket had been opened, but he had said nothing about it. As he had spoken about me, she had not been able to resist the pleasure of telling him that I was her sole benefactor, at which, so far from being offended, he seemed to trust in her more than ever.

"But has he not questioned you indirectly as to the connection between us?"

"Not at all. I told him that you went to my confessor after having spoken to me once only in the church, where I told you what a good chance I had of being married to him."

"Do you think he believed you?"

"I am not sure; however, even if it were otherwise, it is enough that he pretends to, for I am determined to win his esteem."

"You are right, and I think all the better of him for his suspicions, for it is better to marry a man with some sense in his head than to marry a fool."

I was so pleased with what she told me that when I took leave of the company I embraced the hairdresser, and drawing a handsome gold watch from my fob I begged him to accept it as a souvenir of me. He received it with the utmost gratitude. From my pocket I took a ring, worth at least six hundred francs, and put it on his wife's finger, wishing them a fair posterity and all manner of happiness, and I then went home to bed, telling Le Duc and Costa that we must begin to pack up next day.

I was just getting up when they brought me a note from Lord Lismore, begging me to come and speak to him at noon at the Villa Borghese.

I had some suspicion of what he might want, and kept the appointment. I felt in a mood to give him some good advice. Indeed, considering the friendship between his mother and myself, it was my duty to do so.

He came up to me and gave me a letter he had received the evening before from his mother. She told him that Paris de Monmartel had just informed her that he was in possession of a bill for two hundred thousand francs drawn by her son, and that he would honour it if she would furnish him with the funds. She had replied that she would let him know in two or three days if she could do so; but she warned her son that she had only asked for this delay to give him time to escape, as the bill would certainly be protested and returned, it being absolutely out of the question for her to get the money.

"You had better make yourself scarce as soon as you can," said I, returning him the letter.

"Buy this ring, and so furnish me with the means for my escape. You would not know that it was not my property if I had not told you so in confidence."

I made an appointment with him, and had the stone taken out and valued by one of the best jewellers in Rome.

"I know this stone," said he, "it is worth two thousand Roman crowns."

At four o'clock I took the earl five hundred crowns in gold and fifteen hundred crowns in paper, which he would have to take to a banker, who would give him a bill of exchange in Amsterdam.

"I will be off at nightfall," said he, "and travel by myself to Amsterdam, only taking such effects as are absolutely necessary, and my beloved blue ribbon."

"A pleasant journey to you," said I, and left him. In ten days I had the stone mounted at Bologna.

I got a letter of introduction from Cardinal Albani for Onorati, the nuncio at Florence, and another letter from M. Mengs to Sir —— Mann, whom he begged to receive me in his house. I was going to Florence for the sake of the Corticelli and my dear Thérèse, and I reckoned on the auditor's feigning to ignore my return, in spite of his unjust order, especially if I were residing at the English minister's.

On the second day of Lent the disappearance of Lord Lismore was the talk of the town. The English tailor was ruined, the Jew who owned the ring was in despair, and all the silly fellow's servants were turned out of the house in almost a state of nakedness, as the tailor had

unceremoniously taken possession of everything in the
way of clothes that he could lay his hands on.

Poor Poinsinet came to see me in a pitiable condition ;
he had only his shirt and overcoat. He had been despoiled of everything, and threatened with imprisonment.
"I haven't a farthing," said the poor child of the muses,
"I have only the shirt on my back. I know nobody here,
and I think I shall go and throw myself into the Tiber."

He was destined, not to be drowned in the Tiber but
in the Guadalquivir. I calmed him by offering to take
him to Florence with me, but I warned him that I must
leave him there, as someone was expecting me at Florence. He immediately took up his abode with me, and
wrote verses incessantly till it was time to go.

My brother Jean made me a present of an onyx of
great beauty. It was a cameo, representing Venus bath-
ing, and a genuine antique, as the name of the artist,
Sostrates, was cut on the stone. Two years later I sold
it to Dr. Masti, at London, for three hundred pounds,
and it is possibly still in the British Museum.

I went my way with Poinsinet who amused me, in
spite of his sadness, with his droll fancies. In two days
I got down at Dr. Vannini's, who tried to conceal his
surprise at seeing me. I lost no time, but waited on Sir
—— Mann immediately, and found him sitting at table.
He gave me a very friendly reception, but he seemed
alarmed when, in reply to his question, I told him that
my dispute with the auditor had not been arranged. He
told me plainly that he thought I had made a mistake in
returning to Florence, and that he would be compromised by my staying with him. I pointed out that I was
only passing through Florence.

"That's all very well," said he, "but you know you
ought to call on the auditor."

I promised to do so, and returned to my lodging. I had scarcely shut the door, when an agent of police came and told me that the auditor had something to say to me, and would be glad to see me at an early hour next morning.

I was enraged at this order, and determined to start forthwith rather than obey. Full of this idea I called on Thérèse and found she was at Pisa. I then went to see the Corticelli, who threw her arms round my neck, and made use of the Bolognese grimaces appropriate to the occasion. To speak the truth, although the girl was pretty, her chief merit in my eyes was that she made me laugh.

I gave some money to her mother to get us a good supper, and I took the girl out on pretence of going for a walk. I went with her to my lodging, and left her with Poinsinet, and going to another room I summoned Costa and Vannini. I told Costa in Vannini's presence to go on with Le Duc and my luggage the following day, and to call for me at the "Pilgrim" at Bologna. I gave Vannini my instructions, and he left the room; and then I ordered Costa to leave Florence with Signora Laura and her son, and to tell them that I and the daughter were on in front. Le Duc received similar orders, and calling Poinsinet I gave him ten louis, and begged him to look out for some other lodging that very evening. The worthy but unfortunate young man wept grateful tears, and told me that he would set out for Parma on foot next day, and that there M. Tillot would do something for him.

I went back to the next room, and told the Corticelli to come with me. She did so under the impression that we were going back to her mother's, but without taking the trouble to undeceive her I had a carriage and pair got ready, and told the postillion to drive to Uccellatoio, the first post on the Bologna road.

"Where in the world are we going?" said she.

"Bologna."

"How about mamma?"

"She will come on to-morrow."

"Does she know about it?"

"No, but she will to-morrow when Costa comes to tell her, and to fetch her and your brother."

She liked the joke, and got into the carriage laughing, and we drove away.

CHAPTER XI

*My Arrival at Bologna—I Am Expelled from Modena—
I Visit Parma and Turin—The Pretty Jewess—The
Dressmaker*

T HE Corticelli had a good warm mantle, but the fool
who carried her off had no cloak, even of the most
meagre kind, to keep off the piercing cold, which was
increased by a keen wind blowing right in our faces.

In spite of all I would not halt, for I was afraid I
might be pursued and obliged to return, which would
have greatly vexed me.

When I saw that the postillion was slackening his
speed, I increased the amount of the present I was going
to make him, and once more we rushed along at a head-
long pace. I felt perishing with the cold; while the postillions seeing me so lightly clad, and so prodigal of my
money to speed them on their way, imagined that I was
a prince carrying off the heiress of some noble family.
We heard them talking to this effect while they changed
horses, and the Corticelli was so much amused that she
did nothing but laugh for the rest of the way. In five
hours we covered forty miles; we started from Florence
at eight o'clock, and at one in the morning we stopped
at a post in the Pope's territory, where I had nothing to
fear. The stage goes under the name of "The Ass Un-
burdened."

The odd name of the inn made my mistress laugh
afresh. Everybody was asleep, but the noise I made and

the distribution of a few pauls procured me the privilege
of a fire. I was dying of hunger, and they coolly told
me there was nothing to eat. I laughed in the landlord's
face, and told him to bring me his butter, his eggs, his
macaroni, a ham, and some Parmesan cheese, for I knew
that so much will be found in the inns all over Italy.
The repast was soon ready, and I shewed the idiot host
that he had materials for an excellent meal. We ate like
four, and afterwards they made up an impromptu bed
and we went to sleep, telling them to call me as soon as a
carriage and four drew up.

Full of ham and macaroni, slightly warmed with the
Chianti and Montepulciano, and tired with our journey,
we stood more in need of slumber than of love, and so
we gave ourselves up to sleep till morning. Then we
gave a few moments to pleasure, but it was so slight an
affair as not to be worth talking about.

At one o'clock we began to feel hungry again and got
up, and the host provided us with an excellent dinner,
after receiving instructions from me. I was astonished
not to see the carriage draw up, but I waited patiently
all day. Night came on and still no coach, and I began
to feel anxious; but the Corticelli persisted in laughing
at everything. Next morning I sent off an express messenger with instructions for Costa. In the event of any
violence having taken place, I was resolved to return to
Florence, of which city I could at any time make myself
free by the expenditure of two hundred crowns.

The messenger started at noon, and returned at two
o'clock with the news that my servants would shortly
be with me. My coach was on its way, and behind it a
smaller carriage with two horses, in which sat an old
woman and a young man.

"That's the mother," said Corticelli; "now we shall

have some fun. Let's get something for them to eat, and be ready to hear the history of this marvellous adventure which she will remember to her dying day."

Costa told me that the auditor had revenged my contempt of his orders by forbidding the post authorities to furnish any horses for my carriage. Hence the delay. But here we heard the allocution of the Signora Laura.

"I got an excellent supper ready," she began, "according to your orders; it cost me more than ten pauls, as I shall shew you, and I hope you will make it up to me as I'm but a poor woman. All was ready and I joyfully expected you, but in vain; I was in despair. At last when midnight came I sent my son to your lodging to enquire after you, but you may imagine my grief when I heard that nobody knew what had become of you. I passed a sleepless night, weeping all the time, and in the morning I went and complained to the police that you had taken off my daughter, and asked them to send after you and make you give her back to me. But only think, they laughed at me! 'Why did you let her go out without you?' laughing in my face. 'Your daughter's in good hands,' says another, 'you know perfectly well where she is.' In fact I was grossly slandered."

"Slandered?" said the Corticelli.

"Yes, slandered, for it was as much as to say that I had consented to your being carried off, and if I had done that the fools might have known I would not have come to them about it. I went away in a rage to Dr. Vannini's, where I found your man, who told me that you had gone to Bologna, and that I could follow you if I liked. I consented to this plan, and I hope you will pay my travelling expenses. But I can't help telling you that this is rather beyond a joke."

I consoled her by telling her I would pay all she had spent, and we set off for Bologna the next day, and reached that town at an early hour. I sent my servants to the inn with my carriage, and I went to lodge with the Corticelli.

I spent a week with the girl, getting my meals from the inn, and enjoying a diversity of pleasures which I shall remember all my days; my young wanton had a large circle of female friends, all pretty and all kind. I lived with them like a sultan, and still I delight to recall this happy time, and I say with a sigh, *Tempi passati!*

There are many towns in Italy where one can enjoy all the pleasures obtainable at Bologna; but nowhere so cheaply, so easily, or with so much freedom. The living is excellent, and there are arcades where one can walk in the shade in learned and witty company. It is a great pity that either from the air, the water, or the wine—for men of science have not made up their minds on the subject—persons who live at Bologna are subject to a slight itch. The Bolognese, however, far from finding this unpleasant, seem to think it an advantage; it gives them the pleasure of scratching themselves. In springtime the ladies distinguish themselves by the grace with which they use their fingers.

Towards mid-Lent I left the Corticelli, wishing her a pleasant journey, for she was going to fulfil a year's engagement at Prague as second dancer. I promised to fetch her and her mother to Paris, and my readers will see how I kept my word.

I got to Modena the evening after I left Bologna, and I stopped there, with one of those sudden whims to which I have always been subject. Next morning I went out to see the pictures, and as I was returning to my lodging for dinner a blackguardly-looking fellow came up and ordered me, on the part of the Government, to continue my journey on the day following at latest.

"Very good," said I, and the fellow went away.

"Who is that man?" I said to the landlord.

"A spy."

"A spy; and the Government dares to send such a fellow to me?"

"The *borgello* must have sent him."

"Then the *borgello* is the Governor of Modena—the infamous wretch!"

"Hush! hush! all the best families speak to him in the street."

"Then the best people are very low here, I suppose?"

"Not more than anywhere else. He is the manager of the opera house, and the greatest noblemen dine with him and thus secure his favour."

"It's incredible! But why should the high and mighty *borgello* send me away from Modena?"

"I don't know, but do you take my advice and go and speak to him; you will find him a fine fellow."

Instead of going to see this b . . . I called on the Abbé Testa Grossa, whom I had known at Venice in 1753. Although he was a man of low extraction he had a keen wit. At this time he was old and resting on his laurels; he had fought his way into favour by the sheer force of merit, and his master, the Duke of Modena, had long chosen him as his representative with other powers.

Abbé Testa Grossa recognized me and gave me the most gracious reception, but when he heard of what had befallen me he seemed much annoyed.

"What can I do?" said I.

"You had better go, as the man may put a much more grievous insult on you."

"I will do so, but could you oblige me by telling me the reason for such a high-handed action?"

"Come again this evening; I shall probably be able to satisfy you."

I called on the abbé again in the evening, for I felt anxious to learn in what way I had offended the lord *borgello,* to whom I thought I was quite unknown. The abbé satisfied me.

"The *borgello,*" said he, "saw your name on the bill which he receives daily containing a list of the names of those who enter or leave the city. He remembered that you were daring enough to escape from The Leads, and as he does not at all approve of that sort of thing he resolved not to let the Modenese be contaminated by so egregious an example of the defiance of justice, however unjust it may be; and in short he has given you the order to leave the town."

"I am much obliged, but I really wonder how it is that while you were telling me this you did not blush to be a subject of the Duke of Modena's. What an unworthy action! How contrary is such a system of government to all the best interests of the state!"

"You are quite right, my dear sir, but I am afraid that as yet men's eyes are not open to what best serves their interests."

"That is doubtless due to the fact that so many men are unworthy."

"I will not contradict you."

"Farewell, abbé."

"Farewell, M. Casanova."

Next morning, just as I was going to get into my carriage, a young man between twenty-five and thirty, tall and strong and broad shouldered, his eyes black and glittering, his eyebrows strongly arched, and his general

air being that of a cut-throat, accosted me and begged
me to step aside and hear what he had to say.

"If you like to stop at Parma for three days, and if
you will promise to give me fifty sequins when I bring
you the news that the *borgello* is dead, I promise to
shoot him within the next twenty-four hours."

"Thanks. Such an animal as that should be allowed to
die a natural death. Here's a crown to drink my health."

At the present time I feel very thankful that I acted
as I did, but I confess that if I had felt sure that it was
not a trap I should have promised the money. The fear
of committing myself spared me this crime.

The next day I got to Parma, and I put up at the
posting-house under the name of the Chevalier de Seingalt, which I still bear. When an honest man adopts a
name which belongs to no one, no one has a right to
contest his use of it; it becomes a man's duty to keep
the name. I had now borne it for two years, but I often
subjoined to it my family name.

When I got to Parma I dismissed Costa, but in a week
after I had the misfortune to take him on again. His
father, who was a poor violin player, as I had once been,
with a large family to provide for, excited my pity.

I made enquiries about M. Antonio, but he had left
the place; and M. Dubois Chalelereux, Director of the
Mint, had gone to Venice with the permission of the
Duke of Parma, to set up the beam, which was never
brought into use. Republics are famous for their superstitious attachment to old customs; they are afraid that
changes for the better may destroy the stability of the
state, and the government of aristocratic Venice still
preserves its original Greek character.

My Spaniard was delighted when I dismissed Costa,
and proportionately sorry when I took him back.

"He's no profligate," said Le Duc; "he is sober, and has no liking for bad company. But I think he's a robber, and a dangerous robber, too. I know it, because he seems so scrupulously careful not to cheat you in small things. Remember what I say, sir; he will do you. He is waiting to gain your confidence, and then he will strike home. Now, I am quite a different sort of fellow, a rogue in a small way; but you know me."

His insight was keener than mine, for five or six months later the Italian robbed me of fifty thousand crowns. Twenty-three years afterwards, in 1784, I found him in Venice, valet to Count Hardegg, and I felt inclined to have him hanged. I shewed him by proof positive that I could do so if I liked; but he had resource to tears and supplications, and to the intercession of a worthy man named Bertrand, who lived with the ambassador of the King of Sardinia. I esteemed this individual, and he appealed to me successfully to pardon Costa. I asked the wretch what he had done with the gold and jewels he had stolen from me, and he told me that he had lost the whole of it in furnishing funds for a bank at Biribi, that he had been despoiled by his own associates, and had been poor and miserable ever since.

In the same year in which he robbed me he married Momolo's daughter, and after making her a mother he abandoned her.

To pursue our story.

At Turin I lodged in a private house with the Abbé Gama, who had been expecting me. In spite of the good abbé's sermon on economy, I took the whole of the first floor, and a fine suite it was.

We discussed diplomatic topics, and he assured me that I should be accredited in May, and that he would give me instructions as to the part I was to play. I was pleased with his commission, and I told the abbé that I should be ready to go to Augsburg whenever the ambassadors of the belligerent powers met there.

After making the necessary arrangements with my landlady with regard to my meals I went to a coffee-house to read the papers, and the first person I saw was the Marquis Desarmoises, whom I had known in Savoy. The first thing he said was that all games of chance were forbidden, and that the ladies I had met would no doubt be delighted to see me. As for himself, he said that he lived by playing backgammon, though he was not at all lucky at it, as talent went for more than luck at that game. I can understand how, if fortune is neutral, the best player will win, but I do not see how the contrary can take place.

We went for a walk in the promenade leading to the citadel, where I saw numerous extremely pretty women. In Turin the fair sex is most delightful, but the police regulations are troublesome to a degree. Owing to the town being a small one and thinly peopled, the police spies find out everything. Thus one cannot enjoy any little freedoms without great precautions and the aid of cunning procuresses, who have to be well paid, as they would be cruelly punished if they were found out. No prostitutes and no kept women are allowed, much to the delight of the married women, and with results which the ignorant police might have anticipated. As well be imagined, pederasty has a fine field in this town, where the passions are kept under lock and key.

Amongst the beauties I looked at, one only attracted me. I asked Desarmoises her name, as he knew all of them.

"That's the famous Leah," said he; "she is a Jewess, and impregnable. She has resisted the attacks of the best strategists in Turin. Her father's a famous horse-dealer; you can go and see her easily enough, but there's nothing to be done there."

The greater the difficulty the more I felt spurred on to attempt it.

"Take me there," said I, to Desarmoises.

"As soon as you please."

I asked him to dine with me, and we were on our way when we met M. Zeroli and two or three other persons whom I had met at Aix. I gave and received plenty of compliments, but not wishing to pay them any visits I excused myself on the pretext of business.

When we had finished dinner Desarmoises took me to the horse-dealer's. I asked if he had a good saddle horse. He called a lad and gave his orders, and whilst he was speaking the charming daughter appeared on the scene. She was dazzlingly beautiful, and could not be more than twenty-two. Her figure was as lissom as a nymph's, her hair a raven black, her complexion a meeting of the lily and the rose, her eyes full of fire, her lashes long, and her eye-brows so well arched that they seemed ready to make war on any who would dare the conquest of her charms. All about her betokened an educated mind and knowledge of the world.

I was so absorbed in the contemplation of her charms that I did not notice the horse when it was brought to me. However, I proceeded to scrutinise it, pretending to be an expert, and after feeling the knees and legs, turning back the ears, and looking at the teeth, I tested its behaviour at a walk, a trot, and a gallop, and then told the Jew that I would come and try it myself in top-boots the next day. The horse was a fine dappled bay, and was priced at forty Piedmontese pistoles—about a hundred sequins.

"He is gentleness itself," said Leah, "and he ambles as fast as any other horse trots."

"You have ridden it, then?"

"Often, sir, and if I were rich I would never sell him."

"I won't buy the horse till I have seen you ride it."

She blushed at this.

"You must oblige the gentleman," said her father. She consented to do so, and I promised to come again at nine o'clock the next day.

I was exact to time, as may be imagined, and I found Leah in riding costume. What proportions! What a Venus Callipyge! I was captivated.

Two horses were ready, and she leapt on hers with the ease and grace of a practised rider, and I got up on my horse. We rode together for some distance. The horse went well enough, but what of that; all my eyes were for her.

As we were turning, I said,——

"Fair Leah, I will buy the horse, but as a present for you; and if you will not take it I shall leave Turin to-day. The only condition I attach to the gift is, that you will ride with me whenever I ask you."

I saw she seemed favourably inclined to my proposal, so I told her that I should stay six weeks at Turin, that I had fallen in love with her on the promenade, and that the purchase of the horse had been a mere pretext for discovering to her my feelings. She replied modestly that she was vastly flattered by the liking I had taken to her, and that I need not have made her such a present to assure myself of her friendship.

"The condition you impose on me is an extremely pleasant one, and I am sure that my father will like me to accept it."

To this she added,——

"All I ask is for you to make me the present before him, repeating that you will only buy it on the condition that I will accept it."

I found the way smoother than I had expected, and I did what she asked me. Her father, whose name was Moses, thought it a good bargain, congratulated his daughter, took the forty pistoles and gave me a receipt, and begged me to do them the honour of breakfasting with them the next day. This was just what I wanted.

The following morning Moses received me with great respect. Leah, who was in her ordinary clothes, told me that if I liked to ride she would put on her riding habit.

"Another day," said I; "to-day I should like to converse with you in your own house."

But the father, who was as greedy as most Jews are, said that if I liked driving he could sell me a pretty phaeton with two excellent horses.

"You must shew them to the gentleman," said Leah, possibly in concert with her father.

Moses said nothing, but went out to get the horses harnessed.

"I will look at them," I said to Leah, "but I won't buy, as I should not know what to do with them."

"You can take your lady-love out for a drive."

"That would be you; but perhaps you would be afraid?"

"Not at all, if you drove in the country or the suburbs."

"Very good, Leah, then I will look at them."

The father came in, and we went downstairs. I liked the carriage and the horses, and I told Leah so.

"Well," said Moses, "you can have them now for four hundred sequins, but after Easter the price will be five hundred sequins at least."

Leah got into the carriage, and I sat beside her, and we went for an hour's drive into the country. I told Moses I would give him an answer by the next day, and he went about his business, while Leah and I went upstairs again.

"It's quite worth four hundred sequins," said I, "and to-morrow I will buy it with pleasure; but on the same condition as that on which I bought the horse, and something more—namely, that you will grant me all the favours that a tender lover can desire."

"You speak plainly, and I will answer you in the same way. I'm an honest girl, sir, and not for sale."

"All women, dear Leah, whether they are honest or not, are for sale. When a man has plenty of time he buys the woman his heart desires by unremitting attentions; but when he's in a hurry he buys her with presents, and even with money."

"Then he's a clumsy fellow; he would do better to let sentiment and attention plead his cause and gain the victory."

"I wish I could give myself that happiness, fair Leah, but I'm in a great hurry."

As I finished this sentence her father came in, and I left the house telling him that if I could not come the next day I would come the day after, and that we could talk about the phaeton then.

It was plain that Leah thought I was lavish of my money, and would make a capital dupe. She would relish the phaeton, as she had relished the horse, but I knew that I was not quite such a fool as that. It had not cost me much trouble to resolve to chance the loss of a hundred sequins, but beyond that I wanted some value for my money.

I temporarily suspended my visits to see how Leah and her father would settle it amongst themselves. I reckoned on the Jew's greediness to work well for me. He was very fond of money, and must have been angry that his daughter had not made me buy the phaeton by some means or another, for so long as the phaeton was bought the rest would be perfectly indifferent to him. I felt almost certain that they would come and see me.

The following Saturday I saw the fair Jewess on the promenade. We were near enough for me to accost her without seeming to be anxious to do so, and her look seemed to say, "Come."

"We see no more of you now," said she, "but come and breakfast with me to-morrow, or I will send you back the horse."

I promised to be with her in good time, and, as the reader will imagine, I kept my word.

The breakfast party was almost confined to ourselves, for though her aunt was present she was only there for decency's sake. After breakfast we resolved to have a ride, and she changed her clothes before me, but also before her aunt. She first put on her leather breeches, then let her skirts fall, took off her corset, and donned a jacket. With seeming indifference I succeeded in catching a glimpse of a magnificent breast; but the sly puss knew how much my indifference was worth.

"Will you arrange my frill?" said she.

This was a warm occupation for me, and I am afraid my hand was indiscreet. Nevertheless, I thought I detected a fixed design under all this seeming complaisance, and I was on my guard.

Her father came up just as we were getting on horse-back.

"If you will buy the phaeton and horses," said he, "I will abate twenty sequins."

"All that depends on your daughter," said I.

We set off at a walk, and Leah told me that she had been imprudent enough to confess to her father that she could make me buy the carriage, and that if I did not wish to embroil her with him I would be kind enough to purchase it.

"Strike the bargain," said she, "and you can give it me when you are sure of my love."

"My dear Leah, I am your humble servant, but you know on what condition."

"I promise to drive out with you whenever you please, without getting out of the carriage, but I know you would not care for that. No, your affection was only a temporary caprice."

"To convince you of the contrary I will buy the phaeton and put it in a coach-house. I will see that the horses are taken care of, though I shall not use them. But if you do not make me happy in the course of a week I shall re-sell the whole."

"Come to us to-morrow."

"I will do so, but I must have some pledge of your affection this morning."

"This morning? It's impossible."

"Excuse me; I will go upstairs with you, and you can shew me more than one kindness while you are undressing."

We came back, and I was astonished to hear her telling her father that the phaeton was mine, and all he had to do was to put in the horses. The Jew grinned, and we all went upstairs, and Leah coolly said,——

"Count out the money."

"I have not any money about me, but I will write you a cheque, if you like."

"Here is paper."

I wrote a cheque on Zappata for three hundred sequins, payable at sight. The Jew went off to get the money, and Leah remained alone with me.

"You have trusted me," she said, "and have thus shewn yourself worthy of my love."

"Then undress, quick!"

"No, my aunt is about the house; and as I cannot shut the door without exciting suspicion, she might come in; but I promise that you shall be content with me to-morrow. Nevertheless, I am going to undress, but you must go in this closet; you may come back when I have got my woman's clothes on again."

I agreed to this arrangement, and she shut me in. I examined the door, and discovered a small chink between the boards. I got on a stool, and saw Leah sitting on a sofa opposite to me engaged in undressing herself. She took off her shift and wiped her breasts and her feet with a towel, and just as she had taken off her breeches, and was as naked as my hand, one of her rings happened to slip off her finger, and rolled under the sofa. She got up, looked to right and left, and then stooped to search under the sofa, and to do this she had to kneel with her head down. When she got back to couch, the towel came again into requisition, and she wiped herself all over in such a manner that all her charms were revealed to my eager eyes. I felt sure that she knew I was a witness of all these operations, and she probably guessed what a fire the sight would kindle in my inflammable breast.

At last her toilette was finished, and she let me out. I clasped her in my arms, with the words, "I have seen everything." She pretended not to believe me, so I shewed her the chink, and was going to obtain my just dues, when the accursed Moses came in. He must have been blind or he would have seen the state his daughter had put me in; however, he thanked me, and gave me a receipt for the money, saying, "Everything in my poor house is at your service."

I bade them adieu, and I went away in an ill temper. I got into my phaeton, and drove home and told the coachman to find me a stable for the horses and a coach-house for the carriage.

I did not expect to see Leah again, and I felt enraged with her. She had pleased me only too much by her voluptuous attitudes, but she had set up an irritation wholly hostile to Love. She had made Love a robber, and the hungry boy had consented, but afterwards, when he craved more substantial fare, she refused him, and ardour was succeeded by contempt. Leah did not want to confess herself to be what she really was, and my love would not declare itself knavish.

I made the acquaintance of an amiable chevalier, a soldier, a man of letters, and a great lover of horses, who introduced me to several pleasant families. However, I did not cultivate them, as they only offered me the pleasures of sentiment, while I longed for lustier fare for which I was willing to pay heavily. The Chevalier de Brézé was not the man for me; he was too respectable for a profligate like myself. He bought the phaeton and horses, and I only lost thirty sequins by the transaction.

A certain M. Baretti, who had known me at Aix, and had been the Marquis de Prié's croupier, took me to see the Mazzoli, formerly a dancer, and then mistress to the Chevalier Raiberti, a hardheaded but honest man, who was then secretary for foreign affairs. Although the

Mazzoli was by no means pretty, she was extremely complaisant, and had several girls at her house for me to see; but I did not think any of them worthy of occupying Leah's place. I fancied I no longer loved Leah, but I was wrong.

The Chevalier Cocona, who had the misfortune to be suffering from a venereal disease, gave me up his mistress, a pretty little *soubrette;* but in spite of the evidence of my own eyes, and in spite of the assurances she gave me, I could not make up my mind to have her, and my fear made me leave her untouched. Count Trana, a brother of the chevalier's whom I had known at Aix, introduced me to Madame de Sc——, a lady of high rank and very good-looking, but she tried to involve me in a criminal transaction, and I ceased to call on her. Shortly after, Count Trana's uncle died and he became rich and got married, but he lived an unhappy life.

I was getting bored, and Desarmoises, who had all his meals with me, did not know what to do. At last he advised me to make the acquaintance of a certain Madame R——, a Frenchwoman, and well known in Turin as a milliner and dressmaker. She had six or eight girls working for her in a room adjoining her shop. Desarmoises thought that if I got in there I might possibly be able to find one to my taste. As my purse was well furnished I thought I should not have much difficulty, so I called on Madame R——. I was agreeably surprised to find Leah there, bargaining for a quantity of articles, all of which she pronounced to be too dear. She told me kindly but reproachfully that she had thought I must be ill.

"I have been very busy," I said; and felt all my old ardour revive. She asked me to come to a Jewish wedding, where there would be a good many people and several pretty girls. I knew that ceremonies of this kind are very amusing, and I promised to be present. She proceeded with her bargaining, but the price was still too high and she left the shop. Madame R—— was going to put back all the trifles in their places, but I said,——

"I will take the lot myself."

She smiled, and I drew out my purse and paid the money.

"Where do you live, sir?" said she; "and when shall I send you your purchases?"

"You may bring them to-morrow yourself, and do me the honour of breakfasting with me."

"I can never leave the shop, sir."

In spite of her thirty-five years, Madame R—— was still what would be called a tasty morsel, and she had taken my fancy.

"I want some dark lace," said I.

"Then kindly follow me, sir."

I was delighted when I entered the room to see a lot of young work-girls, all charming, hard at work, and scarcely daring to look at me. Madame R—— opened several cupboards, and shewed me some magnificent lace. I was distracted by the sight of so many delicious nymphs, and I told her that I wanted the lace for two *baoutes* in the Venetian style. She knew what I meant. The lace cost me upwards of a hundred sequins. Madame R—— told two of her girls to bring me the lace the next day, together with the goods which Leah had thought too dear. They meekly replied,——

"Yes, mother."

They rose and kissed the mother's hand, which I thought a ridiculous ceremony; however, it gave me an opportunity of examining them, and I thought them delicious. We went back to the shop, and sitting down by the counter I enlarged on the beauty of the girls, adding, though not with strict truth, that I vastly preferred their mistress. She thanked me for the compliment and told me plainly that she had a lover, and soon after named him. He was the Comte de St. Giles, an infirm and elderly man, and by no means a model lover. I thought Madame R—— was jesting, but next day I ascertained that she was speaking the truth. Well, everyone to his taste, and I suspect that she was more in love with the count's purse than his person. I had met him at the "Exchange" coffeehouse.

The next day the two pretty milliners brought me my goods. I offered them chocolate, but they firmly and persistently declined. The fancy took me to send them to Leah with all the things she had chosen, and I bade them return and tell me what sort of a reception they had had. They said they would do so, and waited for me to write her a note. I could not give them the slightest mark of affection. I dared not shut the door, and the mistress and the ugly young woman of the house kept going and coming all the time; but when they came back I waited for them on the stairs, and giving them a sequin each told each of them that she might command my heart if she would. Leah had accepted my handsome present and sent to say that she was waiting for me.

As I was walking aimlessly about in the afternoon I happened to pass the milliner's shop, and Madame R—— saw me and made me come in and sit down beside her.

"I am really much obliged to you," said she, "for your kindness to my girls. They came home enchanted. Tell me frankly whether you are really in love with the pretty Jewess."

"I am really in love with her, but as she will not make me happy I have signed my own dismissal."

"You were quite right. All Leah thinks of is duping those who are captivated by her charms."

"Do not your charming apprentices follow your maxims?"

"No; but they are only complaisant when I give them leave."

"Then I commend myself to your intercession, for they would not even take a cup of chocolate from me."

"They were perfectly right not to accept your chocolate: but I see you do not know the ways of Turin. Do you find yourself comfortable in your present lodging?"

"Quite so."

"Are you perfectly free to do what you like?"

"I think so."

"Can you give supper to anyone you like in your own rooms? I am certain you can't."

"I have not had the opportunity of trying the experiment so far, but I believe. . . ."

"Don't flatter yourself by believing anything; that house is full of the spies of the police."

"Then you think that I could not give you and two or three of your girls a little supper?"

"I should take very good care not to go to it, that's all I know. By next morning it would be known to all the town, and especially to the police."

"Well, supposing I look out for another lodging?"

"It's the same everywhere. Turin is a perfect nest of spies; but I do know a house where you could live at ease, and where my girls might perhaps be able to bring you your purchases. But we should have to be very careful."

"Where is the house   I will be guided by you in everything."

"Don't trust a Piedmontese; that's the first commandment here."

She then gave me the address of a small furnished house, which was only inhabited by an old door-keeper and his wife.

"They will let it you by the month," said she, "and if you pay a month in advance you need not even tell them your name."

I found the house to be a very pretty one, standing in a lonely street at about two hundred paces from the citadel. One gate, large enough to admit a carriage, led into the country. I found everything to be as Madame R—— had described it. I paid a month in advance without any bargaining, and in a day I had settled in my new lodging. Madame R—— admired my celerity.

I went to the Jewish wedding and enjoyed myself, for there is something at once solemn and ridiculous about the ceremony; but I resisted all Leah's endeavours to get me once more into her meshes. I hired a close carriage from her father, which with the horses I placed in the coach-house and stables of my new house. Thus I was absolutely free to go whenever I would by night or by day, for I was at once in the town and in the country. I was obliged to tell the inquisitive Gama where I was living, and I hid nothing from Desarmoises, whose needs made him altogether dependent on me. Nevertheless I gave orders that my door was shut to them as to everyone else, unless I had given special instructions that they were to be admitted. I had no reason to doubt the fidelity of my two servants.

In this blissful abode I enjoyed all Mdlle. R——'s girls, one after the other. The one I wanted always brought a companion, whom I usually sent back after giving her a slice of the cake. The last of them, whose name was Victorine, as fair as day and as soft as a dove, had the misfortune to be *tied,* though she knew nothing about it. Mdlle. R——, who was equally ignorant on the subject, had represented her to me as a virgin, and so I thought her for two long hours in which I strove with might and main to break the charm, or rather open the shell. All my efforts were in vain. I was exhausted at last, and I wanted to see in what the obstacle consisted. I put her in the proper position, and armed with a candle I began my scrutiny. I found a fleshy membrane pierced by so small a hole that large pin's head could scarcely have gone through. Victorine encouraged me to force a passage with my little finger, but in vain I tried to pierce this wall, which nature had made impassable by all ordinary means. I was tempted to see what I could do with a bistoury, and the girl wanted me to try, but I was afraid of the hæmorrhage which might have been dangerous, and I wisely refrained.

Poor Victorine, condemned to die a maid, unless some clever surgeon performed the same operation that was undergone by Mdlle. Cheruffini shortly after M. Lepri married her, wept when I said,——

"My dear child, your little Hymen defies the most vigorous lover to enter his temple."

But I consoled her by saying that a good surgeon could easily make a perfect woman of her.

In the morning I told Madame R—— of the case. She laughed and said,——

"It may prove a happy accident for Victorine; it may make her fortune."

A few years after the Count of Padua had her operated on, and made her fortune. When I came back from

Spain I found that she was with child, so that I could not exact the due reward for all the trouble I had taken with her.

Early in the morning on Maunday Thursday they told me that Moses and Leah wanted to see me. I had not expected to see them, but I welcomed them warmly. Throughout Holy Week the Jews dared not shew themselves in the streets of Turin, and I advised them to stay with me till the Saturday. Moses began to try and get me to purchase a ring from him, and I judged from that that I should not have to press them very much.

"I can only buy this ring from Leah's hands," said I.

He grinned, thinking doubtless that I intended to make her a present of it, but I was resolved to disappoint him. I gave them a magnificent dinner and supper, and in the evening they were shewn a double-bedded room not far from mine. I might have put them in different rooms, and Leah in a room adjoining mine, which would have facilitated any nocturnal excursions; but after all I had done for her I was resolved to owe nothing to a surprise; she should come of herself.

The next day Moses (who noticed that I had not yet bought the ring) was obliged to go out on business, and asked for the loan of my carriage for the whole day, telling me that he would come for his daughter in the evening. I had the horses harnessed, and when he was gone I bought the ring for six hundred sequins, but on my own terms. I was in my own house, and Leah could not deceive me. As soon as the father was safely out of the way I possessed myself of the daughter. She proved a docile and amorous subject the whole day. I had reduced her to a state of nature, and though her body was as perfect as can well be imagined I used it and abused it in every way imaginable. In the evening her father found her looking rather tired, but he seemed as pleased as I was. Leah was not quite so well satisfied, for till the moment of their departure she was expecting me to give her the ring, but I contented myself with saying that I should like to reserve myself the pleasure of taking it to her.

On Easter Monday a man brought me a note summoning me to appear at the police office.

CHAPTER XII

My Victory Over the Deputy Chief of Police—My De-
parture—Chambéri—Desarmoises's Daughter—M. Mo-
rin—M * * * M * * * At Aix—The Young Boarder
—Lyons—Paris

THIS citation, which did not promise to lead to anything agreeable, surprised and displeased me exceedingly. However, I could not avoid it, so I drove to the
office of the deputy-superintendent of police. I found
him sitting at a long table, surrounded by about a score
of people in a standing posture. He was a man of sixty,
hideously ugly, his enormous nose half destroyed by an
ulcer hidden by a large black silk plaster, his mouth of
huge dimensions, his lips thick, with small green eyes and
eyebrows which had partly turned white. As soon as this
disgusting fellow saw me, he began,——

"You are the Chevalier de Seingalt?"

"That is my name, and I have come here to ask how
I can oblige you?"

"I have summoned you here to order you to leave the
place in three days at latest."

"And as you have no right to give such an order, I
have come here to tell you that I shall go when I please,
and not before."

"I will expel you by force."

"You may do that whenever you please. I cannot
resist force, but I trust you will give the matter a second
thought; for in a well-ordered city they do not expel a

306

man who has committed no crimes, and has a balance of a hundred thousand francs at the bank."

"Very good, but in three days you have plenty of time to pack up and arrange matters with your banker. I advise you to obey, as the command comes from the king."

"If I were to leave the town I should become accessory to your injustice! I will not obey, but since you mention the king's name, I will go to his majesty at once, and he will deny your words or revoke the unjust order you have given me with such publicity."

"Pray, does not the king possess the power to make you go?"

"Yes, by force, but not by justice. He has also the power to kill me, but he would have to provide the executioner, as he could not make me commit suicide."

"You argue well, but nevertheless you will obey."

"I argue well, but I did not learn the art from you, and I will not obey."

With these words I turned my back on him, and left without another word.

I was in a furious rage. I felt inclined to offer overt resistance to all the myrmidons of the infamous superintendent. Nevertheless I soon calmed myself, and summoning prudence to my aid I remembered the Chevalier Raiberti, whom I had seen at his mistress's house, and I decided on asking his advice. He was the chief permanent official in the department of foreign affairs. I told the coachman to drive to his house, and I recounted to him the whole tale, saying, finally, that I should like to speak to the king, as I was resolved that I would not go unless I was forced to do so. The worthy man advised me to go to the Chevalier Osorio, the principal secretary for foreign affairs, who could always get an audience of the king. I was pleased with his advice, and I went immediately to the minister, who was a Sicilian and a man of parts. He gave me a very good reception, and after I had informed him of the circumstances of the case I begged him to communicate the matter to his majesty, adding that as the superintendent's order appeared horribly unjust to me I was resolved not to obey it unless compelled to do so by main force. He promised to oblige me in the way I wished, and told me to call again the next day.

After leaving him I took a short walk to cool myself, and then went to the Abbé Gama, hoping to be the first to impart my ridiculous adventure to him. I was disappointed; he already knew that I had been ordered to go, and how I had answered the superintendent. When he saw that I persisted in my determination to resist, he did not condemn my firmness, though he must have thought it very extraordinary, for the good abbé could not understand anybody's disobeying the order of the authorities. He assured me that if I had to go he would send me the necessary instructions to any address I liked to name.

The next day the Chevalier Osorio received me with the utmost politeness, which I thought a good omen. The Chevalier Raiberti had spoken to him in my behalf, and he had laid the matter before the king and also before the Count d'Aglié, and the result was that I could stay as long as I liked. The Count d'Aglié was none other than the horrible superintendent. I was told that I must wait on him, and he would give me leave to remain at Turin till my affairs were settled.

"My only business here," said I, "is to spend my money till I have instructions from the Court of Portugal to at-

tend the Congress of Augsburg on behalf of his most
faithful majesty."

"Then you think that this Congress will take place?"

"Nobody doubts it."

"Somebody believes it will all end in smoke. However, I am delighted to have been of service to you, and
I shall be curious to hear what sort of reception you get
from the superintendent."

I felt ill at ease. I went to the police office immediately, glad to shew myself victorious, and anxious to
see how the superintendent would look when I came in.
However, I could not flatter myself that he looked
ashamed of himself; these people have a brazen forehead, and do not know what it is to blush.

As soon as he saw me, he began,——

"The Chevalier Osorio tells me that you have business
in Turin which will keep you for some days. You may
therefore stay, but you must tell me as nearly as possible
how long a time you require."

"I cannot possibly tell you that."

"Why? if you don't mind telling me."

"I am awaiting instructions from the Court of Portugal to attend the Congress to be held at Augsburg, and
before I could tell you how long I shall have to stay I
should be compelled to ask his most faithful majesty.
If this time is not sufficient for me to do my business, I
will intimate the fact to you."

"I shall be much obliged by your doing so."

This time I made him a bow, which was returned, and
on leaving the office I returned to the Chevalier Osorio,
who said, with a smile, that I had caught the superintendent, as I had taken an indefinite period, which left
me quite at my ease.

The diplomatic Gama, who firmly believed that the

Congress would meet, was delighted when I told him that the Chevalier Osorio was incredulous on the subject. He was charmed to think his wit keener than the minister's; it exalted him in his own eyes. I told him that whatever the chevalier might say I would go to Augsburg, and that I would set out in three or four weeks.

Madame R—— congratulated me over and over again, for she was enchanted that I had humiliated the superintendent; but all the same we thought we had better give up our little suppers. As I had had a taste of all her girls, this was not such a great sacrifice for me to make.

I continued thus till the middle of May, when I left Turin, after receiving letters from the Abbé Gama to Lord Stormont, who was to represent England at the approaching Congress. It was with this nobleman that I was to work in concert at the Congress.

Before going to Germany I wanted to see Madame d'Urfé, and I wrote to her, asking her to send me a letter of introduction to M. de Rochebaron, who might be useful to me. I also asked M. Raiberti to give me a letter for Chambéri, where I wanted to visit the divine M—— M—— (of whom I still thought with affection) at her convent grating. I wrote to my friend Valenglard, asking him to remind Madame Morin that she had promised to shew me a likeness to somebody at Chambéri.

But here I must note down an event worthy of being recorded, which was extremely prejudicial to me.

Five or six days before my departure Desarmoises came to me looking very downcast, and told me that he had been ordered to leave Turin in twenty-four hours.

"Do you know why?" I asked him.

"Last night when I was at the coffee-house, Count Scarnafis dared to say that France subsidised the Berne newspapers. I told him he lied, at which he rose and left.

the place in a rage, giving me a glance the meaning of
which is not doubtful. I followed him to bring him to
reason or to give him satisfaction; but he would do
nothing and I suspect he went to the police to complain.
I shall have to leave Turin early to-morrow morning."

"You're a Frenchman, and as you can claim the protection of your ambassador you will be wrong to leave so
suddenly."

"In the first place the ambassador is away, and in the
second my cruel father disavows me. No, I would rather
go, and wait for you at Lyons. All I want is for you to
lend me a hundred crowns, for which I will give you an
account."

"It will be an easy account to keep," said I, "but a
long time before it is settled."

"Possibly; but if it is in my power I will shew my
gratitude for the kindnesses you have done me."

I gave him a hundred crowns and wished him a pleasant journey, telling him that I should stop some time at
Lyons.

I got a letter of credit on an Augsburg house, and
three days after I left Turin I was at Chambéri. There
was only one inn there in those days, so I was not much
puzzled to choose where I would go, but for all that I
found myself very comfortable.

As I entered my room, I was struck by seeing an extremely pretty girl coming out of an adjacent room.

"Who is that young lady?" said I to the chamber-
maid who was escorting me.

"That's the wife of a young gentleman who has to
keep his bed to get cured of a sword-thrust which he
received four days ago on his way from France."

I could not look at her without feeling the sting of con-
cupiscence. As I was leaving my room I saw the door

half open, and I stopped short and offered my services as a neighbour. She thanked me politely, and asked me in. I saw a handsome young man sitting up in bed, so I went up to enquire how he felt.

"The doctor will not let him talk," said the young lady, "on account of a sword-thrust in the chest he received at half a league from here. We hope he will be all right in a few days, and then we can continue our journey."

"Where are you going, madam?"

"To Geneva."

Just as I was leaving, a maid came to ask me if I would take supper in my own room or with the lady. I laughed at her stupidity, and said I would sup in my own apartment, adding that I had not the honour of the lady's acquaintance.

At this the young lady said it would give her great pleasure if I would sup with her, and the husband repeated this assurance in a whisper. I accepted the invitation gratefully, and I thought that they were really pleased. The lady escorted me out as far as the stairs, and I took the liberty of kissing her hand, which in France is a declaration of tender though respectful affection.

At the post-office I found a letter from Valenglard, telling me that Madame Morin would wait on me at Chambéri if I would send her a carriage, and another from Desarmoises dated from Lyons. He told me that as he was on his way from Chambéri he had encountered his daughter in company with a rascal who had carried her off. He had buried his sword in his body, and would have killed them if he had been able to stop their carriage. He suspected that they had been staying in Chambéri, and he begged me to try and persuade his daughter to return to Lyons; and he added that if she would not do so I ought to oblige him by sending her back by force. He assured me that they were not married, and he begged me to answer his letter by express, for which purpose he sent me his address.

I guessed at once that this daughter of his was my fair neighbour, but I did not feel at all inclined to come to the aid of the father in the way he wished.

As soon as I got back to the inn I sent off Le Duc in a travelling carriage to Madame Morin, whom I informed by letter that as I was only at Chambéri for her sake I would await her convenience. This done, I abandoned myself to the delight I felt at the romantic adventure which fortune had put in my way.

I repeated Mdlle. Desarmoises and her ravisher, and I did not care to enquire whether I was impelled in what I did by virtue or vice; but I could not help perceiving that my motives were of a mixed nature; for if I were amorous, I was also very glad to be of assistance to two young lovers, and all the more from my knowledge of the father's criminal passion.

On entering their room I found the invalid in the surgeon's hands. He pronounced the wound not to be dangerous, in spite of its depth; suppuration had taken place without setting up inflammation—in short, the young man only wanted time and rest. When the doctor had gone I congratulated the patient on his condition, advising him to be careful what he ate, and to keep silent. I then gave Mdlle. Desarmoises her father's letter, and I said farewell for the present, telling them that I would go to my own room till supper-time. I felt sure that she would come and speak to me after reading her father's letter.

In a quarter of an hour she knocked timidly at my

door, and when I let her in she gave me back the letter
and asked me what I thought of doing.

"Nothing. I shall be only too happy, however, if I
can be of any service to you."

"Ah! I breathe again!"

"Could you imagine me pursuing any other line of
conduct? I am much interested in you, and will do all
in my power to help you. Are you married?"

"Not yet, but we are going to be married when we get
to Geneva."

"Sit down and tell me all about yourself. I know
that your father is unhappily in love with you, and that
you avoid his attentions."

"He has told you that much? I am glad of it. A
year ago he came to Lyons, and as soon as I knew he
was in the town I took refuge with a friend of my
mother's, for I was aware that I could not stay in the
same house with my father for an hour without exposing
myself to the most horrible outrage. The young man
in bed is the son of a rich Geneva merchant. My father
introduced him to me two years ago, and we soon fell
in love with each other. My father went away to Marseilles, and my lover asked my mother to give me in
marriage to him; but she did not feel authorized to do so
without my father's consent. She wrote and asked him,
but he replied that he would announce his decision when
he returned to Lyons. My lover went to Geneva, and as
his father approved of the match he returned with all
the necessary documents and a strong letter of commendation from M. Tolosan. When my father came to
Lyons I escaped, as I told you, and my lover got M.
Tolosan to ask my hand for him of my father. His
reply was, 'I can give no answer till she returns to my
house!' M. Tolosan brought this reply to me, and I told

him that I was ready to obey if my mother would guarantee my safety. She replied, however, that she knew her husband too well to dare to have us both under the same roof. Again did M. Tolosan endeavour to obtain my father's consent, but to no purpose. A few days after he left Lyons, telling us that he was first going to Aix and then to Turin, and as it was evident that he would never give his consent my lover proposed that I should go off with him, promising to marry me as soon as we reached Geneva. By ill luck we travelled through Savoy, and thus met my father. As soon as he saw us he stopped the carriage and called to me to get out. I began to shriek, and my lover taking me in his arms to protect me my father stabbed him in the chest. No doubt he would have killed him, but seeing that my shrieks were bringing people to our rescue, and probably believing that my lover was as good as dead, he got on horseback again and rode off at full speed. I can shew you the sword still covered with blood."

"I am obliged to answer this letter of his, and I am thinking how I can obtain his consent."

"That's of no consequence; we can marry and be happy without it."

"True, but you ought not to despise your dower."

"Good heavens! what dower? He has no money."

"But on the death of his father, the Marquis Desarmoises. . . ."

"That's all a lie. My father has only a small yearly pension for having served thirty years as a Government messenger. His father has been dead these thirty years, and my mother and my sister only live by the work they do."

I was thunderstruck at the impudence of the fellow, who, after imposing on me so long, had himself put me in a position to discover his deceit. I said nothing. Just then we were told that supper was ready, and we sat at table for three hours talking the matter over. The poor wounded man had only to listen to me to know my feelings on the subject. His young mistress, as witty as she was pretty, jested on the foolish passion of her father, who had loved her madly ever since she was eleven.

"And you were always able to resist his attempts?" said I.

"Yes, whenever he pushed things too far."

"And how long did this state of things continue?"

"For two years. When I was thirteen he thought I was ripe, and tried to gather the fruit; but I began to shriek, and escaped from his bed stark naked, and I went to take refuge with my mother, who from that day forth would not let me sleep with him again."

"You used to sleep with him? How could your mother allow it?"

"She never thought that there was anything criminal in his affection for me, and I knew nothing about it. I thought that what he did to me, and what he made me do to him, were mere trifles."

"But you have saved the little treasure?"

"I have kept it for my lover."

The poor lover, who was suffering more from the effects of hunger than from his wounds, laughed at this speech of hers, and she ran to him and covered his face with kisses. All this excited me intensely. Her story had been told with too much simplicity not to move me, especially when I had her before my eyes, for she possessed all the attractions which a woman can have, and I almost forgave her father for forgetting she was his daughter and falling in love with her.

When she escorted me back to my room I made her

feel my emotion, and she began to laugh; but as my servants were close by I was obliged to let her go.

Early next morning I wrote to her father that his daughter had resolved not to leave her lover, who was only slightly wounded, that they were in perfect safety and under the protection of the law at Chambéri, and finally that having heard their story, and judging them to be well matched, I could only approve of the course they had taken. When I had finished I went into their room and gave them the letter to read, and seeing the fair runaway at a loss how to express her gratitude, I begged the invalid to let me kiss her.

"Begin with me," said he, opening his arms.

My hypocritical love masked itself under the guise of paternal affection. I embraced the lover, and then more amorously I performed the same office for the mistress, and shewed them my purse full of gold, telling them it was at their service. While this was going on the surgeon came in, and I retired to my room.

At eleven o'clock Madame Morin and her daughter arrived, preceded by Le Duc on horseback, who announced their approach by numerous smacks of his whip. I welcomed her with open arms, thanking her for obliging me.

The first piece of news she gave me was that Mdlle. Roman had become mistress to Louis XV., that she lived in a beautiful house at Passi, and that she was five months gone with child. Thus she was in a fair way to become queen of France, as my divine oracle had predicted.

"At Grenoble," she added, "you are the sole topic of conversation; and I advise you not to go there unless you wish to settle in the country, for they would never let you go. You would have all the nobility at your feet, and above all, the ladies anxious to know the lot of their daughters. Everybody believes in judicial astrology now, and Valenglard triumphs. He has bet a hundred louis to fifty that my niece will be delivered of a young prince, and he is certain of winning; though to be sure, if he loses, everybody will laugh at him."

"Don't be afraid of his losing."

"Is it quite certain?"

"Has not the horoscope proved truthful in the principal particular? If the other circumstances do not follow, I must have made a great mistake in my calculations."

"I am delighted to hear you say so."

"I am going to Paris and I hope you will give me a letter of introduction to Madame Varnier, so that I may have the pleasure of seeing your niece."

"You shall have the letter to-morrow without fail."

I introduced Mdlle. Desarmoises to her under the family name of her lover, and invited her to dine with Madame Morin and myself. After dinner we went to the convent, and M—— M—— came down very surprised at this unexpected visit from her aunt; but when she saw me she had need of all her presence of mind. When her aunt introduced me to her by name, she observed with true feminine tact that during her stay at Aix she had seen me five or six times at the fountain, but that I could not remember her features as she had always worn her veil. I admired her wit as much as her exquisite features. I thought she had grown prettier than ever, and no doubt my looks told her as much. We spent an hour in talking about Grenoble and her old friends, whom she gladly recalled to her memory, and then she went to fetch a young girl who was boarding at the convent, whom she liked and wanted to present to her aunt.

I seized the opportunity of telling Madame Morin that

I was astonished at the likeness, that her very voice was like that of my Venetian M—— M——, and I begged her to obtain me the privilege of breakfasting with her niece the next day, and of presenting her with a dozen pounds of capital chocolate. I had brought it with me from Genoa.

"You must make her the present yourself," said Madame Morin, "for though she's a nun she's a woman, and we women much prefer a present from a man's than from a woman's hand."

M—— M—— returned with the superior of the convent, two other nuns, and the young boarder, who came from Lyons, and was exquisitely beautiful. I was obliged to talk to all the nuns, and Madame Morin told her niece that I wanted her to try some excellent chocolate I had brought from Genoa, but that I hoped her lay-sister would make it.

"Sir," said M—— M——, "kindly send me the chocolate, and to-morrow we will breakfast together with these dear sisters."

As soon as I got back to my inn I sent the chocolate with a respectful note, and I took supper in Madame Morin's room with her daughter and Mdlle. Desarmoises, of whom I was feeling more and more amorous, but I talked of M—— M—— all the time, and I could see that the aunt suspected that the pretty nun was not altogether a stranger to me.

I breakfasted at the convent and I remember that the chocolate, the biscuits, and the sweetmeats were served with a nicety which savoured somewhat of the world. When we had finished breakfast I told M—— M—— that she would not find it so easy to give me a dinner, with twelve persons sitting down to table, but I added that half the company could be in the convent and half in the parlour, separated from the convent by a light grating.

"It's a sight I should like to see," said I, "if you will allow me to pay all expenses."

"Certainly," replied M—— M——, and this dinner was fixed for the next day.

M—— M—— took charge of the whole thing, and promised to ask six nuns. Madame Morin, who knew my tastes, told her to spare nothing, and I warned her that I would send in the necessary wines.

I escorted Madame Morin, her daughter, and Mdlle. Desarmoises back to the hotel, and I then called on M. Magnan, to whom I had been recommended by the Chevalier Raiberti. I asked him to get me some of the best wine, and he took me down to his cellar, and told me to take what I liked. His wines proved to be admirable.

This M. Magnan was a clever man, of a pleasant appearance, and very comfortably off. He occupied an extremely large and convenient house outside the town, and there his agreeable wife dispensed hospitality. She had ten children, amongst whom there were four pretty daughters; the eldest, who was nineteen, was especially good-looking.

We went to the convent at eleven o'clock, and after an hour's conversation we were told that dinner was ready. The table was beautifully laid, covered with a fair white cloth, and adorned with vases filled with artificial flowers so strongly scented that the air of the parlour was quite balmy. The fatal grill was heavier than I had hoped. I found myself seated to the left of M—— M——, and totally unable to see her. The fair Desarmoises was at my right, and she entertained us all the time with her amusing stories.

We in the parlour were waited on by Le Duc and Costa, and the nuns were served by their lay-sisters. The abundant provision, the excellent wines, the pleasant though sometimes equivocal conversation, kept us all merrily employed for three hours. Mirth had the mastery over reason, or, to speak more plainly, we were all drunk; and if it had not been for the fatal grill, I could have had the whole eleven ladies without much trouble. The young Desarmoises was so gay, indeed, that if I had not restrained her she would probably have scandalised all the nuns, who would have liked nothing better. I was longing to have her to myself, that I might quench the flame she had kindled in my breast, and I had no doubt of my success on the first attempt. After coffee had been served, we went into another parlour and stayed there till night came on. Madame Morin took leave of her niece, and the hand-shakings, thanks, and promises of remembrance between me and the nuns, lasted for a good quarter of an hour. After I had said aloud to M—— M—— that I hoped to have the pleasure of seeing her before I left, we went back to the inn in high good humour with our curious party which I still remember with pleasure.

Madame Morin gave me a letter for her cousin Madame Varnier, and I promised to write to her from Paris, and tell her all about the fair Mdlle. Roman. I presented the daughter with a beautiful pair of ear-rings, and I gave Madame Morin twelve pounds of good chocolate which M. Magnan got me, and which the lady thought had come from Genoa. She went off at eight o'clock preceded by Le Duc, who had orders to greet the doorkeeper's family on my behalf.

At Magnan's I had a dinner worthy of Lucullus, and I promised to stay with him whenever I passed

Chambéri, which promise I have faithfully performed.

On leaving the gourmand's I went to the convent, and M—— M—— came down alone to the grating. She thanked me for coming to see her, and added that I had come to disturb her peace of mind.

"I am quite ready, dearest, to climb the garden wall, and I shall do it more dexterously than your wretched humpback."

"Alas! that may not be, for, trust me, you are already spied upon. Everybody here is sure that we knew each other at Aix. Let us forget all, and thus spare ourselves the torments of vain desires."

"Give me your hand."

"No. All is over. I love you still, probably I shall always love you; but I long for you to go, and by doing so, you will give me a proof of your love."

"This is dreadful; you astonish me. You appear to me in perfect health, you are prettier than ever, you are made for the worship of the sweetest of the gods, and I can't understand how, with a temperament like yours, you can live in continual abstinence."

"Alas! lacking the reality we console ourselves by pretending. I will not conceal from you that I love my young boarder. It is an innocent passion, and keeps my mind calm. Her caresses quench the flame which would otherwise kill me."

"And that is not against your conscience?"

"I do not feel any distress on the subject."

"But you know it is a sin."

"Yes, so I confess it."

"And what does the confessor say?"

"Nothing. He absolves me, and I am quite content."

"And does the pretty boarder confess, too?"

"Certainly, but she does not tell the father of a matter which she thinks is no sin."

"I wonder the confessor has not taught her, for that kind of instruction is a great pleasure."

"Our confessor is a wise old man."

"Am I to leave you, then, without a single kiss?"

"Not one."

"May I come again to-morrow? I must go the day after."

"You may come, but I cannot see you by myself as the nuns might talk. I will bring my little one with me to save appearances. Come after dinner, but into the other parlour."

If I had not known M—— M—— at Aix, her religious ideas would have astonished me; but such was her character. She loved God, and did not believe that the kind Father who made us with passions would be too severe because we had not the strength to subdue them. I returned to the inn, feeling vexed that the pretty nun would have no more to do with me, but sure of consolation from the fair Desarmoises.

I found her sitting on her lover's bed; his poor diet and the fever had left him in a state of great weakness. She told me that she would sup in my room to leave him in quiet, and the worthy young man shook my hand in token of his gratitude.

As I had a good dinner at Magnan's I ate very little supper, but my companion who had only had a light meal ate and drank to an amazing extent. I gazed at her in a kind of wonder, and she enjoyed my astonishment. When my servants had left the room I challenged her to drink a bowl of punch with me, and this put her into a mood which asked for nothing but laughter, and which laughed to find itself deprived of reasoning power. Nevertheless, I cannot accuse myself of taking an advantage of her condition, for in her voluptuous excitement she entered eagerly into the pleasure to which I excited her till two o'clock in the morning. By the time we separated we were both of us exhausted.

I slept till eleven, and when I went to wish her good day I found her smiling and as fresh as a rose. I asked her how she had passed the rest of the night.

"Very pleasantly," said she, "like the beginning of the night."

"What time would you like to have dinner?"

"I won't dine; I prefer to keep my appetite for supper."

Here her lover joined in, saying in a weak voice,——

"It is impossible to keep up with her."

"In eating or drinking?" I asked.

"In eating, drinking, and in other things," he replied, with a smile. She laughed, and kissed him affectionately.

This short dialogue convinced me that Mdlle. Desarmoises must adore her lover; for besides his being a handsome young man, his disposition was exactly suitable to hers. I dined by myself, and Le Duc came in as I was having dessert. He told me that the door-keeper's daughters and their pretty cousin had made him wait for them to write to me, and he gave me three letters and three dozen of gloves which they had presented me. The letters urged me to come and spend a month with them, and gave me to understand that I should be well pleased with my treatment. I had not the courage to return to a town, where with my reputation I should have been obliged to draw horoscopes for all the young ladies or to make enemies by refusing.

After I had read the letters from Grenoble I went to the convent and announced my presence, and then entered the parlour which M—— M—— had indicated. She soon came down down with the pretty boarder, who feebly sustained my part in her amorous ecstacies. She had not yet completed her twelfth year, but she was extremely tall and well developed for her age. Gentleness, liveliness, candour, and wit were united in her features, and gave her expression an exquisite charm. She wore a well-made corset which disclosed a white throat, to which the fancy easily added the two spheres which would soon appear there. Her entrancing face, her raven locks, and her ivory throat indicated what might be concealed, and my vagrant imagination made her into a budding Venus. I began by telling her that she was very pretty, and would make her future husband a happy man. I knew she would blush at that. It may be cruel, but it is thus that the language of seduction always begins. A girl of her age who does not blush at the mention of marriage is either an idiot or already an expert in profligacy. In spite of this, however, the blush which mounts to a young girl's cheek at the approach of such ideas is a puzzling problem. Whence does it arise? It may be from pure simplicity, it may be from shame, and often from a mixture of both feelings. Then comes the fight between vice and virtue, and it is usually virtue which has to give in. The desires—the servants of vice—usually attain their ends. As I knew the young boarder from M—— M——'s description, I could not be ignorant of the source of those blushes which added a fresh attraction to her youthful charms.

Pretending not to notice anything, I talked to M—— M—— for a few moments, and then returned to the assault. She had regained her calm.

"What age are you, pretty one?" said I.

"I am thirteen."

"You are wrong," said M—— M——, "you have not yet completed your twelfth year."

"The time will come," said I, "when you will diminish the tale of your years instead of increasing it."

"I shall never tell a lie, sir; I am sure of that."

"So you want to be a nun, do you?"

"I have not yet received my vocation; but even if I live in the world I need not be a liar."

"You are wrong; you will begin to lie as soon as you have a lover."

"Will my lover tell lies, too?"

"Certainly he will."

"If the matter were really so, then, I should have a bad opinion of love; but I do not believe it, for I love my sweetheart here, and I never conceal the truth from her."

"Yes, but loving a man is a different thing to loving a woman."

"No, it isn't; it's just the same."

"Not so, for you do not go to bed with a woman and you do with your husband."

"That's no matter, my love would be the same."

"What? You would not rather sleep with me than with M—— M——?"

"No, indeed I should not, because you are a man and would see me."

"You don't want a man to see you, then?"

"No."

"Do you think you are so ugly, then?"

At this she turned to M—— M—— and said, with evident vexation, "I am not really ugly, am I?"

"No, darling," said M—— M——, bursting with

laughter, "it is quite the other way; you are very pretty." With these words she took her on her knee and embraced her tenderly.

"Your corset is too tight; you can't possibly have such a small waist as that."

"You make a mistake, you can put your hand there and see for yourself."

"I can't believe it."

M—— M—— then held her close to the grill and told me to see for myself. At the same moment she turned up her dress.

"You were right," said I, "and I owe you an apology;" but in my heart I cursed the grating and the chemise.

"My opinion is," said I to M—— M——, "that we have here a little boy."

I did not wait for a reply, but satisfied myself by my sense of touch as to her sex, and I could see that the little one and her governess were both pleased that my mind was at rest on the subject.

I drew my hand away, and the little girl looked at M—— M——, and reassured by her smiling air asked if she might go away for a moment. I must have reduced her to a state in which a moment's solitude was necessary, and I myself was in a very excited condition.

As soon as she was gone I said to M—— M——:

"Do you know that what you have shewn me has made me unhappy?"

"Has it? Why?"

"Because your boarder is charming, and I am longing to enjoy her."

"I am sorry for that, for you can't possibly go any further; and besides, I know you, and even if you could satisfy your passion without danger to her, I would not give her up to you, you would spoil her."

"How?"

"Do you think that after enjoying you she would care to enjoy me? I should lose too heavily by the comparison."

"Give me your hand."

"No."

"Stay, one moment."

"I don't want to see anything."

"Not a little bit?"

"Nothing at all."

"Are you angry with me, then?"

"Not at all. If you have been pleased I am glad, and if you have filled her with desires she will love me all the better."

"How pleasant it would be, sweetheart, if we could all three of us be together alone and at liberty!"

"Yes; but it is impossible."

"Are you sure that no inquisitive eye is looking upon us?"

"Quite sure."

"The height of that fatal grill has deprived me of the sight of many charms."

"Why didn't you go to the other parlour; it is much lower there."

"Let us go there, then."

"Not to-day; I should not be able to give any reason for the change."

"I will come again to-morrow, and start for Lyons in the evening."

The little boarder came back, and I stood up facing her. I had a number of beautiful seals and trinkets hanging from my watch-chain, and I had not had the time to put myself in a state of perfect decency again.

She noticed it, and by way of pretext she asked if she might look at them.

"As long as you like; you may look at them and touch them as well."

M—— M—— foresaw what would happen and left the room, saying that she would soon be back. I has-tened to deprive the young boarder of all interest in my seals by shewing her a curiosity of another kind. She did not conceal her pleasure in satisfying her inquisitive-ness on an object which was quite new to her, and which she was able to examine minutely for the first time in her life. But soon an effusion changed her curiosity into surprise, and I did not interrupt her in her delighted gaze.

I saw M—— M—— coming back slowly, and I low-ered my shirt again, and sat down. My watch and chains were still on the ledge of the grating, and M—— M—— asked her young friend if the trinkets had pleased her.

"Yes," she replied, but in a dreamy and melancholy voice. She had learnt so much in the course of less than two hours that she had plenty to think over. I spent the rest of the day in telling M—— M—— the adventures I had encountered since I had left her; but as I had not time to finish my tale I promised to return the next day at the same time.

The little girl, who had been listening to me all the time, though I appeared to be only addressing her friend, said that she longed to know the end of my adventure with the Duke of Matelone's mistress.

I supped with the fair Desarmoises, and after giving her sundry proofs of my affection till midnight, and tell-ing her that I only stopped on for her sake, I went to bed.

The next day after dinner I returned to the convent, and having sent up my name to M—— M—— I entered the room where the grating was more convenient.

Before long M—— M—— arrived alone, but she anticipated my thoughts by telling me that her pretty friend would soon join her.

"You have fired her imagination. She has told me all about it, playing a thousand wanton tricks, and calling me her dear husband. You have seduced the girl, and I am very glad you are going or else you would drive her mad. You will see how she has dressed herself."

"Are you sure of her discretion?"

"Perfectly, but I hope you won't do anything in my presence. When I see the time coming I will leave the room."

"You are an angel, dearest, but you might be something better than that if you would——"

"I want nothing for myself; it is out of the question."

"You could——"

"No, I will have nothing to do with a pastime which would rekindle fires that are hardly yet quenched. I have spoken; I suffer, but let us say no more about it."

At this moment the young adept came in smiling, with her eyes full of fire. She was dressed in a short pelisse, open in front, and an embroidered muslin skirt which did not go beyond her knees. She looked like a sylph.

We had scarcely sat down when she reminded me of the place where my tale had stopped. I continued my recital, and when I was telling them how Donna Lucrezia shewed me Leonilda naked, M—— M—— went out, and the sly little puss asked me how I assured myself that my daughter was a maid.

I took hold of her through the fatal grating, against

which she placed her pretty body, and shewed her how I
assured myself of the fact, and the girl liked it so much
that she pressed my hand to the spot. She then gave me
her hand that I might share her pleasure, and whilst this
enjoyable occupation was in progress M—— M—— appeared. My sweetheart said hastily,——

"Never mind, I told her all about it. She is a good
creature and will not be vexed." Accordingly M——
M—— pretended not to see anything, and the precocious
little girl wiped her hand in a kind of voluptuous ecstacy,
which shewed how well she was pleased.

I proceeded with my history, but when I came to
the episode of the poor girl who was *tied,* describing all
the trouble I had vainly taken with her, the little boarder
got so curious that she placed herself in the most seducing attitude so that I might be able to shew her what I
did. Seeing this M—— M—— made her escape.

"Kneel down on the ledge, and leave the rest to me,"
said the little wanton.

The reader will guess what she meant, and I have no
doubt that she would have succeeded in her purpose if
the fire which consumed me had not distilled itself away
just at the happy moment.

The charming novice felt herself sprinkled, but after
ascertaining that nothing more could be done she withdrew in some vexation. My fingers, however, consoled
her for the disappointment, and I had the pleasure of
seeing her look happy once more.

I left these charming creatures in the evening, promising to visit them again in a year, but as I walked
home I could not help reflecting how often these asylums,
supposed to be devoted to chastity and prayer, contain in
themselves the hidden germs of corruption. How many
a timorous and trustful mother is persuaded that the

child of her affection will escape the dangers of the world by taking refuge in the cloister. But behind these bolts and bars desires grow to a frenzied extreme; they crave in vain to be satisfied.

When I returned to the inn I took leave of the wounded man, whom I was happy to see out of danger. In vain I urged him to make use of my purse; he told me, with an affectionate embrace, that he had sufficient money, and if not, he had only to write to his father. I promised to stop at Lyons, and to oblige Desarmoises to desist from any steps he might be taking against them, telling them I had a power over him which would compel him to obey. I kept my word. After we had kissed and said good-bye, I took his future bride into my room that we might sup together and enjoy ourselves till midnight; but she could not have been very pleased with my farewell salute, for I was only able to prove my love for her once, as M—— M——'s young friend had nearly exhausted me.

I started at day-break, and the next day I reached the "Hotel du Parc," at Lyons. I sent for Desarmoises, and told him plainly that his daughter's charms had seduced me, that I thought her lover worthy of her, and that I expected him out of friendship for me to consent to the marriage. I went further, and told him that if he did not consent to everything that very instant I could no longer be his friend, and at this he gave in. He executed the requisite document in the presence of two witnesses, and I sent it to Chambéri by an express messenger.

This false marquis made me dine with him in his poor house. There was nothing about his younger daughter to remind me of the elder, and his wife inspired me with pity. Before I left I managed to wrap up six louis in a piece of paper, and gave it to her without the knowledge of her husband. A grateful look shewed me how welcome the present was.

I was obliged to go to Paris, so I gave Desarmoises sufficient money for him to go to Strasburg, and await me there in company with my Spaniard.

I thought myself wise in only taking Costa, but the inspiration came from my evil genius.

I took the Bourbonnais way, and on the third day I arrived at Paris, and lodged at the Hotel du St. Esprit," in the street of the same name.

Before going to bed I sent Costa with a note to Madame d'Urfé, promising to come and dine with her the next day. Costa was a good-looking young fellow, and as he spoke French badly and was rather a fool I felt sure that Madame d'Urfé would take him for some extraordinary being. She wrote to say that she was impatiently expecting me.

"How did the lady receive you, Costa?"

"She looked into a mirror, sir, and said some words I could make nothing of; then she went round the room three times burning incense; then she came up to me with a majestic air and looked me in the face; and at last she smiled very pleasantly, and told me to wait for a reply in the ante-chamber."

CHAPTER XIII

My Stay at Paris and My Departure for Strasburg,
Where I Find the Renaud—My Misfortunes at Mu-
nich and My Sad Visit to Augsburg

A T ten o'clock in the morning, cheered by the pleasant feeling of being once more in that Paris which
is so imperfect, but which is the only true town in the
world, I called on my dear Madame d'Urfé, who received me with open arms. She told me that the young
Count d'Aranda was quite well, and if I liked she would
ask him to dinner the next day. I told her I should be
delighted to see him, and then I informed her that the
operation by which she was to become a man could not
be performed till Querilinto, one of the three chiefs of
the Fraternity of the Rosy Cross, was liberated from the
dungeons of the Inquisition, at Lisbon.

"This is the reason," I added, "that I am going to
Augsburg in the course of next month, where I shall
confer with the Earl of Stormont as to the liberation of
the adept, under the pretext of a mission from the
Portuguese Government. For these purposes I shall
require a good letter of credit, and some watches and
snuff-boxes to make presents with, as we shall have to
win over certain of the profane."

"I will gladly see to all that, but you need not hurry
yourself as the Congress will not meet till September."

"Believe me, it will never meet at all, but the ambassadors of the belligerent powers will be there all the

same. If, contrary to my expectation, the Congress is held, I shall be obliged to go to Lisbon. In any case, I promise to see you again in the ensuing winter. The fortnight that I have to spend here will enable me to defeat a plot of St. Germain's."

"St. Germain—he would never dare to return to Paris."

"I am certain that he is here in disguise. The state messenger who ordered him to leave London has convinced him the English minister was not duped by the demand for his person to be given up, made by the Comte d'Afri in the name of the king to the States-General."

All this was mere guess-work, and it will be seen that I guessed rightly.

Madame d'Urfé then congratulated me on the charming girl whom I had sent from Grenoble to Paris. Valenglard had told her the whole story.

"The king adores her," said she, "and before long she will make him a father. I have been to see her at Passi with the Duchesse de l'Oraguais."

"She will give birth to a son who will make France happy, and in thirty years time you will see wondrous things, of which, unfortunately, I can tell you nothing until your transformation. Did you mention my name to her?"

"No, I did not; but I am sure you will be able to see her, if only at Madame Varnier's."

She was not mistaken; but shortly afterwards an event happened which made the madness of this excellent woman much worse.

Towards four o'clock, as we were talking over my travels and our designs, she took a fancy to walk in the Bois du Boulogne. She begged me to accompany her, and I acceded to her request. We walked into the deepest recesses of the wood and sat down under a tree.

"It is eighteen years ago," said she, "since I fell asleep on the same spot that we now occupy. During my sleep the divine Horosmadis came down from the sun and stayed with me till I awoke. As I opened my eyes I saw him leave me and ascend to heaven. He left me with child, and I bore a girl which he took away from me years ago, no doubt to punish me for having so far forgotten myself as to love a mortal after him. My lovely Iriasis was like him."

"You are quite sure that M. d'Urfé was not the child's father?"

"M. d'Urfé did not know me after he saw me lying beside the divine Anael."

"That's the genius of Venus. Did he squint?"

"To excess. You are aware, then, that he squints?"

"Yes, and I know that at the amorous crisis he ceases to squint."

"I did not notice that. He too left me on account of my sinning with an Arab."

"The Arab was sent to you by an enemy of Anael's, the genius of Mercury."

"It must have been so; it was a great misfortune."

"On the contrary, it rendered you more fit for transformation."

We were walking towards the carriage when all at once we saw St. Germain, but as soon as he noticed us he turned back and we lost sight of him.

"Did you see him?" said I. "He is working against us, but our genie makes him tremble."

"I am quite thunderstruck. I will go and impart this piece of news to the Duc de Choiseul to-morrow morning. I am curious to hear what he will say when I tell him."

As we were going back to Paris I left Madame d'Urfé,

and walked to the Porte St. Denis to see my brother. He and his wife received me with cries of joy. I thought the wife very pretty but very wretched, for Providence had not allowed my brother to prove his manhood, and she was unhappily in love with him. I say unhappily, because her love kept her faithful to him, and if she had not been in love she might easily have found a cure for her misfortune as her husband allowed her perfect liberty. She grieved bitterly, for she did not know that my brother was impotent, and fancied that the reason of his abstention was that he did not return her love; and the mistake was an excusable one, for he was like a Hercules, and indeed he was one, except where it was most to be desired. Her grief threw her into a consumption of which she died five or six years later. She did not mean her death to be a punishment to her husband, but we shall see that it was so.

The next day I called on Madame Varnier to give her Madame Morin's letter. I was cordially welcomed, and Madame Varnier was kind enough to say that she had rather see me than anybody else in the world; her niece had told her such strange things about me that she had got quite curious. This, as is well known, is a prevailing complaint with women.

"You shall see my niece," she said, "and she will tell you all about herself."

She wrote her a note, and put Madame Morin's letter under the same envelope.

"If you want to know what my niece's answer is," said Madame Varnier, "you must dine with me."

I accepted the invitation, and she immediately told her servant that she was not at home to anyone.

The small messenger who had taken the note to Passi returned at four o'clock with the following epistle:

"The moment in which I see the Chevalier de Seingalt once more will be one of the happiest of my life. Ask him to be at your house at ten o'clock the day after to-morrow, and if he can't come then please let me know."

After reading the note and promising to keep the appointment, I left Madame Varnier and called on Madame de Rumain, who told me I must spend a whole day with her as she had several questions to put to my oracle.

Next day Madame d'Urfé told me the reply she had from the Duc de Choiseul, when she told him that she had seen the Comte de St. Germain in the Bois du Bologne.

"I should not be surprised," said the minister, "considering that he spent the night in my closet."

The duke was a man of wit and a man of the world. He only kept secrets when they were really important ones; very different from those make-believe diplomatists, who think they give themselves importance by making a mystery of trifles of no consequence. It is true that the Duc de Choiseul very seldom thought anything of great importance; and, in point of fact, if there were less intrigue and more truth about diplomacy (as there ought to be), concealment would be rather ridiculous than necessary.

The duke had pretended to disgrace St. Germain in France that he might use him as a spy in London; but Lord Halifax was by no means taken in by this stratagem. However, all governments have the politeness to afford one another these services, so that none of them can reproach the others.

The small Conte d'Aranda after caressing me affectionately begged me to come and breakfast with him at his boarding-house, telling me that Mdlle. Viar would be glad to see me.

The next day I took care not to fail in my appointment with the fair lady. I was at Madame Varnier's a quarter of an hour before the arrival of the dazzling brunette, and I waited for her with a beating at the heart which shewed me that the small favours she had given me had not quenched the flame of love. When she made her appearance the stoutness of her figure carried respect with it, so that I did not feel as if I could come forward and greet her tenderly; but she was far from thinking that more respect was due to her than when she was at Grenoble, poor but also pure. She kissed me affectionately and told me as much.

"They think I am happy," said she, "and envy my lot; but can one be happy after the loss of one's self-respect? For the last six months I have only smiled, not laughed; while at Grenoble I laughed heartily from true gladness. I have diamonds, lace, a beautiful house, a superb carriage, a lovely garden, waiting-maids, and a maid of honour who perhaps despises me; and although the highest Court ladies treat me like a princess, I do not pass a single day without experiencing some mortification."

"Mortification?"

"Yes; people come and bring pleas before me, and I am obliged to send them away as I dare not ask the king anything."

"Why not?"

"Because I cannot look on him as my lover only; he is always my sovereign, too. Ah! happiness is to be sought for in simple homes, not in pompous palaces."

"Happiness is gained by complying with the duties

of whatever condition of life one is in, and you must constrain yourself to rise to that exalted station in which destiny has placed you."

"I cannot do it; I love the king and I am always afraid of vexing him. I am always thinking that he does too much for me, and thus I dare not ask for anything for others."

"But I am sure the king would be only too glad to shew his love for you by benefiting the persons in whom you take an interest."

"I know he would, and that thought makes me happy, but I cannot overcome my feeling of repugnance to asking favours. I have a hundred louis a month for pin-money, and I distribute it in alms and presents, but with due economy, so that I am not penniless at the end of the month. I have a foolish notion that the chief reason the king loves me is that I do not importune him."

"And do you love him?"

"How can I help it? He is good-hearted, kindly, handsome, and polite to excess; in short, he possesses all the qualities to captivate a woman's heart.

"He is always asking me if I am pleased with my furniture, my clothes, my servants, and my garden, and if I desire anything altered. I thank him with a kiss, and tell him that I am pleased with everything."

"Does he ever speak of the scion you are going to present to him?"

"He aften says that I ought to be careful of myself in my situation. I am hoping that he will recognize my son as a prince of the blood; he ought in justice to do so, as the queen is dead."

"To be sure he will."

"I should be very happy if I had a son. I wish I felt

sure that I would have one. But I say nothing about this to anyone. If I dared speak to the king about the horoscope, I am certain he would want to know you; but I am afraid of evil tongues."

"So am I. Continue in your discreet course and nothing will come to disturb your happiness, which may become greater, and which I am pleased to have procured for you."

We did not part without tears. She was the first to go, after kissing me and calling me her best friend. I stayed a short time with Madame Varnier to compose my feelings, and I told her that I should have married her instead of drawing her horoscope.

"She would no doubt have been happier. You did not foresee, perhaps, her timidity and her lack of ambition."

"I can assure you that I did not reckon upon her courage or ambition. I laid aside my own happiness to think only of hers. But what is done cannot be recalled, and I shall be consoled if I see her perfectly happy at last. I hope, indeed, she will be so, above all if she is delivered of a son."

I dined with Madame d'Urfé, and we decided to send back Aranda to his boarding-school that we might be more free to pursue our cabalistic operations; and afterwards I went to the opera, where my brother had made an appointment with me. He took me to sup at Madame Vanloo's, and she received me in the friendliest manner possible.

"You will have the pleasure of meeting Madame Blondel and her husband," said she.

The reader will recollect that Madame Blondel was Manon Baletti, whom I was to have married.

"Does she know I am coming?" I enquired.

"No, I promise myself the pleasure of seeing her surprise."

"I am much obliged to you for not wishing to enjoy my surprise as well. We shall see each other again, but not to-day, so I must bid you farewell; for as I am a man of honour I hope never to be under the same roof as Madame Blondel again."

With this I left the room, leaving everybody in astonishment, and not knowing where to go I took a coach and went to sup with my sister-in-law, who was extremely glad to see me. But all through supper-time this charming woman did nothing but complain of her husband, saying that he had no business to marry her, knowing that he could not shew himself a man.

"Why did you not make the trial before you married?"

"Was it for me to propose such a thing? How should I suppose that such a fine man was impotent? But I will tell you how it all happened. As you know, I was a dancer at the Comédie Italienne, and I was the mistress of M. de Sauci, the ecclesiastical commissioner. He brought your brother to my house, I liked him, and before long I saw that he loved me. My lover advised me that it was an opportunity for getting married and making my fortune. With this idea I conceived the plan of not granting him any favours. He used to come and see me in the morning, and often found me in bed; we talked together, and his passions seemed to be aroused, but it all ended in kissing. On my part, I was waiting for a formal declaration and a proposal of marriage. At that period, M. de Sauci settled an annuity of a thousand crowns on me on the condition that I left the stage.

"In the spring M. de Sauci invited your brother to spend a month in his country house. I was of the party, but for propriety's sake it was agreed that I should pass as your brother's wife. Casanova enjoyed the idea, looking upon it as a jest, and not thinking of the consequences. I was therefore introduced as his wife to my lover's family, as also to his relations, who were judges, officers, and men about town, and to their wives, who were all women of fashion. Your brother was in high glee that to play our parts properly we were obliged to sleep together. For my part, I was far from disliking the idea, or at all events I looked upon it as a short cut to the marriage I desired.

"But how can I tell you? Though tender and affectionate in everything, your brother slept with me for a month without our attaining what seemed the natural result under the circumstances."

"You might have concluded, then, that he was impotent; for unless he were made of stone, or had taken a vow of chastity, his conduct was inexplicable."

"The fact is, that I had no means of knowing whether he was capable or incapable of giving me substantial proof of his love."

"Why did you not ascertain his condition for yourself?"

"A feeling of foolish pride prevented me from putting him to the test. I did not suspect the truth, but imagined reasons flattering to myself. I thought that he loved me so truly that he would not do anything before I was his wife. That idea prevented me humiliating myself by making him give me some positive proof of his powers."

"That supposition would have been tenable, though highly improbable, if you had been an innocent young maid, but he knew perfectly well that your novitiate was long over."

"Very true; but what can you expect of a woman impelled by love and vanity?"

"Your reasoning is excellent, but it comes rather late."

"Well, at last we went back to Paris, your brother to his house, and I to mine, while he continued his courtship, and I could not understand what he meant by such strange behaviour. M. de Sauci, who knew that nothing serious had taken place between us, tried in vain to solve the enigma. 'No doubt he is afraid of getting you with child,' he said, 'and of thus being obliged to marry you.' I began to be of the same opinion, but I thought it a strange line for a man in love to take.

"M. de Nesle, an officer in the French Guards, who had a pretty wife I had met in the country, went to your brother's to call on me. Not finding me there he asked why we did not live together. Your brother replied openly that our marriage had been a mere jest. M. de Nesle then came to me to enquire if this were the truth, and when he heard that it was he asked me how I would like him to make Casanova marry me. I answered that I should be delighted, and that was enough for him. He went again to your brother, and told him that his wife would never have associated with me on equal terms if I had not been introduced to her as a married woman; that the deceit was an insult to all the company at the country-house, which must be wiped out by his marrying me within the week or by fighting a duel. M. de Nesle added that if he fell he would be avenged by all the gentlemen who had been offended in the same way. Casanova replied, laughing, that so far from fighting to escape marrying me, he was ready to break a lance to get me. 'I love her,' he said, 'and if she loves me I am quite ready to give her my hand. Be kind enough,' he added, 'to prepare the way for me, and I will marry her whenever you like.'

"M. de Nesle embraced him, and promised to see to

everything; he brought me the joyful news, and in a week all was over. M. de Nesle gave us a splendid supper on our wedding-day, and since then I have had the title of his wife. It is an empty title, however, for, despite the ceremony and the fatal yes, I am no wife, for your brother is completely impotent. I am an unhappy wretch, and it is all his fault, for he ought to have known his own condition. He has deceived me horribly."

"But he was obliged to act as he did; he is more to be pitied than to be blamed. I also pity you, but I think you are in the wrong, for after his sleeping with you for a month without giving any proof of his manhood you might have guessed the truth. Even if you had been a perfect novice, M. de Sauci ought to have known what was the matter; he must be aware that it is beyond the power of man to sleep beside a pretty woman, and to press her naked body to his breast without becoming, in spite of himself, in a state which would admit of no concealment; that is, in case he were not impotent."

"All that seems very reasonable, but nevertheless neither of us thought of it; your brother looks such a Hercules."

"There are two remedies open to you; you can either have your marriage annulled, or you can take a lover; and I am sure that my brother is too reasonable a man to offer any opposition to the latter course."

"I am perfectly free, but I can neither avail myself of a divorce nor of a lover; for the wretch treats me so kindly that I love him more and more, which doubtless makes my misfortune harder to bear."

The poor woman was so unhappy that I should have been delighted to console her, but it was out of the question. However, the mere telling of her story had afforded her some solace, and after kissing her in such a way as to convince her that I was not like my brother, I wished her good night.

The next day I called on Madame Vanloo, who informed me that Madame Blondel had charged her to thank me for having gone away, while her husband wished me to know that he was sorry not to have seen me to express his gratitude.

"He seems to have found his wife a maid, but that's no fault of mine; and Manon Baletti is the only person he ought to be grateful to. They tell me that he has a pretty baby, and that he lives at the Louvre, while she has another house in the Rue Neuve-des-Petits-Champs."

"Yes, but he has supper with her every evening."

"It's an odd way of living."

"I assure you it answers capitally. Blondel regards his wife as his mistress. He says that that keeps the flame of love alight, and that as he never had a mistress worthy of being a wife, he is delighted to have a wife worthy of being a mistress."

The next day I devoted entirely to Madame de Rumain, and we were occupied with knotty questions till the evening. I left her well pleased. The marriage of her daughter, Mdlle. Cotenfau, with M. de Polignac, which took place five or six years later, was the result of our cabalistic calculations.

The fair stocking-seller of the Rue des Prouvères, whom I had loved so well, was no longer in Paris. She had gone off with a M. de Langlade, and her husband was inconsolable. Camille was ill. Coralline had become the titulary mistress of the Comte de la Marche, son of the Prince of Conti, and the issue of this union was a son, whom I knew twenty years later. He called himself the Chevalier de Montréal, and wore the cross of the Knights of Malta. Several other girls I had known were widowed and in the country, or had become inaccessible in other ways.

Such was the Paris of my day. The actors on its stage changed as rapidly as the fashions.

I devoted a whole day to my old friend Baletti, who had left the theatre and married a pretty ballet-girl on the death of his father; he was making experiments with a view to finding the philosopher's stone.

I was agreeably surprised at meeting the poet Poinsinet at the Comédie Française. He embraced me again and again, and told me that M. du Tillot had overwhelmed him with kindness at Parma.

"He would not get me anything to do," said Poinsinet, "because a French poet is rather at a discount in Italy."

"Have you heard anything of Lord Lismore?"

"Yes, he wrote to his mother from Leghorn, telling her that he was going to the Indies, and that if you had not been good enough to give him a thousand louis he would have been a prisoner at Rome."

"His fate interests me extremely, and I should be glad to call on his lady-mother with you."

"I will tell her that you are in Paris, and I am sure that she will invite you to supper, for she has the greatest desire to talk to you."

"How are you getting on here? Are you still content to serve Apollo?"

"He is not the god of wealth by any means. I have no money and no room, and I shall be glad of a supper, if you will ask me. I will read you my play, the *Cercle*, which has been accepted. I am sure it will be successful."

The *Cercle* was a short prose play, in which the poet

satirised the jargon of Dr. Herrenschwand, brother of
the doctor I had consulted at Soleure. The play proved
to be a great success.

I took Poinsinet home to supper, and the poor nursling of the muses ate for four. In the morning he came
to tell me that the Countess of Lismore expected me to
supper.

I found the lady, still pretty, in company with her
aged lover, M. de St. Albin, Archbishop of Cambrai, who
spent all the revenues of his see on her. This worthy
prelate was one of the illegitimate children of the Duc
d'Orleans, the famous Regent, by an actress. He supped
with us, but he only opened his mouth to eat, and his
mistress only spoke of her son, whose talents she lauded
to the skies, though he was in reality a mere scamp; but
I felt in duty bound to echo what she said. It would
have been cruel to contradict her. I promised to let
her know if I saw anything more of him.

Poinsinet, who was hearthless and homeless, as they
say, spent the night in my room, and in the morning I
gave him two cups of chocolate and some money where-
with to get a lodging. I never saw him again, and a
few years after he was drowned, not in the fountain of
Hippocrene, but in the Guadalquivir. He told me that
he had spent a week with M. de Voltaire, and that he
had hastened his return to Paris to obtain the release
of the Abbé Morellet from the Bastile.

I had nothing more to do at Paris, and I was only
waiting for some clothes to be made and for a cross of
the order, with which the Holy Father had decorated
me, to be set with diamonds and rubies.

I had waited for five or six days when an unfortunate
incident obliged me to take a hasty departure. I am
loth to write what follows, for it was all my own fault

that I was nearly losing my life and my honour. I pity those simpletons who blame fortune and not themselves for their misfortunes.

I was walking in the Tuileries at ten o'clock in the morning, when I was unlucky enough to meet the Dangenancour and another girl. This Dangenancour was a dancer at the opera-house, whom I had desired to meet previously to my last departure from Paris. I congratulated myself on the lucky chance which threw her in my way, and accosted her, and had not much trouble in inducing her to dine with me at Choisi.

We walked towards the Pont-Royal, where we took a coach. After dinner had been ordered we were taking a turn in the garden, when I saw a carriage stop and two adventurers whom I knew getting out of it, with two girls, friends of the ones I had with me. The wretched landlady, who was standing at the door, said that if we liked to sit down together she could give us an excellent dinner, and I said nothing, or rather I assented to the *yes* of my two nymphs. The dinner was excellent, and after the bill was paid, and we were on the point of returning to Paris, I noticed that a ring, which I had taken off to shew to one of the adventurers named Santis, was still missing. It was an exceedingly pretty miniature, and the diamond setting had cost me twenty-five louis. I politely begged Santis to return me the ring, and he replied with the utmost coolness that he had done so already.

"If you had returned it," said I, "it would be on my finger, and you see that it is not."

He persisted in his assertion; the girls said nothing, but Santis's friend, a Portuguese, named Xavier, dared to tell me that he had seen the ring returned.

"You're a liar," I exclaimed; and without more ado I

took hold of Santis by the collar, and swore I would not
let him go till he returned me my ring. The Portuguese
rose to come to his friend's rescue, while I stepped back
and drew my sword, repeating my determination not to
let them go. The landlady came on the scene and began
to shriek, and Santis asked me to give him a few words
apart. I thought in all good faith that he was ashamed
to restore the ring before company, but that he would
give it me as soon as we were alone. I sheathed my
sword, and told him to come with me. Xavier got into
the carriage with the four girls, and they all went back
to Paris.

Santis followed me to the back of the inn, and then
assuming a pleasant smile he told me that he had put
the ring into his friend's pocket for a joke, but that I
should have it back at Paris.

"That's an idle tale," I exclaimed, "your friend said
that he saw you return it, and now he has escaped me.
Do you think that I am green enough to be taken in by
this sort of thing? You're a couple of robbers."

So saying, I stretched out my hand for his watch-
chain, but he stepped back and drew his sword. I drew
mine, and we had scarcely crossed swords when he
thrust, and I parrying rushed in and ran him through
and through. He fell to the ground calling, "Help!" I
sheathed my sword, and, without troubling myself about
him, got into my coach and drove back to Paris.

I got down in the Place Maubert, and walked by a
circuitous way to my hotel. I was sure that no one could
have come after me there, as my landlord did not even
know my name.

I spent the rest of the day in packing up my trunks,
and after telling Costa to place them on my carriage I
went to Madame d'Urfé. After I had told her of what

had happened, I begged her, as soon as that which she had for me was ready, to send it to me at Augsburg by Costa. I should have told her to entrust it to one of her own servants, but my good genius had left me that day. Besides I did not look upon Costa as a thief.

When I got back to the hotel I gave the rascal his instructions, telling him to be quick and to keep his own counsel, and then I gave him money for the journey.

I left Paris in my carriage, drawn by four hired horses, which took me as far as the second post, and I did not stop till I got to Strasburg, where I found Desarmoises and my Spaniard.

There was nothing to keep me in Strasburg, so I wanted to cross the Rhine immediately; but Desarmoises persuaded me to come with him to see an extremely pretty woman who had only delayed her departure for Augsburg in the hope that we might journey there together.

"You know the lady," said the false marquis, "but she made me give my word of honour that I would not tell you. She has only her maid with her, and I am sure you will be pleased to see her."

My curiosity made me give in. I followed Desarmoises, and came into a room where I saw a nice-looking woman whom I did not recognize at first. I collected my thoughts, and the lady turned out to be a dancer whom I had admired on the Dresden boards eight years before. She was then mistress to Count Brühl, but I had not even attempted to win her favour. She had an excellent carriage, and as she was ready to go to Augsburg I immediately concluded that we could make the journey together very pleasantly.

After the usual compliments had passed, we decided on leaving for Augsburg the following morning. The lady was going to Munich, but as I had no business there we agreed that she should go by herself.

"I am quite sure," she said, afterwards, "that you will come too, for the ambassadors do not assemble at Augsburg till next September."

We supped together, and next morning we started on our way; she in her carriage with her maid, and I in mine with Desarmoises, preceded by Le Duc on horseback. At Rastadt, however, we made a change, the Renaud (as she was called) thinking that she would give less opportunity for curious surmises by riding with me while Desarmoises went with the servant. We soon became intimate. She told me about herself, or pretended to, and I told her all that I did not want to conceal. I informed her that I was an agent of the Court of Lisbon, and she believed me, while, for my part, I believed that she was only going to Munich and Augsburg to sell her diamonds.

We began to talk about Desarmoises, and she said that it was well enough for me to associate with him, but I should not countenance his styling himself marquis.

"But," said I, "he is the son of the Marquis Desarmoises, of Nancy."

"No, he isn't; he is only a retired messenger, with a small pension from the department of foreign affairs. I know the Marquis Desarmoises; he lives at Nancy, and is not so old as our friend."

"Then one can't see how he can be Desarmoises's father."

"The landlord of the inn at Strasburg knew him when he was a messenger."

"How did you make his acquaintance?"

"We met at the table d'hôte. After dinner he came

up to my room, and told me he was waiting for a gentleman who was going to Augsburg, and that we might make the journey together. He told me the name, and after questioning him I concluded that the gentleman was yourself, so here we are, and I am very glad of it. But listen to me; I advise you to drop all false styles and titles. Why do you call yourself Seingalt?"

"Because it's my name, but that doesn't prevent my old friends calling me Casanova, for I am both. You understand?"

"Oh, yes! I understand. Your mother is at Prague, and as she doesn't get her pension on account of the war, I am afraid she must be rather in difficulties."

"I know it, but I do not forget my filial duties. I have sent her some money."

"That's right. Where are you going to stay at Augsburg?"

"I shall take a house, and if you like you shall be the mistress and do the honours."

"That would be delightful! We will give little suppers, and play cards all night."

"Your programme is an excellent one."

"I will see that you get a good cook; all the Bavarian cooks are good. We shall cut a fine figure, and people will say we love each other madly."

"You must know, dearest, that I do not understand jokes at the expense of fidelity."

"You may trust me for that. You know how I lived at Dresden."

"I will trust you, but not blindly, I promise you. And now let us address each other in the same way; you must call me *tu*. You must remember we are lovers."

"Kiss me!"

The fair Renaud did not like traveling by night;

she preferred to eat a good supper, to drink heavily, and to go to bed just as her head began to whirl. The heat of the wine made her into a Bacchante, hard to appease; but when I could do no more I told her to leave me alone, and she had to obey.

When we reached Augsburg we alighted at the "Three Moors," but the landlord told us that though he could give us a good dinner he could not put us up, as the whole of the hotel had been engaged by the French ambassador. I called on M. Corti, the banker to whom I was accredited, and he soon got me a furnished house with a garden, which I took for six months. The Renaud liked it immensely.

No one had yet arrived at Augsburg. The Renaud contrived to make me feel that I should be lonely at Augsburg without her, and succeeded in persuading me to come with her to Munich. We put up at the "Stag," and made ourselves very comfortable, while Desarmoises went to stay somewhere else. As my business and that of my new mate had nothing in common, I gave her a servant and a carriage to herself, and made myself the same allowance.

The Abbé Gama had given me a letter from the Commendatore Almada for Lord Stormont, the English ambassador at the Court of Bavaria. This nobleman being then at Munich I hastened to deliver the letter. He received me very well, and promised to do all he could as soon as he had time, as Lord Halifax had told him all about it. On leaving his Britannic Lordship's I called on M. de Folard, the French ambassador, and gave him a letter from M. de Choiseul. M. de Folard gave me a hearty welcome, and asked me to dine with him the next day, and the day after introduced me to the Elector.

During the four fatal weeks I spent at Munich, the

ambassador's house was the only one I frequented. I
call these weeks fatal, and with reason, for in them I lost
all my money, I pledged jewels (which I never recovered) to the amount of forty thousand francs, and finally
I lost my health. My assassins were the Renaud and
Desarmoises, who owed me so much and paid me so
badly.

The third day after my arrival I had to call on the
Dowager Electress of Saxony. It was my brother-in-
law, who was in her train, that made me go, by telling
me that it must be done, as she knew me and had been
enquiring for me. I had no reason to repent of my
politeness in going, as the Electress gave me a good
reception, and made me talk to any extent. She was
extremely curious, like most people who have no employment, and have not sufficient intelligence to amuse
themselves.

I have done a good many foolish things in the course
of my existence. I confess it as frankly as Rousseau,
and my Memoirs are not so egotistic as those of that unfortunate genius; but I never committed such an act of
folly as I did when I went to Munich, where I had
nothing to do. But it was a crisis in my life. My evil
genius had made me commit one folly after another since
I left Turin. The evening at Lord Lismore's, my connection with Desarmoises, my party at Choisi, my trust
in Costa, my union with the Renaud, and worse than
all, my folly in letting myself play at faro at a place
where the knavery of the gamesters is renowned all over
Europe, followed one another in fatal succession. Among
the players was the famous, or rather infamous, Af-
flisio, the friend of the Duc de Deux-Ponts, whom the
duke called his aide-de-camp, and who was known for
the keenest rogue in the world.

I played every day, and as I often lost money on my word of honour, the necessity of paying the next day often caused me the utmost anxiety. When I had exhausted my credit with the bankers, I had recourse to the Jews who require pledges, and in this Desarmoises and the Renaud were my agents, the latter of whom ended by making herself mistress of all my property. This was not the worst thing she did to me; for she gave me a disease which devoured her interior parts and left no marks outwardly, and was thus all the more dangerous, as the freshness of her complexion seemed to indicate the most perfect health. In short, this serpent, who must have come from hell to destroy me, had acquired such a mastery over me that she persuaded me that she would be dishonoured if I called in a doctor during our stay at Munich, as everybody knew that we were living together as man and wife.

I cannot imagine what had become of my wits to let myself be so beguiled, while every day I renewed the poison that she had poured into my veins.

My stay at Munich was a kind of curse; throughout that dreadful month I seemed to have a foretaste of the pains of the damned. The Renaud loved gaming, and Desarmoises was her partner. I took care not to play with them, for the false marquis was an unmitigated cheat and often tricked with less skill than impudence. He asked disreputable people to my house and treated them at my expense; every evening scenes of a disgraceful character took place.

The Dowager Electress mortified me extremely by the way she addressed me on my last two visits to her.

"Everybody knows what kind of a life you lead here, and the way the Renaud behaves, possibly without your knowing it. I advise you to have done with her, as your character is suffering."

She did not know what a thraldom I was under. I had left Paris for a month, and I had neither heard of Madame d'Urfé nor of Costa. I could not guess the reason, but I began to suspect my Italian's fidelity. I also feared lest my good Madame d'Urfé might be dead or have come to her senses, which would have come to the same thing so far as I was concerned; and I could not possibly return to Paris to obtain the information which was so necessary both for calming my mind and refilling my purse.

I was in a terrible state, and my sharpest pang was that I began to experience a certain abatement of my vigous, the natural result of advancing years. I had no longer that daring born of youth and the knowledge of one's strength, and I was not yet old enough to have learnt how to husband my forces. Nevertheless, I made an effort and took a sudden leave of my mistress, telling her I would await her at Augsburg. She did not try to detain me, but promised to rejoin me as soon as possible; she was engaged in selling her jewellery. I set out preceded by Le Duc, feeling very glad that Desarmoises had chosen to say with the wretched woman to whom he had introduced me. When I reached my pretty house at Augsburg I took to my bed, determined not to rise till I was cured or dead. M. Carli, my banker, recommended to me a doctor named Cephalides, a pupil of the famous Fayet, who had cured me of a similar complaint several years before. This Cephalides was considered the best doctor in Augsburg. He examined me and declared he could cure me by sudorifics without having recourse to the knife. He began his treatment by putting me on a severe regimen, ordering baths, and applying mercury locally. I endured this treatment for six weeks, at the end of which time I found myself worse than at the beginning. I had become terribly thin, and I had two enormous ingunial tumours. I had to make up my mind to have them lanced, but though the operation nearly killed me it did not to make me any better. He was so clumsy as to cut the artery, causing great loss of blood which was arrested with difficulty, and would have proved fatal if it had not been for the care of M. Algardi, a Bolognese doctor in the service of the Prince-Bishop of Augsburg.

I had enough of Cephalides, and Dr. Algardi prepared in my presence eighty-six pills containing eighteen grains of manna. I took one of these pills every morning, drinking a large glass of curds after it, and in the evening I had another pill with barley water, and this was the only sustenance I had. This heroic treatment gave me back my health in two months and a half, in which I suffered a great deal of pain; but I did not begin to put on flesh and get back my strength till the end of the year.

It was during this time that I heard about Costa's flight with my diamonds, watches, snuff-box, linen, rich suits, and a hundred louis which Madame d'Urfé had given him for the journey. The worthy lady sent me a bill of exchange for fifty thousand francs, which she had happily not entrusted to the robber, and the money rescued me very opportunely from the state to which my imprudence had reduced me.

At this period I made another discovery of an extremely vexatious character; namely, that Le Duc had robbed me. I would have forgiven him if he had not forced me to a public exposure, which I could only have avoided with the loss of my honour. However, I kept him in my service till my return to Paris at the commencement of the following year.

Towards the end of September, when everybody knew that the Congress would not take place, the Renaud passed through Augsburg with Desarmoises on her way to Paris; but she dared not come and see me for fear I should make her return my goods, of which she had taken possession without telling me. Four or five years later she married a man named Böhmer, the same that gave the Cardinal de Rohan the famous necklace, which he supposed was destined for the unfortunate Marie Antoinette. The Renaud was at Paris when I returned, but I made no endeavour to see her, as I wished, if possible, to forget the past. I had every reason to do so, for amongst all the misfortunes I had gone through during that wretched year the person I found most at fault was myself. Nevertheless, I would have given myself the pleasure of cutting off Desarmoises's ears; but the old rascal, who, no doubt, foresaw what kind of treatment I was likely to mete to him, made his escape. Shortly after, he died miserably of consumption in Normandy.

My health had scarcely returned, when I forgot all my woes and began once more to amuse myself. My excellent cook, Anna Midel, who had been idle so long, had to work hard to satisfy my ravenous appetite. My landlord and pretty Gertrude, his daughter, looked at me with astonishment as I ate, fearing some disastrous results. Dr. Algardi, who had saved my life, prophesied a dyspepsia which would bring me to the tomb, but my need of food was stronger than his arguments, to which I paid no kind of attention; and I was right, for I required an immense quantity of nourishment to recover my former state, and I soon felt in a condition to renew my sacrifices to the deity for whom I had suffered so much.

I fell in love with the cook and Gertrude, who were both young and pretty. I imparted my love to both of them at once, for I had foreseen that if I attacked them separately I should conquer neither. Besides, I felt that I had not much time to lose, as I had promised to sup with Madame d'Urfé on the first night of the year 1761 in a suite of rooms she had furnished for me in the Rue de Bacq. She had adorned the rooms with superb tapestry made for Réné of Savoy, on which were depicted all the operations of the Great Work. She wrote to me that she had heard that Santis had recovered from the wound I had given him, and had been committed to the Bicêtre for fraud.

Gertrude and Anna Midel occupied my leisure moments agreeably enough during the rest of my stay at Augsburg, but they did not make me neglect society. I spent my evenings in a very agreeable manner with Count Max de Lamberg, who occupied the position of field-marshal to the prince-bishop. His wife had all the attractions which collect good company together. At this house I made the acquaintance of the Baron von Selentin, a captain in the Prussian service, who was recruiting for the King of Prussia at Augsburg. I was particularly drawn to the Count Lamberg by his taste for literature. He was an extremely learned man, and has published some excellent works. I kept up a correspondence with him till his death, by his own fault, in 1792, four years from the time of my writing. I say by his fault, but I should have said by the fault of his doctors, who treated him mercurially for a disease which was not venereal; and this treatment not only killed him but took away his good name.

His widow is still alive, and lives in Bavaria, loved by her friends and her daughters, who all made excellent marriages.

At this time a miserable company of Italian actors made their appearance in Augsburg, and I got them permission to play in a small and wretched theatre. As this was the occasion of an incident which diverted me, the hero, I shall impart it to my readers in the hope of its amusing them also.

CHAPTER XIV

The Actors—Bassi—The Girl From Strasburg—The Female Count—My Return to Paris—I Go to Metz—Pretty Raton—The Pretended Countess Lascaris

A WOMAN, ugly enough, but lively like all Italians, called on me, and asked me to intercede with the police to obtain permission for her company to act in Augsburg. In spite of her ugliness she was a poor fellow-countrywoman, and without asking her name, or ascertaining whether the company was good or bad, I promised to do my best, and had no difficulty in obtaining the favour.

I went to the first performance, and saw to my surprise that the chief actor was a Venetian, and a fellow-student of mine, twenty years before, at St. Cyprian's College. His name was Bassi, and like myself he had given up the priesthood. Fortune had made an actor of him, and he looked wretched enough, while I, the adventurer, had a prosperous air.

I felt curious to hear his adventures, and I was also actuated by that feeling of kindliness which draws one towards the companions of one's youthful and especially one's school days, so I went to the back as soon as the curtain fell. He recognized me directly, gave a joyful cry, and after he had embraced me he introduced me to his wife, the woman who had called on me, and to his daughter, a girl of thirteen or fourteen, whose dancing had delighted me. He did not stop here, but turning

362

to his mates, of whom he was chief, introduced me to them as his best friend. These worthy people, seeing me dressed like a lord, with a cross on my breast, took me for a cosmopolitan charlatan who was expected at Augsburg, and Bassi, strange to say, did not undeceive them. When the company had taken off its stage rags and put on its everyday rags, Bassi's ugly wife took me by the arm and said I must come and sup with her. I let myself be led, and we soon got to just the kind of room I had imagined. It was a huge room on the ground floor, which served for kitchen, dining-room, and bed-room all at once. In the middle stood a long table, part of which was covered with a cloth which looked as if it had been in use for a month, and at the other end of the room somebody was washing certain earthenware dishes in a dirty pan. This den was lighted by one candle stuck in the neck of a broken bottle, and as there were no snuffers Bassi's wife snuffed it cleverly with her finger and thumb, wiping her hand on the table-cloth after throwing the burnt wick on the floor. An actor with long moustaches, who played the villain in the various pieces, served an enormous dish of hashed-up meat, swimming in a sea of dirty water dignified with the name of sauce; and the hungry family proceeded to tear pieces of bread off the loaf with their fingers or teeth, and then to dip them in the dish; but as all did the same no one had a right to be disgusted. A large pot of ale passed from hand to hand, and with all this misery mirth displayed itself on every countenance, and I had to ask myself what is happiness. For a second course there was a dish of fried pork, which was de-voured with great relish. Bassi was kind enough not to press me to take part in this banquet, and I felt obliged to him.

The meal over, he proceeded to impart to me his adventures, which were ordinary enough, and like those which many a poor devil has to undergo; and while he talked his pretty daughter sat on my knee. Bassi brought his story to an end by saying that he was going to Venice for the carnival, and was sure of making a lot of money. I wished him all the luck he could desire, and on his asking me what profession I followed the fancy took me to reply that I was a doctor.

"That's a better trade than mine," said he, "and I am happy to be able to give you a valuable present."

"What is that?" I asked.

"The receipt for the Venetian Specific, which you can sell at two florins a pound, while it will only cost you four gros."

"I shall be delighted; but tell me, how is the treasury?"

"Well, I can't complain for a first night. I have paid all expenses, and have given my actors a florin apiece. But I am sure I don't know how I am to play to-morrow, as the company has rebelled; they say they won't act unless I give each of them a florin in advance."

"They don't ask very much, however."

"I know that, but I have no money, and nothing to pledge; but they will be sorry for it afterwards, as I am sure I shall make at least fifty florins to-morrow."

"How many are there in the company?"

"Fourteen, including my family. Could you lend me ten florins? I would pay you back tomorrow night."

"Certainly, but I should like to have you all to supper at the nearest inn to the theatre. Here are the ten florins."

The poor devil overflowed with gratitude, and said he would order supper at a florin a head, according to my instructions. I thought the sight of fourteen famished actors sitting down to a good supper would be rather amusing.

The company gave a play the next evening, but as only thirty or at most forty people were present, poor Bassi did not know where to turn to pay for the lighting and the orchestra. He was in despair; and instead of returning my ten florins he begged me to lend him another ten, still in the hope of a good house next time. I consoled him by saying we would talk it over after supper, and that I would go to the inn to wait for my guests.

I made the supper last three hours by dint of passing the bottle freely. My reason was that I had taken a great interest in a young girl from Strasburg, who played singing chamber-maids. Her features were exquisite and her voice charming, while she made me split my sides with laughing at her Italian pronounced with an Alsatian accent, and at her gestures which were of the most comic description.

I was determined to possess her in the course of the next twenty-four hours, and before the party broke up I spoke as follows:

"Ladies and gentlemen, I will engage you myself for a week at fifty florins a day on the condition that you acknowledge me as your manager for the time being, and pay all the expenses of the theatre. You must charge the prices I name for seats, five members of the company to be chosen by me must sup with me every evening. If the receipts amount to more than fifty florins, we will share the overplus between us."

My proposal was welcomed with shouts of joy, and I called for pen, ink, and paper, and drew up the agreement.

"For to-morrow," I said to Bassi, "the prices for admission shall remain the same, but the day after we will see what can be done. You and your family will sup with me to-morrow, as also the young Alsatian whom I could never separate from her dear Harlequin."

He issued bills of an enticing description for the following evening; but, in spite of all, the pit only contained a score of common people, and nearly all the boxes were empty.

Bassi had done his best, and when we met at supper he came up to me looking extremely confused, and gave me ten or twelve florins.

"Courage!" said I; and I proceeded to share them among the guests present.

We had a good supper, and I kept them at table till midnight, giving them plenty of choice wine and playing a thousand pranks with Bassi's daughter and the young Alsatian, who sat one on each side of me. I did not heed the jealous Harlequin, who seemed not to relish my familiarities with his sweetheart. The latter lent herself to my endearments with a bad enough grace, as she hoped Harlequin would marry her, and consequently did not want to vex him. When supper was over, we rose, and I took her between my arms, laughing, and caressing her in a manner which seemed too suggestive to the lover, who tried to pull me away. I thought this rather too much in my turn, and seizing him by his shoulders I dismissed him with a hearty kick, which he received with great humility. However, the situation assumed a melancholy aspect, for the poor girl began to weep bitterly. Bassi and his wife, two hardened sinners, laughed at her tears, and Bassi's daughter said that her lover had offered me great provocation; but the young Alsatian continued weeping, and told me that she would never sup with me again if I did not make her lover return.

"I will see to all that," said I; and four sequins soon made her all smiles again. She even tried to shew me that she was not really cruel, and that she would be still less so if I could manage the jealous Harlequin. I promised everything, and she did her best to convince me that she would be quite complaisant on the first opportunity.

I ordered Bassi to give notice that the pit would be two florins and the boxes a ducat, but that the gallery would be opened freely to the first comers.

"We shall have nobody there," said he, looking alarmed.

"Maybe, but that remains to be seen. You must request twelve soldiers to keep order, and I will pay for them."

"We shall want some soldiers to look after the mob which will beseige the gallery, but as for the rest of the house . . . ."

"Again I tell you, we shall see. Carry out my instructions, and whether they prove successful or no, we will have a merry supper as usual."

The next day I called upon the Harlequin in his little den of a room, and with two louis, and a promise to respect his mistress, I made him as soft as a glove.

Bassi's bills made everybody laugh. People said he must be mad; but when it was ascertained that it was the lessee's speculation, and that I was the lessee, the accusation of madness was turned on me, but what did I care? At night the gallery was full an hour before the rise of the curtain; but the pit was empty, and there was nobody in the boxes with the exception of Count Lamberg, a Genoese abbé named Bolo, and a young man who appeared to me a woman in disguise.

The actors surpassed themselves, and the thunders of applause from the gallery enlivened the performance.

When we got to the inn, Bassi gave me the three ducats for the three boxes, but of course I returned them to him; it was quite a little fortune for the poor actors. I sat down at table between Bassi's wife and daughter, leaving the Alsatian to her lover. I told the manager to persevere in the same course, and to let those laugh who would, and I made him promise to play all his best pieces.

When the supper and the wine had sufficiently raised my spirits, I devoted my attention to Bassi's daughter, who let me do what I liked, while her father and mother only laughed, and the silly Harlequin fretted and fumed at not being able to take the same liberties with his Dulcinea. But at the end of supper, when I had made the girl in a state of nature, I myself being dressed like Adam before he ate the fatal apple, Harlequin rose, and taking his sweetheart's arm was going to draw her away. I imperiously told him to sit down, and he obeyed me in amazement, contenting himself with turning his back. His sweetheart did not follow his example, and so placed herself on the pretext of defending my victim that she increased my enjoyment, while my vagrant hand did not seem to displease her.

The scene excited Bassi's wife, and she begged her husband to give her a proof of his love for her, to which request he acceded, while modest Harlequin sat by the fire with his head on his hands. The Alsatian was in a highly excited state, and took advantage of her lover's position to grant me all I wished, so I proceeded to execute the great work with her, and the violent movements of her body proved that she was taking as active a part in it as myself.

When the orgy was over I emptied my purse on the table, and enjoyed the eagerness with which they shared a score of sequins.

This indulgence at a time when I had not yet recovered my full strength made me enjoy a long sleep. Just as I awoke I was handed a summons to appear before the burgomaster. I made haste with my toilette, for I felt curious to know the reason of this citation, and I was aware I had nothing to fear. When I appeared, the magistrate addressed me in German, to which I turned a deaf ear, for I only knew enough of that language to ask for necessaries. When he was informed of my ignorance of German he addressed me in Latin, not of the Ciceronian kind by any means, but in that peculiar dialect which obtains at most of the German universities.

"Why do you bear a false name?" he asked.

"My name is not false. You can ask Carli, the banker, who has paid me fifty thousand florins."

"I know that; but your name is Casanova, so why do you call yourself Seingalt?"

"I take this name, or rather I have taken it, because it belongs to me, and in such a manner that if anyone else dared to take it I should contest it as my property by every legitimate resource."

"Ah! and how does this name belong to you?"

"Because I invented it; but that does not prevent my being Casanova as well."

"Sir, you must choose between Casanova and Seingalt; a man cannot have two names."

"The Spaniards and Portuguese often have half a dozen names."

"But you are not a Spaniard or a Portuguese; you are an Italian: and, after all, how can one invent a name?"

"It's the simplest thing in the world."

"Kindly explain."

"The alphabet belongs equally to the whole human race; no one can deny that. I have taken eight letters and combined them in such a way as to produce the word Seingalt. It pleased me, and I have adopted it as my surname, being firmly persuaded that as no one had borne it before no one could deprive me of it, or carry it without my consent."

"This is a very odd idea. Your arguments are rather specious than well grounded, for your name ought to be none other than your father's name."

"I suggest that there you are mistaken; the name you yourself bear because your father bore it before you, has not existed from all eternity; it must have been invented by an ancestor of yours who did not get it from his father, or else your name would have been Adam. Does your worship agree to that?"

"I am obliged to; but all this is strange, very strange."

"You are again mistaken. It's quite an old custom, and I engage to give you by to-morrow a long list of names invented by worthy people still living, who are allowed to enjoy their names in peace and quietness without being cited to the town hall to explain how they got them."

"But you will confess that there are laws against false names?"

"Yes, but I repeat this name is my true name. Your name which I honour, though I do not know it, cannot be more true than mine, for it is possible that you are not the son of the gentleman you consider your father."

He smiled and escorted me out, telling me that he would make enquiries about me of M. Carli.

I took the part of going to M. Carli's myself. The story made him laugh. He told me that the burgomaster was a Catholic, a worthy man, well to do, but rather thick-headed; in short, a fine subject for a joke.

The following morning M. Carli asked me to breakfast, and afterwards to dine with the burgomaster.

"I saw him yesterday," said he, "and we had a long talk, in the course of which I succeeded in convincing him on the question of names, and he is now quite of your opinion."

I accepted the invitation with pleasure, as I was sure of seeing some good company. I was not undeceived; there were some charming women and several agreeable men. Amongst others, I noticed the woman in man's dress I had seen at the theatre. I watched her at dinner, and I was the more convinced that she was a woman. Nevertheless, everybody addressed her as a man, and she played the part to admiration. I, however, being in search of amusement, and not caring to seem as if I were taken in, began to talk to her in a stream of gallantry as one talks to a woman, and I contrived to let her know that if I were not sure of her sex I had very strong suspicions. She pretended not to understand me, and everyone laughed at my feigned expression of offence.

After dinner, while we were taking coffee, the pretended gentleman shewed a canon who was present a portrait on one of her rings. It represented a young lady who was in the company, and was an excellent likeness —an easy enough matter, as she was very ugly. My conviction was not disturbed, but when I saw the imposter kissing the young lady's hand with mingled affection and respect, I ceased jesting on the question of her sex. M. Carli took me aside for a moment, and told me that in spite of his effeminate appearance this individual was a man, and was shortly going to marry the young lady whose hand he had just kissed.

"It may be so," said I, "but I can't believe it all the same."

However, the pair were married during the carnival, and the husband obtained a rich dowry with his wife. The poor girl died of grief in the course of a year, but did not say a word till she was on her death-bed. Her foolish parents, ashamed of having been deceived so grossly, dared not say anything, and got the female swindler out of the way; she had taken good care, however, to lay a firm hold on the dowry. The story became known, and gave the good folk of Augsburg much amusement, while I became renowned for my sagacity in piercing the disguise.

I continued to enjoy the society of my two servants and of the fair Alsation, who cost me a hundred louis. At the end of a week my agreement with Bassi came to an end, leaving him with some money in his pocket. He continued to give performances, returning to the usual prices and suppressing the free gallery. He did very fair business.

I left Augsburg towards the middle of December.

I was vexed on account of Gertrude, who believed herself with child, but could not make up her mind to accompany me to France. Her father would have been pleased for me to take her; he had no hopes of getting her a husband, and would have been glad enough to get rid of her by my making her my mistress.

We shall hear more of her in the course of five or six

years, as also of my excellent cook, Anna Midel, to whom I gave a present of four hundred florins. She married shortly afterwards, and when I visited the town again I found her unhappy.

I could not make up my mind to forgive Le Duc, who rode on the coachman's box, and when we were in Paris, half-way along the Rue St. Antoine, I made him take his trunk and get down; and I left him there without a character, in spite of his entreaties. I never heard of him again, but I still miss him, for, in spite of his great failings, he was an excellent servant. Perhaps I should have called to mind the important services he had rendered me at Stuttgart, Soleure, Naples, Florence, and Turin; but I could not pass over his impudence in compromising me before the Augsburg magistrate. If I had not succeeded in bringing a certain theft home to him, it would have been laid to my door, and I should have been dishonoured.

I had done a good deal in saving him from justice, and, besides, I had rewarded him liberally for all the special services he had done me.

From Augsburg I went to Bâle by way of Constance, where I stayed at the dearest inn in Switzerland. The landlord, Imhoff, was the prince of cheats, but his daughters were amusing, and after a three days' stay I continued my journey. I got to Paris on the last day of the year 1761, and I left the coach at the house in the Rue du Bacq, where my good angel Madame d'Urfé had arranged me a suite of rooms with the utmost elegance.

I spent three weeks in these rooms without going anywhere, in order to convince the worthy lady that I had only returned to Paris to keep my word to her, and make her be born again a man.

We spent the three weeks in making preparations for this divine operation, and our preparations consisted of devotions to each of the seven planets on the days consecrated to each of the intelligences. After this I had to seek, in a place which the spirits would point out to me, for a maiden, the daughter of an adept, whom I was to impregnate with a male child in a manner only known to the Fraternity of the Rosy Cross. Madame d'Urfé was to receive the child into her arms the moment it was born, and to keep it beside her in bed for seven days. At the end of the seven days she would die with her lips on the lips of the child, who would thus receive her reasonable soul, whereas before it had only possessed a vegetal soul.

This being done, it was to be my part to care for the child with the magisterium which was known to me, and as soon as it had attained to its third year Madame d'Urfé would begin to recover her self-consciousness, and then I was to begin to initiate her in the perfect knowledge of the Great Work.

The operation must take place under the full moon during the months of April, May, or June. Above all, Madame d'Urfé was to make a will in favour of the child, whose guardian I was to be till its thirteenth year.

This sublime madwoman had no doubts whatever as to the truth of all this, and burned with impatience to see the virgin who was destined to be the vessel of election. She begged me to hasten my departure.

I had hoped, in obtaining my answers from the oracle, that she would be deterred by the prospect of death, and I reckoned on the natural love of life making her defer the operation for an indefinite period. But such was not the case, and I found myself obliged to keep my word, in appearance at all events, and to go on my quest for the mysterious virgin.

What I wanted was some young hussy whom I could teach the part, and I thought of the Corticelli. She had been at Prague for the last nine months, and when we were at Bologna I had promised to come and see her before the end of the year. But as I was leaving Germany—by no means a land of pleasant memories to me —I did not think it was worth while going out of my way for such a trifle in the depth of winter. I resolved to send her enough money for the journey, and to let her meet me in some French town.

M. de Fouquet, a friend of Madame d'Urfé's, was Governor of Metz, and I felt sure that, with a letter of introduction from Madame d'Urfé, this nobleman would give me a distinguished reception. Besides, his nephew, the Comte de Lastic, whom I knew well, was there with his regiment. For these reasons I chose Metz as a meeting-place with the virgin Corticelli, to whom this new part would certainly be a surprise. Madame d'Urfé gave me the necessary introductions, and I left Paris on January 25th, 1762, loaded with presents. I had a letter of credit to a large amount, but I did not make use of it as my purse was abundantly replenished.

I took no servant, for after Costa's robbing me and Le Duc's cheating me I felt as if I could not trust in anyone. I got to Metz in two days, and put up at the "Roi Dagobert," an excellent inn, where I found the Comte de Louvenhaupt, a Swede, whom I had met at the house of the Princess of Anhalt-Zerbst, mother of the Empress of Russia. He asked me to sup with him and the Duc de Deux Ponts, who was travelling incognito to Paris to visit Louis XV., whose constant friend he was.

The day after my arrival I took my letters to the governor, who told me I must dine with him every day. M. de Lastic had left Metz, much to my regret, as he would have contributed in no small degree to the pleasure of my stay. The same day I wrote to the Corticelli, sending her fifty louis, and telling her to come with her mother as soon as possible, and to get someone who knew the way to accompany her. She could not leave Prague before the beginning of Lent, and to make sure of her coming I promised that I would make her fortune.

In four or five days I knew my way about the town, but I did not frequent polite assemblies, preferring to go to the theatre, where a comic opera singer had captivated me. Her name was Raton, and she was only fifteen, after the fashion of actresses who always subtract at least two or three years from their age. However, this failing is common to women, and is a pardonable one, since to be youthful is the greatest of all advantages to them. Raton was not so much handsome as attractive, but what chiefly made her an object of desire was the fact that she had put the price of twenty-five louis on her maidenhead. One could spend a night with her, and make the trial for a louis; the twenty-five were only to be paid on the accomplishment of the great work.

It was notorious that numerous officers in the army and young barristers had undertaken the operation unsuccessfully, and all of them had paid a louis apiece.

This singular case was enough to whet my curiosity. I was not long before I called on Raton, but not wishing to be duped by her I took due precautions. I told her that she must come and sup with me, and that I would give her the twenty-five louis if my happiness was complete, and that if I were unsuccessful she should have six louis instead of one, provided that she was not tied. Her aunt assured me that this was not the case; but I could not help thinking of Victorine.

Raton came to supper with her aunt, who went to bed in an adjoining closet when the dessert was brought in. The girl's figure was exquisitely beautiful, and I felt that I had no small task before me. She was kind, laughing, and defied me to the conquest of a fleece not of gold, but of ebony, which the youth of Metz had assaulted in vain. Perhaps the reader will think that I, who was no longer in my first vigour, was discouraged by the thought of the many who had failed; but I knew my powers, and it only amused me. Her former lovers had been Frenchmen, more skilled in carrying strong places by assault than in eluding the artfulness of a girl who corked herself up. I was an Italian, and knew all about that, so I had no doubts as to my victory.

However, my preparations were superfluous; for as soon as Raton felt from my mode of attack that the trick would be of no avail she met my desires half-way, without trying the device which had made her seem to be what she was no longer to her inexpert lovers. She gave herself up in good faith, and when I had promised to keep the secret her ardours were equal to mine. It was not her first trial, and I consequently need not have given her the twenty-five louis, but I was well satisfied, and not caring much for maidenheads rewarded her as if I had been the first to bite at the cherry.

I kept Raton at a louis a day till the arrival of the Corticelli, and she had to be faithful to me, as I never let her go out of my sight. I liked the girl so well and found her so pleasant that I was sorry that the Corticelli was coming; however, I was told of her arrival one night just as I was leaving my box at the theatre. My foot-man told me in a loud voice that my lady wife, my daughter, and a gentleman had just arrived from Frank-fort, and were awaiting me at the inn.

"Idiot," I exclaimed, "I have no wife and no daugh-ter."

However, all Metz heard that my family had arrived.

The Corticelli threw her arms round my neck, laugh-ing as usual, and her mother presented me to the worthy man who had accompanied them from Prague to Metz. He was an Italian named Monti, who had lived for a long time at Prague, where he taught his native language. I saw that M. Monti and the old woman were suitably accommodated, and I then led the young fool into my room. I found her changed for the better; she had grown, her shape was improved, and her pleasant man-ners made her a very charming girl.

CHAPTER XV

I Returned to Paris With The Corticelli, Now Countess Lascaris—The Hypostasis Fails—Aixla-Chapelle— Duel—Mimi d'Aché—The Corticelli Turns Traitress to Her Own Disadvantage—Journey to Sulzbach

WHY did you allow your mother to call herself my wife, little simpleton? Do you think that's a compliment to my judgment? She might have given herself out for your governess, as she wishes to pass you off as my daughter."

"My mother is an obstinate old woman who had rather be whipped at the cart-tail than call herself my governess. She has very narrow ideas, and always thinks that governess and procuress mean the same thing."

"She's an old fool, but we will make her hear reason either with her will or in spite of it. But you look well dressed, have you made your fortune?"

"At Prague I captivated the affections of Count N——, and he proved a generous lover. But let your first action be to send back M. Monti. The worthy man has his family at Prague to look after; he can't afford to stay long here."

"True, I will see about it directly."

The coach started for Frankfort the same evening, and summoning Monti I thanked him for his kindness and paid him generously, so he went off well pleased.

I had nothing further to do at Metz, so I took leave of my new friends, and in two days time I was at Nancy, where I wrote to Madame d'Urfé that I was on my way back with a virgin, the last of the family of Lascaris, who had once reigned at Constantinople. I begged her to receive her from my hands, at a country house which belonged to her, where we should be occupied for some days in cabalistic ceremonies.

She answered that she would await us at Pont-Carré, an old castle four leagues distant from Paris, and that she would welcome the young princess with all possible kindness.

"I owe her all the more friendship," added the sublime madwoman, "as the family of Lascaris is connected with the family of d'Urfé, and as I am to be born again in the seed of the happy virgin."

I felt that my task would be not exactly to throw cold water on her enthusiasm, but to hold it in check and to moderate its manifestations. I therefore explained to her by return of post that she must be content to treat the virgin as a countess, not a princess, and I ended by informing her that we should arrive, accompanied by the countess's governess, on the Monday of Holy Week.

I spent twelve days at Nancy, instructing the young madcap in the part she had to play, and endeavouring to persuade her mother that she must content herself with being the Countess Lascaris's humble servant. It was a task of immense difficulty; it was not enough to shew her that our success depended on her submitting; I had to threaten to send her back to Bologna by herself. I had good reason to repent of my perseverance. That woman's obstinacy was an inspiration of my good angel's, bidding me avoid the greatest mistake I ever made.

On the day appointed we reached Pont-Carré. Madame d'Urfé, whom I had advised of the exact hour of our arrival, had the drawbridge of the castle lowered, and stood in the archway in the midst of her people, like a general surrendering with all the honours of war. The dear lady, whose madness was but an excess of wit, gave the false princess so distinguished a reception that she would have shewn her amazement if I had not warned her of what she might expect. Thrice did she clasp her to her breast with a tenderness that was quite maternal, calling her her beloved niece, and explaining the entire pedigrees of the families of Lascaris and d'Urfé to make the countess understand how she came to be her niece. I was agreeably surprised to see the polite and dignified air with which the Italian wench listened to all this; she did not even smile, though the scene must have struck her as extremely laughable.

As soon as we got into the castle Madame d'Urfé proceeded to cense the new-comer, who received the attention with all the dignity of an opera queen, and then threw herself into the arms of the priestess, who received her with enthusiastic affection.

At dinner the countess was agreeable and talkative, which won her Madame d'Urfé's entire favour; her broken French being easily accounted for. Laura, the countess's mother, only knew her native Italian, and so kept silence. She was given a comfortable room, where her meals were brought to her, and which she only left to hear mass.

The castle was a fortified building, and had sustained several sieges in the civil wars. As its name, Pont-Carré, indicated, it was square, and was flanked by four crenelated towers and surrounded by a broad moat. The rooms were vast, and richly furnished in an old-fashioned way. The air was full of venomous gnats who devoured us and covered our faces with painful bites; but I had

agreed to spend a week there, and I should have been
hard put to it to find a pretext for shortening the time.
Madame d'Urfé had a bed next her own for her niece,
but I was not afraid of her attempting to satisfy herself
as to the countess's virginity, as the oracle had expressly
forbidden it under pain or failure. The operation was
fixed for the fourteenth day of the April moon.

On that day we had a temperate supper, after which
I went to bed. A quarter of an hour afterwards Madame
d'Urfé came, leading the virgin Lascaris. She undressed
her, scented her, cast a lovely veil over her body, and
when the countess was laid beside me she remained,
wishing to be present at an operation which was to result
in her being born again in the course of nine months.

The act was consummated in form, and then Madame
d'Urfé left us alone for the rest of the night, which was
well employed. Afterwards, the countess slept with her
aunt till the last day of the moon, when I asked the
oracle if the Countess Lascaris had conceived. That
well might be, for I had spared nothing to that intent;
but I thought it more prudent to make the oracle reply
that the operation had failed because the small Count
d'Aranda had watched us behind a screen. Madame
d'Urfé was in despair, but I consoled her by a second
reply, in which the oracle declared that though the operation could only be performed in France in April, it could
take place out of that realm in May; but the inquisitive
young count, whose influence had proved so fatal, must
be sent for at least a year to some place a hundred
leagues from Paris. The oracle also indicated the manner in which he was to travel; he was to have a tutor, a
servant, and all in order.

The oracle had spoken, and no more was wanted.
Madame d'Urfé thought of an abbé she liked for his

tutor, and the count was sent to Lyons, with strong letters of commendation to M. de Rochebaron, a relation
of his patroness. The young man was delighted to travel,
and never had any suspicion of the way in which I had
slandered him. It was not a mere fancy which suggested
this course of action. I had discovered that the Corticelli
was making up to him, and that her mother favoured the
intrigue. I had surprised her twice in the young man's
room, and though he only cared for the girl as a youth
cares for all girls, the Signora Laura did not at all approve of my opposing her daughter's designs.

Our next task was to fix on some foreign town where
we could again attempt the mysterious operation. We
settled on Aix-la-Chapelle, and in five or six days all
was ready for the journey.

The Corticelli, angry with me for having thwarted
her in her projects, reproached me bitterly, and from
that time began to be my enemy; she even allowed herself to threaten me if I did not get back the pretty boy,
as she called him.

"You have no business to be jealous," said she, "and
I am the mistress of my own actions."

"Quite right, my dear," I answered; "but it is my
business to see that you do not behave like a prostitute
in your present position."

The mother was in a furious rage, and said that she
and her daughter would return to Bologna, and to quiet
them I promised to take them there myself as soon as
we had been to Aix-la-Chapelle.

Nevertheless I did not feel at ease, and to prevent
any plots taking place I hastened our departure.

We started in May, in a travelling carriage containing Madame d'Urfé, myself, the false Lascaris, and her
maid and favourite, named Brougnole. We were fol-

lowed by a coach with two seats; in it were the Signora Laura and another servant. Two men-servants in full livery sat on the outside of our travelling carriage. We stopped a day at Brussels, and another at Liège. At Aix there were many distinguished visitors, and at the first ball we attended Madame d'Urfé presented the Lascaris to two Princesses of Mecklenburg as her niece. The false countess received their embraces with much ease and modesty, and attracted the particular attention of the Margrave of Baireuth and the Duchess of Würtemberg, his daughter, who took possession of her, and did not leave her till the end of the ball. I was on thorns the whole time, in terror lest the heroine might make some dreadful slip. She danced so gracefully that everybody gazed at her, and I was the person who was complimented on her performance. I suffered a martyrdom, for these compliments seemed to be given with malicious intent. I suspected that the ballet-girl had been discovered beneath the countess, and I felt myself dishonoured. I succeeded in speaking privately to the young wanton for a moment, and begged her to dance like a young lady, and not like a chorus girl; but she was proud of her success, and dared to tell me that a young lady might know how to dance as well as a professional dancer, and that she was not going to dance badly to please me. I was so enraged with her impudence, that I would have cast her off that instant if it had been possible; but as it was not, I determined that her punishment should lose none of its sharpness by waiting; and whether it be a vice or a virtue, the desire of revenge is never extinguished in my heart till it is satisfied.

The day after the ball Madame d'Urfé presented her

with a casket containing a beautiful watch set with brilliants, a pair of diamond ear-rings, and a ring containing a ruby of fifteen carats. The whole was worth sixty thousand francs. I took possession of it to prevent her going off without my leave.

In the meanwhile I amused myself with play and making bad acquaintances. The worst of all was a French officer, named d'Aché, who had a pretty wife and a daughter prettier still. Before long the daughter had taken possession of the heart which the Corticelli had lost, but as soon as Madame d'Aché saw that I preferred her daughter to herself she refused to receive me at her house.

I had lent d'Aché ten louis, and I consequently felt myself entitled to complain of his wife's conduct; but he answered rudely that as I only went to the house after his daughter, his wife was quite right; that he intended his daughter to make a good match, and that if my intentions were honourable I had only to speak to the mother. His manner was still more offensive than his words, and I felt enraged, but knowing the brutal drunken characteristics of the man, and that he was always ready to draw cold steel for a yes or a no, I was silent and resolved to forget the girl, not caring to become involved with a man like her father.

I had almost cured myself of my fancy when, a few days after our conversation, I happened to go into a billiard-room where d'Aché was playing with a Swiss named Schmit, an officer in the Swedish army. As soon as d'Aché saw me he asked whether I would lay the ten louis he owed me against him.

"Yes," said I, "that will make double or quits."

Towards the end of the match d'Aché made an unfair

stroke, which was so evident that the marker told him of it; but as this stroke made him the winner, d'Aché seized the stakes and put them in his pocket without heeding the marker or the other player, who, seeing himself cheated before his very eyes, gave the rascal a blow across the face with his cue. D'Aché parried the blow with his hand, and drawing his sword rushed at Schmit, who had no arms. The marker, a sturdy young fellow, caught hold of d'Aché round the body, and thus prevented murder. The Swiss went out, saying,——

"We shall see each other again."

The rascally Frenchman cooled down, and said to me,——

"Now, you see, we are quits."

"Very much quits."

"That's all very well; but, by God! you might have prevented the insult which has dishonoured me."

"I might have done so, but I did not care to interfere. You are strong enough to look after yourself. Schmit had not his sword, but I believe him to be a brave man; and he will give you satisfaction if you will return him his money, for there can be no doubt that you lost the match."

An officer, named de Pyène, took me up and said that he himself would give me the twenty louis which d'Aché had taken, but that the Swiss must give satisfaction. I had no hesitation in promising that he would do so, and said I would bring a reply to the challenge the next morning.

I had no fears myself. The man of honour ought always to be ready to use the sword to defend himself from insult, or to give satisfaction for an insult he has offered. I know that the law of duelling is a prejudice which may be called, and perhaps rightly, barbarous, but it is a prejudice which no man of honour can contend against, and I believed Schmit to be a thorough gentleman.

I called on him at day-break, and found him still in bed. As soon as he saw me, he said,——

"I am sure you have come to ask me to fight with d'Aché. I am quite ready to burn powder with him, but he must first pay me the twenty louis he robbed me of."

"You shall have them to-morrow, and I will attend you. D'Aché will be seconded by M. de Pyène."

"Very good. I shall expect you at day-break."

Two hours after I saw de Pyène, and we fixed the meeting for the next day, at six o'clock in the morning. The arms were to be pistols. We chose a garden, half a league from the town, as the scene of the combat.

At day-break I found the Swiss waiting for me at the door of his lodgings, carolling the *ranz-des-vaches*, so dear to his fellow-countrymen. I thought that a good omen.

"Here you are," said he; "let us be off, then."

On the way, he observed, "I have only fought with men of honour up to now, and I don't much care for killing a rascal; it's hangman's work."

"I know," I replied, "that it's very hard to have to risk one's life against a fellow like that."

"There's no risk," said Schmit, with a laugh. "I am certain that I shall kill him."

"How can you be certain?"

"I shall make him tremble."

He was right. This secret is infallible when it is applied to a coward. We found d'Aché and de Pyène on the field, and five or six others who must have been present from motives of curiosity.

D'Aché took twenty louis from his pocket and gave them to his enemy, saying,——

"I may be mistaken, but I hope to make you pay dearly for your brutality." Then turning to me he said,——

"I owe you twenty louis also;" but I made no reply.

Schmit put the money in his purse with the calmest air imaginable, and making no reply to the other's boast placed himself between two trees, distant about four paces from one another, and drawing two pistols from his pocket said to d'Aché,——

"Place yourself at a distance of ten paces, and fire first. I shall walk to and fro between these two trees, and you may walk as far if you like to do so when my turn comes to fire."

Nothing could be clearer or more calmly delivered than this explanation.

"But we must decide," said I, "who is to have the first shot."

"There is no need," said Schmit. "I never fire first, besides, the gentleman has a right to the first shot."

De Pyène placed his friend at the proper distance and then stepped aside, and d'Aché fired on his antagonist, who was walking slowly to and fro without looking at him. Schmit turned round in the coolest manner possible, and said,——

"You have missed me, sir; I knew you would. Try again."

I thought he was mad, and that some arrangement would be come to; but nothing of the kind. D'Aché fired a second time, and again missed; and Schmit, without a word, but as calm as death, fired his first pistol in the air, and then covering d'Aché with his second pistol hit him in the forehead and stretched him dead on the ground. He put back his pistols into his pocket and went off directly by himself, as if he were merely continuing his walk. In two minutes I followed his example, after ascertaining that the unfortunate d'Aché no longer breathed.

I was in a state of amazement. Such a duel was more like a combat of romance than a real fact. I could not understand it; I had watched the Swiss, and had not noticed the slightest change pass over his face.

I breakfasted with Madame d'Urfé, whom I found inconsolable. It was the full moon, and at three minutes past four exactly I ought to perform the mysterious creation of the child in which she was to be born again. But the Lascaris, on whom the work was to be wrought, was twisting and turning in her bed, contorting herself in such a way that it would be impossible for me to accomplish the prolific work.

My grief, when I heard what had happened, was hypocritical; in the first place because I no longer felt any desire for the girl, and in the second because I thought I saw a way in which I could make use of the incident to take vengeance on her.

I lavished consolations on Madame d'Urfé; and on consulting the oracle I found that the Lascaris had been defiled by an evil genius, and that I must search for another virgin whose purity must be under the protection of more powerful spirits. I saw that my madwoman was perfectly happy with this, and I left her to visit the Corticelli, whom I found in bed with her mother beside her.

"You have convulsions, have you, dearest?" said I.

"No, I haven't. I am quite well, but all the same I shall have them till you give me back my jewel-casket."

"You are getting wicked, my poor child; this comes

of following your mother's advice. As for the casket, if you are going to behave like this, probably you will have it."

"I will reveal all."

"You will not be believed; and I shall send you back to Bologna without letting you take any of the presents which Madame d'Urfé has given you."

"You ought to have given me back the casket when I declared myself with child."

Signora Laura told me that this was only too true, though I was not the father.

"Who is, then?" I asked.

"Count N——, whose mistress she was at Prague."

It did not seem probable, as she had no symptoms of pregnancy; still it might be so. I was obliged to plot myself to bring the plots of these two rascally women to nought, and without saying anything to them I shut myself up with Madame d'Urfé to enquire of the oracle concerning the operation which was to make her happy.

After several answers, more obscure than any returned from the oracular tripod at Delphi, the interpretation of which I left to the infatuated Madame d'Urfé, she discovered herself—and I took care not to contradict her —that the Countess Lascaris had gone mad. I encouraged her fears, and succeeded in making her obtain from a cabalistic pyramid the statement that the reason the princess had not conceived was that she had been defiled by an evil genius—an enemy of the Fraternity of the Rosy Cross. This put Madame d'Urfé fairly on the way, and she added on her own account that the girl must be with child by a gnome.

She then erected another pyramid to obtain guidance on our quest, and I so directed things that the answer came that she must write to the moon.

This mad reply, which should have brought her to her senses, only made her more crazy than ever. She was quite ecstatic, and I am sure that if I had endeavoured to shew her the nothingness of all this I should have had nothing for my trouble. Her conclusion would probably have been that I was possessed by an evil spirit, and was no longer a true Rosy Cross. But I had no idea of undertaking a cure which would have done me harm and her no good. Her chimerical notions made her happy, and the cold naked truth would doubtless have made her unhappy.

She received the order to write to the moon with the greater delight as she knew what ceremonies were to be observed in addressing that planet; but she could not dispense with the assistance of an adept, and I knew she would reckon on me. I told her I should always be ready to serve her, but that, as she knew herself, we should have to wait for the first phase of the new moon. I was very glad to gain time, for I had lost heavily at play, and I could not leave Aix-la-Chapelle before a bill, which I had drawn on M. d'O—— of Amsterdam, was cashed. In the mean time we agreed that as the Countess Lascaris had become mad, we must not pay any attention to what she might say, as the words would not be hers but would proceed from the evil spirit who possessed her.

Nevertheless, we determined that as her state was a pitiable one, and should be as much alleviated as possible, she should continue to dine with us, but that in the evening she was to go to her governess and sleep with her.

After having thus disposed of Madame d'Urfé to disbelieve whatever the Corticelli cared to tell her, and to concentrate all her energies on the task of writing to

Selenis, the intelligence of the moon, I set myself seriously to work to regain the money I had lost at play;
and here my cabala was no good to me. I pledged the
Corticelli's casket for a thousand louis, and proceeded
to play in an English club where I had a much better
chance of winning than with Germans or Frenchmen.

Three or four days after d'Aché's death, his widow
wrote me a note begging me to call on her. I found
her in company with de Pyène. She told me in a lugu-
brious voice that her husband had left many debts un-
settled, and that his creditors had seized everything she
possessed; and that she was thus unable to pay the
expenses of a journey, though she wanted to take her
daughter with her to Colmar, and there to rejoin her
family.

"You caused my husband's death," she added, "and I
ask you to give me a thousand crowns; if you refuse me
I shall commence a lawsuit against you, for as the Swiss
officer has left, you are the only person I can prose-
cute."

"I am surprised at your taking such a tone towards
me," I replied, coldly, "and were it not for the respect
I feel for your misfortune, I should answer as bitterly
as you deserve. In the first place I have not a thousand
crowns to throw away, and if I had I would not sacrifice
my money to threats. I am curious to know what kind
of a case you could get up against me in the courts of
law. As for Schmit, he fought like a brave gentleman,
and I don't think you could get much out of him if he
were still here. Good-day, madam."

I had scarcely got fifty paces from the house when
I was joined by de Pyène, who said that rather than
Madame d'Aché should have to complain of me he would
cut my throat on the spot. We neither of us had swords.

"Your intention is not a very flattering one," said I, "and there is something rather brutal about it. I had rather not have any affair of the kind with a man whom I don't know and to whom I owe nothing."

"You are a coward."

"I would be, you mean, if I were to imitate you. It is a matter of perfect indifference to me what opinion you may have on the subject.

"You will be sorry for this."

"Maybe, but I warn you that I never go out unattended by a pair of pistols, which I keep in good order and know how to use." So saying I shewd him the pistols, and took one in my right hand.

At this the bully uttered an oath and we separated.

At a short distance from the place where this scene had occurred I met a Neapolitan named Maliterni, a lieutenant-colonel and *aide* to the Prince de Condé, commander-in-chief of the French army. This Maliterni was a boon companion, always ready to oblige, and always short of money. We were friends, and I told him what had happened.

"I should be sorry," said I, "to have anything to do with a fellow like de Pyène, and if you can rid me of him I promise you a hundred crowns."

"I daresay that can be managed," he replied, "and I will tell you what I can do to-morrow."

In point of fact, he brought me news the next day that my cut-throat had received orders from his superior officer to leave Aix-la-Chapelle at day-break, and at the same time he gave me a passport from the Prince de Condé.

I confess that this was very pleasant tidings. I have never feared to cross my sword with any man, though I never sought the barbarous pleasure of spilling men's

blood; but on this occasion I felt an extreme dislike to
a duel with a fellow who was probably of the same caste
as his friend d'Aché.

I therefore gave Maliterni my heartiest thanks, as well
as the hundred crowns I had promised him, which I considered so well employed that I did not regret their loss.

Maliterni, who was a jester of the first water, and a
creature of the Marshal d'Estrées, was lacking neither
in wit nor knowledge; but he was deficient in a sense of
order and refinement. He was a pleasant companion, for
his gaiety was inexhaustible and he had a large knowledge of the world. He attained the rank of field-marshal
in 1768, and went to Naples to marry a rich heiress,
whom he left a widow a year after.

The day after de Pyène's departure I received a note
from Mdlle. d'Aché, begging me, for the sake of her
sick mother, to come and see her. I answered that I
would be at such a place at such a time, and that she
could say what she liked to me.

I found her at the place and time I appointed, with
her mother, whose illness, it appeared, did not prevent
her from going out. She called me her persecutor, and
said that since the departure of her best friend, de
Pyène, she did not know where to turn; that she had
pledged all her belongings, and that I, who was rich,
ought to aid her, if I were not the vilest of men.

"I feel for your condition," I replied, "as I feel your
abuse of me; and I cannot help saying that you have
shewn yourself the vilest of women in inciting de Pyène,
who may be an honest man for all I know, to assassinate
me. In fine, rich or not, and though I owe you nothing,
I will give you enough money to take your property
out of pawn, and I may possibly take you to Colmar

myself, but you must first consent to my giving your
charming daughter a proof of my affection."

"And you dare to make this horrible proposal to me?"

"Horrible or not, I do make it."

"I will never consent."

"Good day, madam."

I called the waiter to pay him for the refreshments
I had ordered, and I gave the girl six double louis, but
her proud mother forbade her to accept the money from
me. I was not surprised, in spite of her distress; for the
mother was in reality still more charming than the
daughter, and she knew it. I ought to have given her
the preference, and thus have ended the dispute, but
who can account for his whims? I felt that she must
hate me, for she did not care for her daughter, and it
must have humiliated her bitterly to be obliged to
regard her as a victorious rival.

I left them still holding the six double louis, which
pride or scorn had refused, and I went to the faro-table
and decided in sacrificing them to fortune; but that
capricious deity, as proud as the haughty widow, refused
them, and though I left them on the board for five deals
I almost broke the bank. An Englishman, named Martin, offered to go shares with me, and I accepted, as I
knew he was a good player; and in the course of eight
or ten days we did such good business that I was not
only able to take the casket out of pledge and to cover
all losses, but made a considerable profit in addition.

About this period, the Corticelli, in her rage against
me, had told Madame d'Urfé the whole history of her
life, of our acquaintance, and of her pregnancy. But
the more truthfully she told her story so much the more
did the good lady believe her to be mad, and we often

laughed together at the extraordinary fancies of the traitress. Madame d'Urfé put all her trust in the instructions which Selenis would give in reply to her letter.

Nevertheless, as the girl's conduct displeased me, I made her eat her meals with her mother, while I kept Madame d'Urfé company. I assured her that we should easily find another vessel of election, the madness of the Countess Lascaris having made her absolutely incapable of participating in our mysterious rites.

Before long, d'Aché's widow found herself obliged to give me her Mimi; but I won her by kindness, and in such a way that the mother could pretend with decency to know nothing about it. I redeemed all the goods she had pawned, and although the daughter had not yet yielded entirely to my ardour, I formed the plan of taking them to Colmar with Madame d'Urfé. To make up the good lady's mind, I resolved to let that be one of the instructions from the moon, and this she would not only obey blindly but would have no suspicions as to my motive.

I managed the correspondence between Selenis and Madame d'Urfé in the following manner:

On the day appointed, we supped together in a garden beyond the town walls, and in a room on the ground floor of the house I had made all the necessary preparations, the letter which was to fall from the moon, in reply to Madame d'Urfé's epistle, being in my pocket. At a little distance from the chamber of ceremonies I had placed a large bath filled with lukewarm water and perfumes pleasing to the deity of the night, into which we were to plunge at the hour of the moon, which fell at one o'clock.

When we had burnt incense, and sprinkled the essences appropriate to the cult of Selenis, we took off all our clothes, and holding the letter concealed in my left hand, with the right I graciously led Madame d'Urfé to the brink of the bath. Here stood an alabaster cup containing spirits of wine which I kindled, repeating magical words which I did not understand, but which she said after me, giving me the letter addressed to Selenis. I burnt the letter in the flame of the spirits, beneath the light of the moon, and the credulous lady told me she saw the characters she had traced ascending in the rays of the planet.

We then got into the bath, and the letter, which was written in silver characters on green paper appeared on the surface of the water in the course of ten minutes. As soon as Madame d'Urfé saw it, she picked it up reverently and got out of the bath with me.

We dried and scented ourselves, and proceeded to put on our clothes. As soon as we were in a state of decency I told Madame d'Urfé that she might read the epistle, which she had placed on a scented silk cushion. She obeyed, and I saw sadness visibly expressed on her features when she saw that her hypostasis was deferred till the arrival of Querilinthus, whom she would see with me at Marseilles in the spring of next year. The genius also said that the Countess Lascaris could not only do her harm, and that she should consult me as to the best means of getting rid of her. The letter ended by ordering her not to leave at Aix a lady who had lost her husband, and had a daughter who was destined to be of great service to the fraternity of the R. C. She was to take them to Alsace, and not to leave them till they were there, and safe from that danger which threatened them if they were left to themselves.

Madame d'Urfé, who with all her folly was an exceedingly benevolent woman, commended the widow to

my care enthusiastically, and seemed impatient to hear
her whole history. I told her all the circumstances which
I thought would strengthen her in her resolution to be-
friend them, and promised to introduce the ladies to
them at the first opportunity.

We returned to Aix, and spent the night in discussing
the phantoms which coursed through her brain. All
was going on well, and my only care was for the journey
to Aix, and how to obtain the complete enjoyment of
Mimi after having so well deserved her favours.

I had a run of luck at play the next day, and in the
evening I gave Madame d'Aché an agreeable surprise
by telling her that I should accompany her and her
Mimi to Colmar. I told her that I should begin by
introducing her to the lady whom I had the honour to
accompany, and I begged her to be ready by the next
day as the marchioness was impatient to see her. I
could see that she could scarcely believe her ears, for
she thought Madame d'Urfé was in love with me, and
she could not understand her desire to make the acquaintance of two ladies who might be dangerous rivals.

I conducted them to Madame d'Urfé at the appointed
hour, and they were received with a warmth which surprised them exceedingly, for they could not be expected
to know that their recommendation came from the
moon. We made a party of four, and while the two
ladies talked together in the fashion of ladies who have
seen the world, I paid Mimi a particular attention, which
her mother understood very well, but which Madame
d'Urfé attributed to the young lady's connection with
the Rosy Cross.

In the evening we all went to a ball, and there the
Corticelli, who was always trying to annoy me, danced
as no young lady would dance. She executed rapid steps,

pirouetted, cut capers, and shewed her legs; in short, she behaved like a ballet-girl. I was on thorns. An officer, who either ignored, or pretended to ignore, my supposed relation to her, asked me if she was a professional dancer. I heard another man behind me say that he thought he remembered seeing her on the boards at Prague. I resolved on hastening my departure, as I foresaw that if I stayed much longer at Aix the wretched girl would end by costing me my life.

As I have said, Madame d'Aché had a good society manner, and this put her in Madame d'Urfé's good graces, who saw in her politeness a new proof of the favour of Selenis. Madame d'Aché felt, I suppose, that she owed me some return after all I had done for her, and left the ball early, so that when I took Mimi home I found myself alone with her, and at perfect liberty to do what I liked. I profited by the opportunity, and remained with Mimi for two hours, finding her so complaisant and even passionate that when I left her I had nothing more to desire.

In three days time I provided the mother and daughter with their outfit, and we left Aix gladly in an elegant and convenient travelling carriage which I had provided. Half an hour before we left I made an acquaintance which afterwards proved fatal to me. A Flemish officer, unknown to me, accosted me, and painted his destitute condition in such sad colours that I felt obliged to give him twelve louis. Ten minutes after, he gave me a paper in which he acknowledged the debt, and named the time in which he could pay it. From the paper I ascertained that his name was Malingan. In ten months the reader will hear the results.

Just as we were starting I shewed the Corticelli a carriage with four places, in which she, her mother, and

the two maids, were to travel. At this she trembled,
her pride was wounded, and for a moment I thought she
was going out of her mind; she rained sobs, abuse, and
curses on me. I stood the storm unmoved, however, and
Madame d'Urfé only laughed at her niece's paroxysms,
and seemed delighted to find herself sitting opposite to
me with the servant of Selenis beside her, while Mimi
was highly pleased to be so close to me.

We got to Liège at nightfall on the next day, and I
contrived to make Madame d'Urfé stay there the day
following, wishing to get horses to take us through the
Ardennes, and thus to have the charming Mimi longer in
my possession.

I rose early and went out to see the town. By the
great bridge, a woman, so wrapped up in a black mantilla that only the tip of her nose was visible, accosted
me, and asked me to follow her into a house with an
open door which she shewed me.

"As I have not the pleasure of knowing you," I replied, "prudence will not allow me to do so."

"You do know me, though," she replied, and taking
me to the corner of a neighbouring street she shewed me
her face. What was my surprise to see the fair Stuart
of Avignon, the statue of the Fountain of Vaucluse. I
was very glad to meet her.

In my curiosity I followed her into the house, to a
room on the first floor, where she welcomed me most
tenderly. It was all no good, for I felt angry with her,
and despised her advances, no doubt, because I had
Mimi, and wished to keep all my love for her. However,
I took three louis out of my purse and gave them to
her, asking her to tell me her history.

"Stuart," she said, "was only my keeper; my real
name is Ranson, and I am the mistress of a rich landed

proprietor. I got back to Liège after many sufferings."

"I am delighted to hear that you are more prosperous now, but it must be confessed that your behaviour at Avignon was both preposterous and absurd. But the subject is not worth discussing. Good day, madam."

I then returned to my hotel to write an account of what I had seen to the Marquis Grimaldi.

The next day we left Liège, and were two days passing through the Ardennes. This is one of the strangest tracts in Europe: a vast forest, the traditions of which furnished Ariosto with some splendid passages.

There is no town in the forest, and though one is obliged to cross it to pass from one country to another, hardly any of the necessaries of life are to be found in it.

The enquirer will seek in vain for vices or virtues, or manners of any kind. The inhabitants are devoid of correct ideas, but have wild notions of their own on the power of men they style scholars. It is enough to be a doctor to enjoy the reputation of an astrologer and a wizard. Nevertheless the Ardennes have a large population, as I was assured that there were twelve hundred churches in the forest. The people are good-hearted and even pleasant, especially the young girls; but as a general rule the fair sex is by no means fair in those quarters. In this vast district watered by the Meuse is the town of Bouillon—a regular hole, but in my time it was the freest place in Europe. The Duke of Bouillon was so jealous of his rights that he preferred the exercise of his prerogatives to all the honours he might have enjoyed at the Court of France. We stayed a day at Metz, but did not call on anyone; and in three days we reached Colmar, where we left Madame d'Aché, whose good graces I had completely won. Her family, in extremely comfortable circumstances, received the mother and daughter with great affection. Mimi wept bitterly when I left her, but I consoled her by saying that I would come back before long. Madame d'Urfé seemed not to mind leaving them, and I consoled myself easily enough. While congratulating myself on having made mother and daughter happy, I adored the secret paths and ways of Divine Providence.

On the following day we went to Sulzbach, where the Baron of Schaumburg, who knew Madame d'Urfé, gave us a warm welcome. I should have been sadly boared in this dull place if it had not been for gaming. Madame d'Urfé, finding herself in need of company, encouraged the Corticelli to hope to regain my good graces, and, consequently, her own. The wretched girl, seeing how easily I had defeated her projects, and to what a pass of humiliation I had brought her, had changed her part, and was now submissive enough. She flattered herself that she would regain the favour she had completely lost, and she thought the day was won when she saw that Madame d'Aché and her daughter stayed at Colmar. But what she had more at heart than either my friendship or Madame d'Urfé's was the jewel-casket; but she dared not ask for it, and her hopes of seeing it again were growing dim. By her pleasantries at table which made Madame d'Urfé laugh she succeeded in giving me a few amorous twinges; but still I did not allow my feelings to relax my severity, and she continued to sleep with her mother.

A week after our arrival at Sulzbach I left Madame d'Urfé with the Baron of Schaumburg, and I went to Colmar in the hope of good fortune. But I was disappointed, as the mother and daughter had both made arrangements for getting married.

A rich merchant, who had been in love with the mother eighteen years before, seeing her a widow and still pretty, felt his early flames revive, and offered his hand and was accepted. A young advocate found Mimi to his taste, and asked her in marriage. The mother and daughter, fearing the results of my affection, and finding it would be a good match, lost no time in giving their consent. I was entertained in the family, and supped in the midst of a numerous and choice assemblage; but seeing that I should only annoy the ladies and tire myself in waiting for some chance favour if I stayed, I bade them adieu and returned to Sulzbach the next morning. I found there a charming girl from Strasburg, named Salzmann, three or four gamesters who had come to drink the waters, and several ladies, to whom I shall introduce the reader in the ensuing chapter.

CHAPTER XVI

I Send The Corticelli to Turin—Helen is Initiated Into The Mysteries of Love—I Go to Lyons—My Arrival at Turin

ONE of the ladies, Madame Saxe, was intended by nature to win the devotion of a man of feeling; and if she had not had a jealous officer in her train who never let her go out of his sight, and seemed to threaten anyone who aspired to please, she would probably have had plenty of admirers. This officer was fond of piquet, but the lady was always obliged to sit close beside him, which she seemed to do with pleasure.

In the afternoon I played with him, and continued doing so for five or six days. After that I could stand it no longer, as when he had won ten or twelve louis he invariably rose and left me to myself. His name was d'Entragues; he was a fine-looking man, though somewhat thin, and had a good share of wit and knowledge of the world.

We had not played together for two days, when one afternoon he asked if I would like to take my revenge.

"No, I think not," said I, "for we don't play on the same principle. I play for amusement's sake and you play to win money."

"What do you mean? Your words are offensive."

"I didn't mean them to be offensive, but as a matter of fact, each time we have played you have risen after a quarter of an hour."

"You ought to be obliged to me, as otherwise you would have lost heavily."

"Possibly; but I don't think so."

"I can prove it to you."

"I accept the offer, but the first to leave the table must forfeit fifty louis."

"I agree; but money down."

"I never play on credit."

I ordered a waiter to bring cards, and I went to fetch four or five rolls of a hundred louis each. We began playing for five louis the game, each player putting down the fifty louis wagered.

We began to play at three, and at nine o'clock d'Entragues said we might take some supper.

"I am not hungry," I replied, "but you can go if you want me to put the hundred louis in my pocket."

He laughed at this and went on playing, but this lady fair scowled at me, though I did not care in the least for that. All the guests went to supper, and returned to keep us company till midnight, but at that hour we found ourselves alone. D'Entragues saw what kind of man he had got hold of and said never a word, while I only opened my lips to score; we played with the utmost coolness.

At six o'clock the ladies and gentlemen who were taking the waters began to assemble. We were applauded for our determination, in spite of our grim looks. The louis were on the table; I had lost a hundred, and yet the game was going in my favour.

At nine the fair Madame Saxe put in an appearance, and shortly after Madame d'Urfé came in with M. de Schaumburg. Both ladies advised us to take a cup of chocolate. D'Entragues was the first to consent, and thinking that I was almost done he said,——

"Let us agree that the first man who asks for food, who absents himself for more than a quarter of an hour, or who falls asleep in his chair, loses the bet."

"I will take you at your word," I replied, "and I adhere to all your conditions."

The chocolate came, we took it, and proceeded with our play. At noon we were summoned to dinner, but we both replied that we were not hungry. At four o'clock we allowed ourselves to be persuaded into taking some soup. When supper-time came and we were still playing, people began to think that the affair was getting serious, and Madame Saxe urged us to divide the wager. D'Entragues, who had won a hundred louis, would have gladly consented, but I would not give in, and M. de Schaumburg pronounced me within my rights. My adversary might have abandoned the stake and still found himself with a balance to the good, but avarice rather than pride prevented his doing so. I felt the loss myself, but what I cared chiefly about was the point of honour. I still looked fresh, while he resembled a disinterred corpse. As Madame Saxe urged me strongly to give way, I answered that I felt deeply grieved at not being able to satisfy such a charming woman, but that there was a question of honour in the case; and I was determined not to yield to my antagonist if I sat there till I fell dead to the ground.

I had two objects in speaking thus: I wanted to frighten him and to make him jealous of me. I felt certain that a man in a passion of jealousy would be quite confused, and I hoped his play would suffer accordingly, and that I should not have the mortification of losing a hundred louis to his superior play, though I won the fifty louis of the wager.

The fair Madame Saxe gave me a glance of contempt

and left us, but Madame d'Urfé, who believed I was infallible, avenged me by saying to d'Entragues, in a tone of the profoundest conviction,——

"O Lord! I pity you, sir."

The company did not return after supper, and we were left alone to our play. We played on all the night, and I observed my antagonist's face as closely as the cards. He began to lose his composure, and made mistakes, his cards got mixed up, and his scoring was wild. I was hardly less done up than he; I felt myself growing weaker, and I hoped to see him fall to the ground every moment, as I began to be afraid of being beaten in spite of the superior strength of my constitution. I had won back my money by day-break, and I cavilled with him for being away for more than a quarter of an hour. This quarrel about nothing irritated him, and roused me up; the difference of our natures produced these different results, and my stratagem succeeded because it was impromptu, and could not have been foreseen. In the same way in war, sudden stratagems succeed.

At nine o'clock Madame Saxe came in, her lover was losing.

"Now, sir," she said to me, "you may fairly yield."

"Madam," said I, "in hope of pleasing you, I will gladly divide the stakes and rise from the table."

The tone of exaggerated gallantry with which I pronounced these words, put d'Entragues into a rage, and he answered sharply that he would not desist till one of us was dead.

With a glance at the lady which was meant to be lovelorn, but which must have been extremely languid in my exhausted state, I said,——

"You see, Madam, that I am not the more obstinate of the two."

A dish of soup was served to us, but d'Entragues, who was in the last stage of exhaustion, had no sooner swallowed the soup than he fell from his chair in a dead faint. He was soon taken up, and after I had given six louis to the marker who had been watching for forty-eight hours, I pocketed the gold, and went to the apothecary's where I took a mild emetic. Afterwards I went to bed and slept for a few hours, and at three o'clock I made an excellent dinner.

D'Entragues remained in his room till the next day. I expected a quarrel, but the night brings counsel, and I made a mistake. As soon as he saw me he ran up to me and embraced me, saying,——

"I made a silly bet, but you have given me a lesson which will last me all my days, and I am much obliged to you for it."

"I am delighted to hear it, provided that your health has not suffered."

"No, I am quite well, but we will play no more together."

"Well, I hope we shan't play against each other any more."

In the course of eight or ten days I took Madame d'Urfé and the pretended Lascaris to Bâle. We put up at the inn of the famous Imhoff, who swindled us, but, all the same, the "Three Kings" is the best inn in the town. I think I have noted that noon at Bâle is at eleven o'clock—an absurdity due to some historic event, which I had explained to me but have forgotten. The inhabitants are said to be subject to a kind of madness, of which they are cured by taking the waters of Sulzbach; but they get it again as soon as they return.

We should have stayed at Bâle some time, if it had

not been for an incident which made me hasten our departure. It was as follows:

My necessities had obliged me to forgive the Corticelli to a certain extent, and when I came home early I spent the night with her; but when I came home late, as often happened, I slept in my own room. The little hussy, in the latter case, slept also alone in a room next to her mother's, through whose chamber one had to pass to get to the daughter's.

One night I came in at one o'clock, and not feeling inclined to sleep, I took a candle and went in search of my charmer. I was rather surprised to find Signora Laura's door half open, and just as I was going in the old woman came forward and took me by the arm, begging me not to go into her daughter's room.

"Why?" said I.

"She has been very poorly all the evening, and she is in need of sleep."

"Very good; then I will sleep too."

So saying I pushed the mother to one side, and entering the girl's room I found her in bed with someone who was hiding under the sheets.

I gazed at the picture for a moment and then began to laugh, and sitting down on the bed begged to enquire the name of the happy individual whom I should have the pleasure of throwing out of the window. On a chair I saw the coat, trousers, hat, and cane of the gentleman; but as I had my two trusty pistols about me I knew I had nothing to fear; however, I did not want to make a noise.

With tears in her eyes, and trembling all over, the girl took my hand and begged me to forgive her.

"It's a young lord," said she, "and I don't even know his name."

"Oh, he is a young lord, is he? and you don't know his name, you little hussy, don't you? Well, he will tell me himself."

So saying, I took a pistol and vigorously stripped the sheets off the cuckoo who had got into my nest. I saw the face of a young man whom I did not know, his head covered with a nightcap, but the rest perfectly naked, as indeed was my mistress. He turned his back to me to get his shirt which he had thrown on the floor, but seizing him by the arm I held him firmly, with my pistol to his forehead.

"Kindly tell me your name, fair sir."

"I am Count B——, canon of Bâle."

"And do you think you have been performing an ecclesiastical function here?"

"No sir, no, and I hope you will forgive me and the lady too, for I am the only guilty party."

"I am not asking you whether she is guilty or not."

"Sir, the countess is perfectly innocent."

I felt in a good temper, and far from being angry I was strongly inclined to laugh. I found the picture before me an attractive one; it was amusing and voluptuous. The sight of the two nudities on the bed was a truly lascivious one, and I remained contemplating it in silence for a quarter of an hour, occupied in resisting a strong temptation to take off my clothes and lie beside them. The only thing which prevented my yielding to it was the fear that I might find the canon to be a fool, incapable of playing the part with dignity. As for the Corticelli, she soon passed from tears to laughter, and would have done it well, but if, as I feared, the canon was a blockhead, I should have been degrading myself.

I felt certain that neither of them had guessed my

thoughts, so I rose and told the canon to put on his clothes.

"No one must hear anything more of this," said I, "but you and I will go to a distance of two hundred paces and burn a little powder."

"No, no, sir," cried my gentleman, "you may take me where you like, and kill me if you please, but I was not meant for a fighting man."

"Really?"

"Yes, sir, and I only became a priest to escape the fatal duty of duelling."

"Then you are a coward, and will not object to a good thrashing?"

"Anything you like, but it would be cruelty, for my love blinded me. I only came here a quarter of an hour ago, and the countess and her governess were both asleep."

"You are a liar."

"I had only just taken off my shirt when you came, and I have never seen this angel before."

"And that's gospel truth," said the Corticelli.

"Are you aware that you are a couple of impudent scoundrels? And as for you, master canon, you deserve to be roasted like St. Laurence."

In the meanwhile the wretched ecclesiastic had huddled on his clothes.

"Follow me, sir," said I, in a tone which froze the marrow of his bones; and I accordingly took him to my room.

"What will you do," said I, "if I forgive you and let you go without putting you to shame?"

"I will leave in an hour and a half, and you shall never see me here again; but even if we meet in the

future, you will find me always ready to do you a
service."

"Very good. Begone, and in the future take more
precautions in your amorous adventures."

After this I went to bed, well pleased with what I had
seen and what I had done, for I now had complete
power over the Corticelli.

In the morning I called on her as soon as I got up,
and told her to pack up her things, forbidding her to
leave her room till she got into the carriage.

"I shall say I am ill."

"Just as you please, but nobody will take any notice
of you."

I did not wait for her to make any further objections,
but proceeded to tell the tale of what had passed to
Madame d'Urfé, slightly embroidering the narrative. She
laughed heartily, and enquired of the oracle what must
be done with the Lascaris after her evident pollution by
the evil genius disguised as a priest. The oracle replied
that we must set out the next day for Besançon, whence
she would go to Lyons and await me there, while I would
take the countess to Geneva, and thus send her back to
her native country.

The worthy visionary was enchanted with this arrangement, and saw in it another proof of the benevolence of Selenis, who would thus give her an opportunity
of seeing young Aranda once more. It was agreed that
I was to rejoin her in the spring of the following year,
to perform the great operation which was to make her
be born a man. She had not the slightest doubts as to
the reasonableness of this performance.

All was ready, and the next day we started; Madame
d'Urfé and I in the travelling carriage, and the Corti-

celli, her mother, and the servants in another convey-
ance.

When we got to Besançon Madame d'Urfé left me,
and on the next day I journeyed towards Geneva with
the mother and daughter.

On the way I not only did not speak to my companions, I did not so much as look at them. I made them
have their meals with a servant from the Franche
Comté, whom I had taken on M. de Schaumburg's
recommendation.

I went to my banker, and asked him to get me a good
coachman, who would take two ladies of my acquaintance to Turin.

When I got back to the inn I wrote to the Chevalier
Raiberti, sending him a bill of exchange. I warned him
that in three or four days after the receipt of my letter
he would be accosted by a Bolognese dancer and her
mother, bearing a letter of commendation. I begged
him to see that they lodged in a respectable house, and
to pay for them on my behalf. I also said that I should
be much obliged if he would contrive that she should
dance, even for nothing, at the carnival, and I begged
him to warn her that, if I heard any tales about her
when I came to Turin, our relations would be at an end.

The following day a clerk of M. Tronchin's brought
a coachman for me to see. The man said he was ready
to start as soon as he had had his dinner. I confirmed
the agreement he had made with the banker, I summoned
the two Corticellis, and said to the coachman,——

"These are the persons you are to drive, and they will
pay you when they reach Turin in safety with their
luggage. You are to take four days and a half for the
journey. as is stipulated in the agreement, of which

they have one copy and you another." An hour after he called to put the luggage in.

The Corticelli burst into tears, but I was not so cruel as to send her away without any consolation. Her bad conduct had been severely enough punished already. I made her dine with me, and as I gave her the letter for M. Raiberti, and twenty-five louis for the journey, I told her what I had written to the gentleman, who would take good care of them. She asked me for a trunk containing three dresses and a superb mantle which Madame d'Urfé had given her before she became mad, but I said that we would talk of that at Turin. She dared not mention the casket, but continued weeping; however, she did not move me to pity. I left her much better off than when I first knew her; she had good clothes, good linen, jewels, and an exceedingly pretty watch I had given her; altogether a good deal more than she deserved.

As she was going I escorted her to the carriage, less for politeness' sake than to commend her once more to the coachman. When she was fairly gone I felt as if a load had been taken off my back, and I went to look up my worthy syndic, whom the reader will not have forgotten. I had not written to him since I was in Florence, and I anticipated the pleasure of seeing his surprise, which was extreme. But after gazing at me for a moment he threw his arms round my neck, kissed me several times, and said he had not expected the pleasure of seeing me.

"How are our sweethearts getting on?"

"Excellently. They are always talking about you and regretting your absence; they will go wild with joy when they know you are here."

"You must tell them directly, then."

"I will go and warn them that we shall all sup together this evening. By the way, M. de Voltaire has given up his house at Delices to M. de Villars, and has gone to live at Ferney."

"That makes no difference to me, as I was not thinking of calling on him this time. I shall be here for two or three weeks, and I mean to devote my time to you."

"You are too good."

"Will you give me writing materials before you go out? I will write a few letters while you are away."

He put me in possession of his desk, and I wrote to my late housekeeper, Madame Lebel, telling her that I was going to spend three weeks at Geneva, and that if I were sure of seeing her I would gladly pay a visit to Lausanne. Unfortunately, I also wrote to the bad Genoese poet, Ascanio Pogomas, or Giaccomo Passano, whom I had met at Leghorn. I told him to go to Turin and to wait for me there. At the same time I wrote to M. F——, to whom I had commended him, asking him to give the poet twelve louis for the journey.

My evil genius made me think of this man, who was an imposing-looking fellow, and had all the air of a magician, to introduce him to Madame d'Urfé as a great adept. You will see, dear reader, in the course of a year whether I had reason to repent of this fatal inspiration.

As the syndic and I were on our way to our young friend's house I saw an elegant English carriage for sale, and I exchanged it for mine, giving the owner a hundred louis as well. While the bargain was going on the uncle of the young theologian who argued so well, and to whom I had given such pleasant lessons in physiology, came up to me, embraced me, and asked me to dine with him the next day.

Before we got to the house the syndic informed me that we should find another extremely pretty but uninitiated girl present.

"All the better," said I, "I shall know how to regulate my conduct, and perhaps I may succeed in initiating her."

In my pocket I had placed a casket containing a dozen exquisite rings. I had long been aware that such trifling presents are often very serviceable.

The moment of meeting those charming girls once more was one of the happiest I have ever enjoyed. In their greeting I read delight and love of pleasure. Their love was without envy or jealousy, or any ideas which would have injured their self-esteem. They felt worthy of my regard, as they had lavished their favours on me without any degrading feelings, and drawn by the same emotion that had drawn me.

The presence of the neophyte obliged us to greet each other with what is called decency, and she allowed me to kiss her without raising her eyes, but blushing violently.

After the usual commonplaces had passed and we had indulged in some double meanings which made us laugh and her look thoughtful, I told her she was pretty as a little love, and that I felt sure that her mind, as beautiful as its casket, could harbour no prejudices.

"I have all the prejudices which honour and religion suggest," she modestly replied.

I saw that this was a case requiring very delicate treatment. There was no question of carrying the citadel by sudden assault. But, as usual, I fell in love with her.

The syndic having pronounced my name, she said,——

"Ah! then, you, sir, are the person who discussed some

very singular questions with my cousin, the pastor's niece. I am delighted to make your acquaintance."

"I am equally pleased to make yours, but I hope the pastor's niece said nothing against me."

"Not at all; she has a very high opinion of you."

"I am going to dine with her to-morrow, and I shall take care to thank her."

"To-morrow! I should like to be there, for I enjoy philosophical discussions though I never dare to put a word in."

The syndic praised her discretion and wisdom in such a manner that I was convinced he was in love with her, and that he had either seduced her or was trying to do so. Her name was Helen. I asked the young ladies if Helen was their sister. The eldest replied, with a sly smile, that she was a sister, but as yet she had no brother; and with this explanation she ran up to Helen and kissed her. Then the syndic and I vied with each other in paying her compliments, telling her that we hoped to be her brothers. She blushed, but gave no answer to our gallantries. I then drew forth my casket, and seeing that all the girls were enchanted with the rings, I told them to choose which ones they liked best. The charming Helen imitated their example, and repaid me with a modest kiss. Soon after she left us, and we were once more free, as in old times.

The syndic had good cause to shew for his love of Helen. She was not merely pleasing, she was made to inspire a violent passion. However, the three friends had no hope of making her join in their pleasures, for they said that she had invincible feelings of modesty where men were concerned.

We supped merrily, and after supper we began our sports again, the syndic remaining as usual a mere looker-on, and well pleased with his part. I treated each of the three nymphs to two courses, deceiving them whenever I was forced by nature to do so. At midnight we broke up, and the worthy syndic escorted me to the door of my lodging.

The day following I went to the pastor's and found a numerous party assembled, amongst others M. d'Harcourt and M. de Ximenes, who told me that M. de Voltaire knew that I was at Geneva and hoped to see me. I replied by a profound bow. Mdlle. Hedvig, the pastor's niece, complimented me, but I was still better pleased to see her cousin Helen. The theologian of twenty-two was fair and pleasant to the eyes, but she had not that *je ne sais quoi*, that shade of bitter-sweet, which adds zest to hope as well as pleasure. However, the evident friendship between Hedvig and Helen gave me good hopes of success with the latter.

We had an excellent dinner, and while it lasted the conversation was restricted to ordinary topics; but at dessert the pastor begged M. de Ximenes to ask his niece some questions. Knowing his world-wide reputation, I expected him to put her some problem in geometry, but he only asked whether a lie could be justified on the principle of a mental reservation.

Hedvig replied that there are cases in which a lie is necessary, but that the principle of a mental reservation is always a cheat.

"Then how could Christ have said that the time in which the world was to come to an end was unknown to Him?"

"He was speaking the truth; it was not known to Him."

"Then he was not God?"

"That is a false deduction, for since God may do all

things, He may certainly be ignorant of an event in futurity."

I thought the way in which she brought in the word "futurity" almost sublime. Hedvig was loudly applauded, and her uncle went all round the table to kiss her. I had a very natural objection on the tip of my tongue, which she might have found difficult to answer, but I wanted to get into her good graces and I kept my own counsel.

M. d'Harcourt was urged to ask her some questions, but he replied in the words of Horace, *Nulla mihi religio est*. Then Hedvig turned to me and asked me to put her some hard question, "something difficult, which you don't know yourself."

"I shall be delighted. Do you grant that a god possesses in a supreme degree the qualities of man?"

"Yes, excepting man's weaknesses."

"Do you class the generative power as a weakness?"

"No."

"Will you tell me, then, of what nature would have been the offspring of a union between a god and a mortal woman?"

Hedvig looked as red as fire.

The pastor and the other guests looked at each other, while I gazed fixedly at the young theologian, who was reflecting. M. d'Harcourt said that we should have to send for Voltaire to settle a question so difficult, but as Hedvig had collected her thoughts and seemed ready to speak everybody was silent.

"It would be absurd," said she, "to suppose that a deity could perform such an action without its having any results. At the end of nine months a woman would be delivered a male child, which would be three parts man and one part god."

At these words all the guests applauded, M. de Ximenes expressed his admiration of the way the question
had been solved, adding,——

"Naturally, if the son of the woman married, his
children would be seven-eighths men and one-eighth
gods."

"Yes," said I, "unless he married a goddess, which
would have made the proportion different."

"Tell me exactly," said Hedvig, "what proportion of
divinity there would be in a child of the sixteenth generation."

"Give me a pencil and I will soon tell you," said M.
de Ximenes.

"There is no need to calculate it," said I; "the child
would have some small share of the wit which you
enjoy."

Everybody applauded this gallant speech, which did
not by any means offend the lady to whom it was addressed.

This pretty blonde was chiefly desirable for the
charms of her intellect. We rose from the table and
made a circle round her, but she told us with much
grace not to pay her any more compliments. I took Helen
aside, and told her to get her cousin to choose a ring
from my casket, which I gave her, and she seemed
glad to execute the commission. A quarter of an hour
afterwards Hedvig came to shew me her hand adorned
with the ring she had chosen. I kissed it rapturously,
and she must have guessed from the warmth of my
kisses with what feelings she had inspired me.

In the evening Helen told the syndic and the three
girls all about the morning's discussion without leaving
out the smallest detail. She told the story with ease
and grace, and I had no occasion to prompt her. We

begged her to stay to supper, but she whispered something to the three friends, and they agreed that it was impossible; but she said that she might spend a couple of days with them in their country house on the lake, if they would ask her mother.

At the syndic's request the girls called on the mother the next day, and the day after that they went off with Helen. The same evening we went and supped with them, but we could not sleep there. The syndic was to take me to a house at a short distance off, where we should be very comfortable. This being the case there was no hurry, and the eldest girl said that the syndic and I could leave whenever we liked, but that they were going to bed. So saying she took Helen to her room, while the two others slept in another room. Soon after the syndic went into the room where Helen was, and I visited the two others.

I had scarcely been with my two sweethearts for an hour when the syndic interrupted my erotic exploits by begging me to go.

"What have you done with Helen?" I asked.

"Nothing; she's a simpleton, and an intractable one. She hid under the sheets and would not look at my performance with her friend."

"You ought to go to her direct."

"I have done so, but she repulsed me again and again. I have given it up, and shall not try it again, unless you will tame her for me."

"How is it to be done?"

"Come to dinner to-morrow. I shall be away at Geneva. I shall be back by supper-time. I wish we could give her too much to drink!"

"That would be a pity. Let me see what I can do."

I accordingly went to dine with them by myself the

next day, and they entertained me in all the force of the word. After dinner we went for a walk, and the three friends understanding my aims left me alone with the intractable girl, who resisted my caresses in a manner which almost made me give up the hope of taming her.

"The syndic," said I, "is in love with you, and last night . . . ."

"Last night," she said, "he amused himself with his old friend. I am for everyone's following their own tastes, but I expect to be allowed to follow mine."

"If I could gain your heart I should be happy."

"Why don't you invite the pastor and my cousin to dine with you? I could come too, for the pastor makes much of everyone who loves his niece."

"I am glad to hear that. Has she a lover?"

"No."

"I can scarcely believe it. She is young, pretty, agreeable, and very clever."

"You don't understand Genevan ways. It is because she is so clever that no young man falls in love with her. Those who might be attracted by her personal charms hold themselves aloof on account of her intellectual capacities, as they would have to sit in silence before her."

"Are the young Genevans so ignorant, then?"

"As a rule they are. Some of them have received excellent educations, but in a general way they are full of prejudice. Nobody wishes to be considered a fool or a blockhead, but clever women are not appreciated; and if a girl is witty or well educated she endeavors to hide her lights, at least if she desires to be married."

"Ah! now I see why you did not open your lips during our discussion."

"No, I know I have nothing to hide. This was not the motive which made me keep silence, but the pleasure of listening. I admired my cousin, who was not afraid to display her learning on a subject which any other girl would have affected to know nothing about."

"Yes, affected, though she might very probably know as much as her grandmother."

"That's a matter of morals, or rather of prejudices."

"Your reasoning is admirable, and I am already longing for the party you so cleverly suggested."

"You will have the pleasure of being with my cousin."

"I do her justice. Hedvig is certainly a very interesting and agreeable girl, but believe me it is your presence that will constitute my chief enjoyment."

"And how if I do not believe you?"

"You would wrong me and give me pain, for I love you dearly."

"In spite of that you have deceived me. I am sure that you have given marks of your affection to those three young ladies. For my part I pity them."

"Why?"

"Because neither of them can flatter herself that you love her, and her alone."

"And do you think that your delicacy of feeling makes you happier than they are?"

"Yes, I think so though of course, I have no experience in the matter. Tell me truly, do you think I am right?"

"Yes, I do."

"I am delighted to hear it; but you must confess that to associate me with them in your attentions would not be giving me the greatest possible proof of your love."

"Yes, I do confess it, and I beg your pardon. But

tell me how I should set to work to ask the pastor to dinner."

"There will be no difficulty. Just call on him and ask him to come, and if you wish me to be of the party beg him to ask my mother and myself."

"Why your mother?"

"Because he has been in love with her these twenty years, and loves her still."

"And where shall I give this dinner?"

"Is not M. Tronchin your banker?"

"Yes."

"He has a nice pleasure house on the lake; ask him to lend it you for the day, he will be delighted to do so. But don't tell the syndic or his three friends anything about it; they can hear of it afterwards."

"But do you think your learned cousin will be glad to be in my company?"

"More than glad, you may be sure."

"Very good, everything will be arranged by to-morrow. The day after, you will be returning to Geneva, and the party will take place two or three days later."

The syndic came back in due course, and we had a very pleasant evening. After supper the ladies went to bed as before, and I went with the eldest girl while the syndic visited the two younger ones. I knew that it would be of no use to try to do anything with Helen, so I contented myself with a few kisses, after which I wished them good night and passed on to the next room. I found them in a deep sleep, and the syndic seemed visibly bored. He did not look more cheerful when I told him that I had had no success with Helen.

"I see," said he, "that I shall waste my time with the little fool. I think I shall give her up."

"I think that's the best thing you could do," I replied, "for a man who languishes after a woman who is either devoid of feeling or full of caprice, makes himself her dupe. Bliss should be neither too easy nor too hard to be won."

The next day we returned to Geneva, and M. Tronchin seemed delighted to oblige me. The pastor accepted my invitation, and said I was sure to be charmed with Helen's mother. It was easy to see that the worthy man cherished a tenderness for her, and if she responded at all it would be all the better for my purposes.

I was thinking of supping with the charming Helen and her three friends at the house on the lake, but an express summoned me to Lausanne. Madame Lebel, my old housekeeper, invited me to sup with her and her husband. She wrote that she had made her husband promise to take her to Lausanne as soon as she got my letter, and she added she was sure that I would resign everything to give her the pleasure of seeing me. She notified the hour at which she would be at her mother's house.

Madame Lebel was one of the ten or twelve women for whom in my happy youth I cherished the greatest affection. She had all the qualities to make a man a good wife, if it had been my fate to experience such felicity. But perhaps I did well not to tie myself down with irrevocable bonds, though now my independence is another name for slavery. But if I had married a woman of tact, who would have ruled me unawares to myself, I should have taken care of my fortune and have had children, instead of being lonely and penniless in my old age.

But I must indulge no longer in digressions on the

past which cannot be recalled, and since my recollections make me happy I should be foolish to cherish idle regrets.

I calculated that if I started directly I should get to Lausanne an hour before Madame Lebel, and I did not hesitate to give her this proof of my regard. I must here warn my readers, that, though I loved this woman well, I was then occupied with another passion, and no voluptuous thought mingled with my desire of seeing her. My esteem for her was enough to hold my passions in check, but I esteemed Lebel too, and nothing would have induced me to disturb the happiness of this married pair.

I wrote in haste to the syndic, telling him that an important and sudden call obliged me to start for Lausanne, but that I should have the pleasure of supping with him and his three friends at Geneva on the following day.

I knocked at Madame Dubois's door at five o'clock, almost dying with hunger. Her surprise was extreme, for she did not know that her daughter was going to meet me at her house. Without more ado I gave her two louis to get us a good supper.

At seven o'clock, Madame Lebel, her husband, and a child of eighteen months, whom I easily recognized as my own, arrived. Our meeting was a happy one indeed; we spent ten hours at table, and mirth and joy prevailed. At day-break she started for Soleure, where Lebel had business. M. de Chavigni had desired to be remembered most affectionately to me. Lebel assured me that the ambassador was extremely kind to his wife, and he thanked me heartily for having given such a woman up to him. I could easily see that he was a happy husband, and that his wife was as happy as he.

My dear housekeeper talked to me about my son. She said that nobody suspected the truth, but that neithei she nor Lebel (who had faithfully kept his promise, and had not consummated the marriage for the two months agreed upon) had any doubts.

"The secret," said Lebel to me, "will never be known, and your son will be my sole heir, or will share my property with my children if I ever have any, which I doubt."

"My dear," said his wife, "there is somebody who has very strong suspicions on the subject, and these suspicions will gain strength as the child grows older; but we have nothing to fear on that score, as she is well paid to keep the secret."

"And who is this person?" said I.

"Madame ———. She has not forgotten the past, and often speaks of you."

"Will you kindly remember me to her?"

"I shall be delighted to do so, and I am sure the message will give her great pleasure."

Lebel shewed me my ring, and I shewed him his, and gave him a superb watch for my son.

"You must give it him," I said, "when you think he is old enough."

We shall hear of the young gentleman in twenty-one years at Fontainebleau.

I passed three hours in telling them of all the adventures I had during the twenty-seven months since we had seen one another. As to their history, it was soon told; it had all the calm which belongs to happiness.

Madame Lebel was as pretty as ever, and I could see no change in her, but I was no longer the same man. She thought me less lively than of old, and she was right. The Renaud had blasted me, and the pretended Lascaris had given me a great deal of trouble and anxiety.

We embraced each other tenderly, and the wedded pair returned to Soleure and I to Geneva; but feeling that I wanted rest I wrote to the syndic that I was not well and could not come till the next day, and after I had done so I went to bed.

The next day, the eve of my dinner party, I ordered a repast in which no expense was to be spared. I did not forget to tell the landlord to get me the best wines, the choicest liqueurs, ices, and all the materials for a bowl of punch. I told him that we should be six in number, for I foresaw that M. Tronchin would dine with us. I was right; I found him at his pretty house ready to receive us, and I had not much trouble in inducing him to stay. In the evening I thought it as well to tell the syndic and his three friends about it in Helen's presence, while she, feigning ignorance, said that her mother had told her they were going somewhere or other to dinner.

"I am delighted to hear it," said I; "it must be at M. Tronchin's."

My dinner would have satisfied the most exacting *gourmet,* but Hedvig was its real charm. She treated difficult theological questions with so much grace, and rationalised so skilfully, that though one might not be convinced it was impossible to help being attracted. I have never seen any theologian who could treat the most difficult points with so much facility, eloquence, and real dignity, and at dinner she completed her conquest of myself. M. Tronchin, who had never heard her speak before, thanked me a hundred times for having procured him this pleasure, and being obliged to leave us by the call of business he asked us to meet again in two days' time.

I was much interested during the dessert by the evident tenderness of the pastor for Helen's mother. His amorous eloquence grew in strength as he irrigated his throat with champagne, Greek wine, and eastern liqueurs. The lady seemed pleased, and was a match for him as far as drinking was concerned, while the two girls and myself only drank with sobriety. However, the mixture of wines, and above all the punch, had done their work, and my charmers were slightly elevated. Their spirits were delightful, but rather pronounced. I took this favourable opportunity to ask the two aged lovers if I might take the young ladies for a walk in the garden by the lake, and they told us enthusiastically to go and enjoy ourselves. We went out arm in arm, and in a few minutes we were out of sight of everyone.

"Do you know," said I to Hedvig, "that you have made a conquest of M. Tronchin?"

"Have I? The worthy banker asked me some very silly questions."

"You must not expect everyone to be able to contend with you."

"I can't help telling you that your question pleased me best of all. A bigoted theologian at the end of the table seemed scandalized at the question and still more at the answer."

"And why?"

"He says I ought to have told you that a deity could not impregnate a woman. He said that he would explain the reason to me if I were a man, but being a woman and a maid he could not with propriety expound such mysteries. I wish you would tell me what the fool meant."

"I should be very glad, but you must allow me to speak plainly, and I shall have to take for granted that you are acquainted with the physical conformation of a man."

"Yes, speak as plainly as you like, for there is nobody to hear what we say; but I must confess that I am only acquainted with the peculiarities of the male by theory and reading. I have no practical knowledge. I have seen statues, but I have never seen or examined a real live man. Have you, Helen?"

"I have never wished to do so."

"Why not? It is good to know everything."

"Well, Hevdig, your theologian meant to say that a god was not capable of this."

"What is that?"

"Give me your hand."

"I can feel it, and have thought it would be something like that; without this provision of nature man would not be able to fecundate his mate. And how could the foolish theologian maintain that this was an imperfection?"

"Because it is the result of desire, Hedvig, and it would not have taken place in me if I had not been charmed with you, and if I had not conceived the most seducing ideas of the beauties that I cannot see from the view of the beauties I can see. Tell me frankly whether feeling that did not give you an agreeable sensation."

"It did, and just in the place where your hand is now. Don't you feel a pleasant tickling there, Helen, after what the gentleman has been saying to us?"

"Yes, I feel it, but I often do, without anything to excite me."

"And then," said I, "nature makes you appease it
. . . thus?"

"Not at all."

"Oh, yes!" said Hedvig. "Even when we are asleep
our hands seek that spot as if by instinct, and if it
were not for that solace I think we should get terribly
ill."

As this philosophical discourse, conducted by the
young theologian in quite a professional manner, proceeded, we reached a beautiful basin of water, with a
flight of marble steps for bathers. Although the air was
cool our heads were hot, and I conceived the idea of
telling them that it would do them good to bathe their
feet, and that if they would allow me I would take off
their shoes and stockings.

"I should like to so much," said Hedvig.

"And I too," said Helen.

"Then sit down, ladies, on the first step."

They proceeded to sit down and I began to take off
their shoes, praising the beauty of their legs, and pretending for the present not to want to go farther than
the knee. When they got into the water they were
obliged to pick up their clothes, and I encouraged them
to do so.

"Well, well," said Hedvig, "men have thighs too."

Helen, who would have been ashamed to be beaten
by her cousin, was not backward in shewing her legs.

"That will do, charming maids," said I, "you might
catch cold if you stayed longer in the water."

They walked up backwards, still holding up their
clothes for fear of wetting them, and it was then my
duty to wipe them dry with all the handkerchiefs I had.
This pleasant task left me at freedom to touch and see,

and the reader will imagine that I did my best in that direction. The fair theologian told me I wanted to know too much, but Helen let me do what I liked with such a tender and affectionate expression that it was as much as I could do to keep within bounds. At last, when I had drawn on their shoes and stockings, I told them that I was delighted to have seen the hidden charms of the two prettiest girls in Geneva.

"What effect had it on you?" asked Hedvig.

"I daren't tell you to look, but feel, both of you."

"Do you bathe, too."

"It's out of the question, a man's undressing takes so much trouble."

"But we have still two hours before us, in which we need not fear any interruption."

This reply gave me a foretaste of the bliss I had to gain, but I did not wish to expose myself to an illness by going into the water in my present state. I noticed a summer-house at a little distance, and feeling sure that M. Tronchin had left the door open, I took the two girls on my arm and led them there without giving them any hint of my intentions. The summer-house was scented with vases of *pot-pourri* and adorned with engravings; but, best of all, there was a large couch which seemed made for repose and pleasure. I sat down on it between my two sweethearts, and as I caressed them I told them I was going to shew them something they had never seen before, and without more ado I displayed to their gaze the principal agent in the preservation of the human race. They got up to admire it, and taking a hand of each one I procured them some enjoyment, but in the middle of their labours an abundant flow of liquid threw them into the greatest astonishment.

"That," said I, "is the Word which makes men."

"It's beautiful!" cried Helen, laughing at the term "word."

"I have a word too," said Hedvig, "and I will shew it to you if you will wait a minute."

"Come, Hedvig, and I will save you the trouble of making it yourself, and will do it better."

"I daresay, but I have never done it with a man."

"No more have I," said Helen.

Placing them in front of me I gave them another ecstacy. We then sat down, and while I felt all their charms I let them touch me as much as they liked till I watered their hands a second time.

We made ourselves decent once more, and spent half an hour in kisses and caresses, and I then told them that they had made me happy only in part, but that I hoped they would make my bliss complete by presenting me with their maidenheads. I shewed them the little safety-bags invented by the English in the interests of the fair sex. They admired them greatly when I explained their use, and the fair theologian remarked to her cousin that she would think it over. We were now close friends, and soon promised to be something more; and we walked back and found the pastor and Helen's mother strolling by the side of the lake.

When I got back to Geneva I went to spend the evening with the three friends, but I took good care not to tell the syndic anything about my victory with Helen. It would only have served to renew his hopes, and he would have had this trouble for nothing. Even I would have done no good without the young theologian; but as Helen admired her she did not like to appear her inferior by refusing to imitate her freedom.

I did not see Helen that evening, but I saw her the next day at her mother's house, for I was in mere polite-

ness bound to thank the old lady for the honour she had
done me. She gave me a most friendly reception, and
introduced me to two very pretty girls who were boarding with her. They might have interested me if I had
been stopping long in Geneva, but as it was Helen
claimed all my attraction.

"To-morrow," said the charming girl, "I shall be able
to get a word with you at Madame Tronchin's dinner,
and I expect Hedvig will have hit on some way for you
to satisfy your desires."

The banker gave us an excellent dinner. He proudly
told me that no inn-keeper could give such a good dinner
as a rich gentleman who has a good cook, a good cellar,
good silver plate, and china of the best quality. We
were twenty of us at table, and the feast was given
chiefly in honour of the learned theologian and myself,
as a rich foreigner who spent money freely. M. de
Ximenes, who had just arrived from Ferney was there,
and told me that M. de Voltaire was expecting me, but
I had foolishly determined not to go.

Hedvig shone in solving the questions put to her by
the company. M. de Ximenes begged her to justify as
best she could our first mother, who had deceived her
husband by giving him the fatal apple to eat.

"Eve," she said, "did not deceive her husband, she
only cajoled him into eating it in the hope of giving him
one more perfection. Besides Eve had not been forbidden to eat the fruit by God, but only by Adam, and
in all probability her woman's sense prevented her regarding the prohibition as serious."

At this reply, which I found full of sense and wit,
two scholars from Geneva and even Hedvig's uncle began
to murmur and shake their heads. Madame Tronchin
said gravely that Eve had received the prohibition from

God himself, but the girl only answered by a humble "I beg your pardon, madam." At this she turned to the pastor with a frightened manner, and said,——

"What do you say to this?"

"Madam, my niece is not infallible."

"Excuse me, dear uncle, I am as infallible as Holy Writ when I speak according to it."

"Bring a Bible, and let me see."

"Hedvig, my dear Hedvig, you are right after all. Here it is. The prohibition was given before woman was made."

Everybody applauded, but Hedvig remained quite calm; it was only the two scholars and Madame Tronchin who still seemed disturbed. Another lady then asked her if it was allowable to believe the history of the apple to be symbolical. She replied,——

"I do not think so, because it could only be a symbol of sexual union, and it is clear that such did not take place between Adam and Eve in the Garden of Eden."

"The learned differ on this point."

"All the worse for them, madam, the Scripture is plain enough. In the first verse of the fourth chapter it is written, that Adam knew his wife after they had been driven from the Garden, and that in consequence she conceived Cain."

"Yes, but the verse does not say that Adam did not know her before, and consequently he might have done so."

"I cannot admit the inference, as in that case she would have conceived; for it would be absurd to suppose that two creatures who had just left God's hands, and were consequently as nearly perfect as is possible, could perform the act of generation without its having any result."

This reply gained everyone's applause, and compliments to Hedvig made the round of the table.

Mr. Tronchin asked her if the doctrine of the immortality of the soul could be gathered from the Old Testament alone.

"The Old Testament," she replied, "does not teach this doctrine; but, nevertheless, human reason teaches it, as the soul is a substance, and the destruction of any substance is an unthinkable proposition."

"Then I will ask you," said the banker, "if the existence of the soul is established in the Bible."

"Where there is smoke there is always fire."

"Tell me, then, if matter can think."

"I cannot answer that question, for it is beyond my knowledge. I can only say that as I believe God to be all powerful, I cannot deny Him the power to make matter capable of thought."

"But what is your own opinion?"

"I believe that I have a soul endowed with thinking capacities, but I do not know whether I shall remember that I had the honour of dining with you to-day after I die."

"Then you think that the soul and the memory may be separable; but in that case you would not be a theologian."

"One may be a theologian and a philosopher, for philosophy never contradicts any truth, and besides, to say 'I do not know' is not the same as 'I am sure' "

Three parts of the guests burst into cries of admiration, and the fair philosopher enjoyed seeing me laugh for pleasure at the applause. The pastor wept for joy, and whispered something to Helen's mother. All at once he turned to me, saying,——

"Ask my niece some question."

"Yes," said Hedvig, "but it must be something quite new."

"That is a hard task," I replied, "for how am I to know that what I ask is new to you? However, tell me if one must stop at the first principle of a thing one wants to understand."

"Certainly, and the reason is that in God there is no first principle, and He is therefore incomprehensible."

"God be praised! that is how I would have you answer. Can God have any self-consciousness?"

"There my learning is baffled. I know not what to reply. You should not ask me so hard a thing as that."

"But you wished for something new. I thought the newest thing would be to see you at a loss."

"That's prettily said. Be kind enough to reply for me, gentlemen, and teach me what to say."

Everybody tried to answer, but nothing was said worthy of record. Hedvig at last said,——

"My opinion is that since God knows all, He knows of His own existence, but you must not ask me how He knows it."

"That's well said," I answered; and nobody could throw any further light on the matter.

All the company looked on me as a polite Atheist, so superficial is the judgment of society, but it did not matter to me whether they thought me an Atheist or not.

M. de Ximenes asked Hedvig if matter had been created.

"I cannot recognize the word 'created,'" she replied. "Ask me whether matter was formed, and I shall reply in the affirmative. The word 'created' cannot have existence, for the existence of anything must be prior to the word which explains it."

"Then what meaning do you assign to the word 'created'?"

"Made out of nothing. You see the absurdity, for nothing must have first existed. I am glad to see you laugh. Do you think that *nothingness* could be created?"

"You are right."

"Not at all, not at all," said one of the guests, superciliously.

"Kindly tell me who was your teacher?" said M. de Ximenes.

"My uncle there."

"Not at all, my dear niece. I certainly never taught you what you have been telling us to-day. But my niece, gentlemen, reads and reflects over what she has read, perhaps with rather too much freedom, but I love her all the same, because she always ends by acknowledging that she knows nothing."

A lady who had not opened her lips hitherto asked Hedvig for a definition of spirit.

"Your question is a purely philosophical one, and I must answer that I do not know enough of spirit or matter to be able to give a satisfactory definition."

"But since you acknowledge the existence of Deity and must therefore have an abstract idea of spirit, you must have some notions on the subject, and should be able to tell me how it acts on matter."

"No solid foundation can be built on abstract ideas. Hobbes calls such ideas mere fantasms. One may have them, but if one begins to reason on them, one is landed in contradiction. I know that God sees me, but I should labour in vain if I endeavoured to prove it by reasoning, for reason tells us no one can see anything without organs of sight; and God being a pure spirit, and therefore without organs, it is scientifically impossible that

He can see us any more than we can see Him. But Moses and several others have seen Him, and I believe it so, without attempting to reason on it."

"You are quite right," said I, "for you would be confronted by blank impossibility. But if you take to reading Hobbes you are in danger of becoming an Atheist."

"I am not afraid of that. I cannot conceive the possibility of Atheism."

After dinner everybody crowded round this truly astonishing girl, so that I had no opportunity of whispering my love. However, I went apart with Helen, who told me that the pastor and his niece were going to sup with her mother the following day.

"Hedvig," she added, "will stay the night and sleep with me as she always does when she comes to supper with her uncle. It remains to be seen if you are willing to hide in a place I will shew you at eleven o'clock to-morrow, in order to sleep with us. Call on my mother at that hour to-morrow, and I will find an opportunity of shewing you where it is. You will be safe though not comfortable, and if you grow weary you can console yourself by thinking that you are in our minds."

"Shall I have to stay there long?"

"Four hours at the most. At seven o'clock the street door is shut, and only opened to anyone who rings."

"If I happen to cough while I am in hiding might I be heard?"

"Yes, that might happen."

"There's a great hazard. All the rest is of no consequence; but no matter, I will risk all for the sake of so great happiness."

In the morning I paid the mother a visit, and as Helen was escorting me out she shewed me a door between the two stairs.

"At seven o'clock," said she, "the door will be open, and when you are in put on the bolt. Take care that no one sees you as you are entering the house."

At a quarter to seven I was already a prisoner. I found a seat in my cell, otherwise I should neither have been able to lie down or to stand up. It was a regular hole, and I knew by my sense of smell that hams and cheeses were usually kept there; but it contained none at present, for I felt all round to see how the land lay. As I was cautiously stepping round I felt my foot encounter some resistance, and putting down my hand I recognized the feel of linen. It was a napkin containing two plates, a nice roast fowl, bread, and a second napkin. Searching again I came across a bottle and a glass. I was grateful to my charmers for having thought of my stomach, but as I had purposely made a late and heavy meal I determined to defer the consumption of my cold collation till a later hour.

At nine o'clock I began, and as I had neither a knife nor a corkscrew I was obliged to break the neck of the bottle with a brick which I was fortunately able to detach from the mouldering floor. The wine was delicious old Neuchâtel, and the fowl was stuffed with truffles, and I felt convinced that my two nymphs must have some rudimentary ideas on the subject of stimulants. I should have passed the time pleasantly enough if it had not been for the occasional visits of a rat, who nearly made me sick with his disgusting odour. I remembered that I had been annoyed in the same way at Cologne under somewhat similar circumstances.

At last ten o'clock struck, and I heard the pastor's voice as he came downstairs talking; he warned the girls not to play any tricks together, and to go to sleep quietly. That brought back to my memory M. Rose leaving

Madame Orio's house at Venice twenty-two years before; and reflecting on my character I found myself much changed, though not more reasonable; but if I was not so sensible to the charms of the sex, the two beauties who were awaiting me were much superior to Madame Orio's nieces.

In my long and profligate career in which I have turned the heads of some hundreds of ladies, I have become familiar with all the methods of seduction; but my guiding principle has been never to direct my attack against novices or those whose prejudices were likely to prove an obstacle except in the presence of another woman. I soon found out that timidity makes a girl averse to being seduced, while in company with another girl she is easily conquered; the weakness of the one brings on the fall of the other. Fathers and mothers are of the contrary opinion, but they are in the wrong. They will not trust their daughter to take a walk or go to a ball with a young man, but if she has another girl with her there is no difficulty made. I repeat, they are in the wrong; if the young man has the requisite skill their daughter is a lost woman. A feeling of false shame hinders them from making an absolute and determined resistance, and the first step once taken the rest comes inevitably and quickly. The girl grants some small favour, and immediately makes her friend grant a much greater one to hide her own blushes; and if the seducer is clever at his trade the young innocent will soon have gone too far to be able to draw back. Besides the more innocence a girl has, the less she knows of the methods of seduction. Before she has had time to think, pleasure attracts her, curiosity draws her a little farther, and opportunity does the rest.

For example, I might possibly have been able to seduce

Hedvig without Helen, but I am certain I should never have succeeded with Helen if she had not seen her cousin take liberties with me which she no doubt thought contrary to the feelings of modesty which a respectable young woman ought to have.

Though I do not repent of my amorous exploits, I am far from wishing that my example should serve for the perversion of the fair sex, who have so many claims on my homage. I desire that what I say may be a warning to fathers and mothers, and secure me a place in their esteem at any rate.

Soon after the pastor had gone I heard three light knocks on my prison door. I opened it, and my hand was folded in a palm as soft as satin. All my being was moved. It was Helen's hand, and that happy moment had already repaid me for my long waiting.

"Follow me on tiptoe," she whispered, as soon as she had shut the door; but in my impatience I clasped her in my arms, and made her feel the effect which her mere presence had produced on me, while at the same time I assured myself of her docility. "There," she said, "now come upstairs softly after me."

I followed her as best I could in the darkness, and she took me along a gallery into a dark room, and then into a lighted one which contained Hedvig almost in a state of nudity. She came to me with open arms as soon as she saw me, and, embracing me ardently, expressed her gratitude for my long and dreary imprisonment.

"Divine Hedvig," I answered, "if I had not loved you madly I would not have stayed a quarter of an hour in that dismal cell, but I am ready to spend four hours there every day till I leave Geneva for your sake. But we must not lose any time; let us go to bed."

"Do you two go to bed," said Helen; "I will sleep on the sofa."

"No, no," cried Hedvig, "don't think of it; our fate must be exactly equal."

"Yes, darling Helen," said I, embracing her; "I love you both with equal ardour, and these ceremonies are only wasting the time in which I ought to be assuring you of my passion. Imitate my proceedings. I am going to undress, and then I shall lie in the middle of the bed. Come and lie beside me, and I'll shew you how I love you. If all is safe I will remain with you till you send me away, but whatever you do do not put out the light."

In the twinkling of an eye, discussing the theory of shame the while with the theological Hedvig, I presented myself to their gaze in the costume of Adam. Hedvig blushed and parted with the last shred of her modesty, citing the opinion of St. Clement Alexandrinus that the seat of shame is in the shirt. I praised the charming perfection of her shape, in the hope of encouraging Helen, who was slowly undressing herself; but an accusation of mock modesty from her cousin had more effect than all my praises. At last this Venus stood before me in a state of nature, covering her most secret parts with her hand, and hiding one breast with the other, and appearing woefully ashamed of what she could not conceal. Her modest confusion, this strife between departing modesty and rising passion, enchanted me.

Hedvig was taller than Helen; her skin was whiter, and her breasts double the size of Helen's; but in Helen there was more animation, her shape was more gently moulded, and her breast might have been the model for the Venus de Medicis.

She got bolder by degrees, and we spent some moments in admiring each other, and then we went to bed. Nature spoke out loudly, and all we wanted was to satisfy its demands. With much coolness I made a woman of Hedvig, and when all was over she kissed me and said that the pain was nothing in comparison with the pleasure.

The turn of Helen (who was six years younger than Hedvig) now came, but the finest fleece that I have ever seen was not won without difficulty. She was jealous of her cousin's success, and held it open with her two hands; and though she had to submit to great pain before being initiated into the amorous mysteries, her sighs were sighs of happiness, as she responded to my ardent efforts. Her great charms and the vivacity of her movements shortened the sacrifice, and when I left the sanctuary my two sweethearts saw that I needed repose.

The alter was purified of the blood of the victims, and we all washed, delighted to serve one another.

Life returned to me under their curious fingers, and the sight filled them with joy. I told them that I wished to enjoy them every night till I left Geneva, but they told me sadly that this was impossible.

"In five or six days time, perhaps, the opportunity may recur again, but that will be all."

"Ask us to sup at your inn to-morrow," said Hedvig; "and maybe, chance will favour the commission of a sweet felony."

I followed this advice.

I overwhelmed them with happiness for several hours, passing five or six times from one to the other before I was exhausted. In the intervals, seeing them to be docile and desirous, I made them execute Aretin's most complicated postures, which amused them beyond words. We kissed whatever took our fancy, and just as Hedvig applied her lips to the mouth of the pistol, it went off and the discharge inundated her face and her bosom. She was delighted, and watched the process to the end with all the curiosity of a doctor. The night seemed short, though we had not lost a moment's time, and at day-break we had to part. I left them in bed and I was fortunate enough to get away without being observed.

I slept till noon, and then having made my toilette I went to call on the pastor, to whom I praised Hedvig to the skies. This was the best way to get him to come to supper at Balances the next day.

"We shall be in the town," said I, "and can remain together as long as we please, but do not forget to bring the amiable widow and her charming daughter."

He promised he would bring them both.

In the evening I went to see the syndic and his three friends, who naturally found me rather insensible to their charms. I excused myself by saying that I had a bad headache. I told them that I had asked the young theologian to supper, and invited the girls and the syndic to come too; but, as I had foreseen, the latter would not hear of their going as it would give rise to gossip.

I took care that the most exquisite wines should form an important feature of my supper. The pastor and the widow were both sturdy drinkers, and I did my best to please them. When I saw that they were pretty mellow and were going over their old recollections, I made a sign to the girls, and they immediately went out as if to go to a retiring-room. Under pretext of shewing them the way I went out too, and took them into a room telling them to wait for me.

I went back to the supper-room, and finding the old

friends taken up with each other and scarcely conscious of my presence, I gave them some punch, and told them that I would keep the young ladies company; they were looking at some pictures, I explained. I lost no time, and shewed them some extremely interesting sights. These stolen sweets have a wonderful charm. When we were to some extent satisfied, we went back, and I plied the punch-ladle more and more freely. Helen praised the pictures to her mother, and asked her to come and look at them.

"I don't care to," she replied.

"Well," said Helen, "let us go and see them again."

I thought this stratagem admissible, and going out with my two sweethearts I worked wonders. Hedvig philosophised over pleasure, and told me she would never have known it if I had not chanced to meet her uncle. Helen did not speak; she was more voluptuous than her cousin, and swelled out like a dove, and came to life only to expire a moment afterwards. I wondered at her astonishing fecundity; while I was engaged in one operation she passed from death to life fourteen times. It is true that it was the sixth time with me, so I made my progress rather slower to enjoy the pleasure she took in it.

Before we parted I agreed to call on Helen's mother every day to ascertain the night I could spend with them before I left Geneva. We broke up our party at two o'clock in the morning.

Three or four days after, Helen told me briefly that Hedvig was to sleep with her that night, and that she would leave the door open at the same time as before.

"I will be there."

"And I will be there to shut you up, but you cannot have a light as the servant might see it."

I was exact to the time, and when ten o'clock struck they came to fetch me in high glee.

"I forgot to tell you," said Helen, "that you would find a fowl there."

I felt hungry, and made short work of it, and then we gave ourselves up to happiness.

I had to set out on my travels in two days. I had received a couple of letters from M. Raiberti. In the first he told me that he had followed my instructions as to the Corticelli, and in the second that she would probably be paid for dancing at the carnival as first *figurante*. I had nothing to keep me at Geneva, and Madame d'Urfé, according to our agreement, would be waiting for me at Lyons. I was therefore obliged to go there. Thus the night that I was to pass with my two charmers would be my last.

My lessons had taken effect, and I found they had become past mistresses in the art of pleasure. But now and again joy gave place to sadness.

"We shall be wretched, sweetheart," said Hedvig, "and if you like we will come with you."

"I promise to come and see you before two years have expired," said I; and in fact they had not so long to wait.

We fell asleep at midnight, and waking at four renewed our sweet battles till six o'clock. Half an hour after I left them, worn out with my exertions, and I remained in bed all day. In the evening I went to see the syndic and his young friends. I found Helen there, and she was cunning enough to feign not to be more vexed at my departure than the others, and to further the deception she allowed the syndic to kiss her. I followed suit, and begged her to bid farewell for me to her learned cousin and to excuse my taking leave of her in person.

The next day I set out in the early morning, and on the following day I reached Lyons. Madame d'Urfé was not there, she had gone to an estate of hers at Bresse. I found a letter in which she said that she would be delighted to see me, and I waited on her without losing any time.

She greeted me with her ordinary cordiality, and I told her that I was going to Turin to meet Frederic Gualdo, the head of the Fraternity of the Rosy Cross, and I revealed to her by the oracle that he would come with me to Marseilles, and that there he would complete her happiness. After having received this oracle she would not go to Paris before she saw us. The oracle also bade her wait for me at Lyons with young d'Aranda, who begged me to take him with me to Turin. It may be imagined that I succeeded in putting him off.

Madame d'Urfé had to wait a fortnight to get me fifty thousand francs which I might require on my journey. In the course of this fortnight I made the acquaintance of Madame Pernon, and spent a good deal of money with her husband, a rich mercer, in refurnishing my wardrobe. Madame Pernon was handsome and intelligent. She had a Milanese lover, named Bono, who did business for a Swiss banker named Sacco. It was through Madame Peron that Bono got Madame d'Urfé the fifty thousand francs I required. She also gave me the three dresses which she had promised to the Countess of Lascaris, but which that lady had never seen.

One of these dresses was furred, and was exquisitely beautiful. I left Lyons equipped like a prince, and journeyed towards Turin, where I was to meet the famous Gualdo, who was none other than Ascanio Pogomas, whom I had summoned from Berne. I thought it would be easy to make the fellow play the part I had destined

for him, but I was cruelly deceived as the reader will
see.

I could not resist stopping at Chambéri to see my fair
nun, whom I found looking beautiful and contented. She
was grieving, however, after the young boarder, who had
been taken from the convent and married.

I got to Turin at the beginning of December, and at
Rivoli I found the Corticelli, who had been warned by
the Chevalier de Raiberti of my arrival. She gave me a
letter from this worthy gentleman, giving the address
of the house he had taken for me as I did not want to
put up at an inn. I immediately went to take possession
of my new lodging.

CHAPTER XVII

*My Old Friends—Pacienza—Agatha—Count Borromeo
—The Ball—Lord Percy*

THE Corticelli was as gentle as a lamb, and left me
as we got into Turin. I promised I would come and
see her, and immediately went to the house the Chevalier
had taken, which I found convenient in every way.

The worthy Chevalier was not long in calling on me.
He gave me an account of the moneys he had spent on
the Corticelli, and handed over the rest to me.

"I am flush of money," I said, "and I intend to invite
my friends to supper frequently. Can you lay your
hands on a good cook?"

"I know a pearl amongst cooks," said he, "and you
can have him directly."

"You, chevalier, are the pearl of men. Get me this
wonder, tell him I am hard to please, and agree on the
sum I am to pay him per month."

The cook, who was an excellent one, came the same
evening.

"It would be a good idea," said Raiberti, "to call on
the Count d'Aglié. He knows that the Corticelli is your
mistress, and he has given a formal order to Madame
Pacienza, the lady with whom she lives, that when
you come and see her you are not to be left alone together."

This order amused me, and as I did not care about the
Corticelli it did not trouble me in the least, though

Raiberti, who thought I was in love with her, seemed to pity me.

"Since she has been here," he said, "her conduct has been irreproachable."

"I am glad to hear that."

"You might let her take some lessons from the dancing-master Dupré," said he. "He will no doubt give her something to do at the carnival."

I promised to follow his advice, and I then paid a visit to the superintendent of police.

He received me well, complimented me on my return to Turin, and then added with a smile——

"I warn you that I have been informed that you keep a mistress, and that I have given strict orders to the respectable woman with whom she lives not to leave her alone with you."

"I am glad to hear it," I replied, "and the more as I fear her mother is not a person of very rigid morals. I advised the Chevalier Raiberti of my intentions with regard to her, and I am glad to see that he has carried them out so well. I hope the girl will shew herself worthy of your protection."

"Do you think of staying here throughout the carnival?"

"Yes, if your excellency approves."

"It depends entirely on your good conduct."

"A few peccadilloes excepted, my conduct is always above reproach."

"There are some peccadilloes we do not tolerate here. Have you seen the Chevalier Osorio?"

"I think of calling on him to-day or to-morrow."

"I hope you will remember me to him."

He rang his bell, bowed, and the audience was over.

The Chevalier Osorio received me at his office, and

gave me a most gracious reception. After I had given him an account of my visit to the superintendent, he asked me, with a smile, if I felt inclined to submit with docility to not seeing my mistress in freedom.

"Certainly," said I, "for I am not in love with her."

Osorio looked at me slyly, and observed, "Somehow I don't think your indifference will be very pleasing to the virtuous duenna."

I understood what he meant, but personally I was delighted not to be able to see the Corticelli save in the presence of a female dragon. It would make people talk, and I loved a little scandal, and felt curious to see what would happen.

When I returned to my house I found the Genoese Passano, a bad poet and worse painter, to whom I had intended to give the part of a Rosicrucian, because there was something in his appearance which inspired, if not respect, at least awe and a certain feeling of fear. In point of fact, this was only a natural presentiment that the man must be either a clever rogue or a morose and sullen scholar.

I made him sup with me and gave him a room on the third floor, telling him not to leave it without my permission. At supper I found him insipid in conversation, drunken, ignorant, and ill disposed, and I already repented of having taken him under my protection; but the thing was done.

The next day, feeling curious to see how the Corticelli was lodged, I called on her, taking with me a piece of Lyons silk.

I found her and her mother in the landlady's room, and as I came in the latter said that she was delighted to see me and that she hoped I would often dine with them. I thanked her briefly and spoke to the girl coolly enough.

"Shew me your room," said I. She took me there in her mother's company. "Here is something to make you a winter dress," said I, shewing her the silk.

"Is this from the marchioness?"

"No, it is from me."

"But where are the three dresses she said she would give me?"

"You know very well on what conditions you were to have them, so let us say no more about it."

She unfolded the silk which she liked very much, but she said she must have some trimmings. The Pacienza offered her services, and said she would send for a dressmaker who lived close by. I acquiesced with a nod, and as soon as she had left the room the Signora Laura said she was very sorry only to be able to receive me in the presence of the landlady.

"I should have thought," said I, "that a virtuous person like you would have been delighted."

"I thank God for it every morning and night."

"You infernal old hypocrite!" said I, looking contemptuously at her. "Upon my word, anybody who didn't know you would be taken in."

In a few minutes Victorine and another girl came in with their band-boxes.

"Are you still at Madame R——'s" said I.

"Yes sir," said she, with a blush.

When the Corticelli had chosen what she wanted I told Victorine to present my compliments to her mistress, and tell her that I would call and pay for the articles.

The landlady had also sent for a dressmaker, and while the Corticelli was being measured, she shewed me her figure and said she wanted a corset. I jested on the pregnancy with which she threatened me, and of which there was now no trace, pitying Count N—— for being deprived of the joys of fatherhood. I then gave her what money she required and took my leave. She escorted me to the door, and asked me if she should have the pleasure of seeing me again before long.

"It's a pleasure, is it?" I replied; "well, I don't know when you will have it again; it depends on my leisure and my fancy."

It is certain that if I had any amorous feelings or even curiosity about the girl, I should not have left her in that house for a moment; but I repeat my love for her had entirely vanished. There was one thing, however, which annoyed me intolerably, namely, that in spite of my coolness towards her, the little hussy pretended to think that I had forgotten and forgiven everything.

On leaving the Corticelli, I proceeded to call on my bankers, amongst others on M. Martin, whose wife was justly famous for her wit and beauty.

I chanced to meet the horse-dealing Jew, who had made money out of me by means of his daughter Leah. She was still pretty, but married; and her figure was too rounded for my taste. She and her husband welcomed me with great warmth, but I cared for her no longer, and did not wish to see her again.

I called on Madame R——, who had been awaiting me impatiently ever since Victorine had brought news of me. I sat down by the counter and had the pleasure of hearing from her lips the amorous histories of Turin for the past few months.

"Victorine and Caton are the only two of the old set that still remain, but I have replaced them with others."

"Has Victorine found anyone to operate on her yet?"

"No, she is just as you left her, but a gentleman who is in love with her is going to take her to Milan."

This gentleman was the Comte de Pérouse, whose acquaintance I made three years afterwards at Milan. I shall speak of him in due time. Madame R—— told me that, in consequence of her getting into trouble several times with the police, she had been obliged to promise the Count d'Aglié only to send the girls to ladies, and, consequently, if I found any of them to my taste I should be obliged to make friends with their relations and take them to the festas. She shewed me the girls in the work-room, but I did not think any of them worth taking trouble about.

She talked about the Pacienza, and when I told her that I kept the Corticelli, and of the hard conditions to which I was obliged to submit, she exclaimed with astonishment, and amused me by her jests on the subject.

"You are in good hands, my dear sir," said she; "the woman is not only a spy of d'Aglié's, but a professional procuress. I wonder the Chevalier Raiberti placed the girl with her."

She was not so surprised when I told her that the chevalier had good reasons for his action, and that I myself had good reasons of my own for wishing the Corticelli to remain there.

Our conversation was interrupted by a customer who wanted silk stockings. Hearing him speak of dancing, I asked him if he could tell me the address of Dupré, the ballet-master.

"No one better, sir, for I am Dupré, at your service."

"I am delighted at this happy chance. The Chevalier Raiberti gave me to understand that you might be able to give dancing lessons to a ballet-girl of my acquaintance."

"M. de Raiberti mentioned your name to me this morning. You must be the Chevalier de Seingalt?"

"Exactly."

"I can give the young lady lessons every morning at nine o'clock at my own home."

"No, do you come to her house, but at whatever hour you like. I will pay you, and I hope you will make her one of your best pupils. I must warn you, however, that she is not a novice."

"I will call on her to-day, and to-morrow I will tell you what I can make of her; but I think I had better tell you my terms: I charge three Piedmontese livres a lesson."

"I think that is very reasonable; I will call on you to-morrow."

"You do me honour. Here is my address. If you like to come in the afternoon you will see the rehearsal of a ballet."

"Is it not rehearsed at the theatre?"

"Yes, but at the theatre no on-lookers are allowed by the orders of the superintendent of police."

"This superintendent of yours puts his finger into a good many pies."

"In too many."

"But at your own house anybody may come?"

"Undoubtedly, but I could not have the dancers there if my wife were not present. The superintendent knows her, and has great confidence in her."

"You will see me at the rehearsal."

The wretched superintendent had erected a fearful system of surveillance against the lovers of pleasure, but it must be confessed that he was often cheated. Voluptuousness was all the more rampant when thus restrained; and so it ever will be while men have passions and women desires. To love and enjoy, to desire and to satisfy one's desires, such is the circle in which we move, and whence we can never be turned. When restrictions are placed upon the passions as in Turkey, they still attain their ends, but by methods destructive to morality.

At the worthy Mazzoli's I found two gentlemen to whom she introduced me. One was old and ugly, decorated with the Order of the White Eagle—his name was Count Borromeo; the other, young and brisk, was Count A—— B—— of Milan. After they had gone I was informed that they were paying assiduous court to the Chevalier Raiberti, from whom they hoped to obtain certain privileges for their lordships which were under the Sardinian rule.

The Milanese count had not a penny, and the Lord of the Borromean Isles was not much better off. He had ruined himself with women, and not being able to live at Milan he had taken refuge in the fairest of his isles, and enjoyed there perpetual spring and very little else. I paid him a visit on my return from Spain, but I shall relate our meeting when I come to my adventures, my pleasures, my misfortunes, and above all my follies there, for of such threads was the weft of my life composed, and folly was the prominent element.

The conversation turned on my house, and the lively Mazzoli asked me how I liked my cook. I replied that I had not yet tried him, but I proposed to put him *to* test the next day, if she and the gentlemen would do me the honour of supping with me.

The invitation was accepted, and she promised to bring her dear chevalier with her, and to warn him of the event, as his health only allowed him to eat once a day.

I called on Dupré in the afternoon. I saw the dancers,

male and female, the latter accompanied by their moth·
ers, who stood on one side muffled up in thick cloaks.
As I passed them under review in my lordly manner, I
noticed that one of them still looked fresh and pretty,
which augured well for her daughter, though the fruit
does not always correspond to the tree.

Dupré introduced me to his wife, who was young and
pretty, but who had been obliged to leave the theatre
owing to the weakness of her chest. She told me that
if the Corticelli would work hard her husband would
make a great dancer of her, as her figure was eminently
suited for dancing. While I was talking with Madame
Dupré, the Corticelli, late Lascaris, came running up
to me with the air of a favourite, and told me she wanted
some ribbons and laces to make a bonnet. The others
girls began to whisper to each other, and guessing what
they must be saying I turned to Dupré without taking
any notice of Madame Madcap, and gave him twelve
pistoles, saying that I would pay for the lessons three
months in advance, and that I hoped he would bring
his new pupil on well. Such a heavy payment in advance
caused general surprise, which I enjoyed, though pretending not to be aware of it. Now I know that I acted
foolishly, but I have promised to speak the truth in these
Memoirs, which will not see the light till all light has
left my eyes, and I will keep my promise. I have always
been greedy of distinction; I have always loved to draw
the eyes of men towards men, but I must also add that
if I have humiliated anyone it has always been a proud
man or a fool, for it has been my rule to please everyone if I can.

I sat on one side, the better to observe the swarm of
girls, and I soon fixed my eyes on one whose appearance

struck me. She had a fine figure, delicate features, a noble air, and a patient look which interested me in the highest degree. She was dancing with a man who did not scruple to abuse her in the coarsest manner when she made any mistakes, but she bore it without replying, though an expression of contempt mingled with the sweetness of her face.

Instinct drew me to the mother I have remarked on, and I asked her to whom the dancer that interested me belonged.

"I am her mother," she replied.

"You, madam! I should not have thought it possible."

"I was very young when she was born."

"I should think so. Where do you come from?"

"I am from Lucca, and what is more—a poor widow."

"How can you be poor, when you are still young and handsome, and have an angel for a daughter?"

She replied only by an expressive glance. I understood her reserve, and I stayed by her without speaking. Soon after, Agatha, as her daughter was named, came up to her to ask for a handkerchief to wipe her face.

"Allow me to offer you mine," said I. It was a white handkerchief, and scented with attar of roses; this latter circumstance gave her an excuse for accepting it, but after smelling it she wanted to return it to me.

"You have not used it," said I; "do so."

She obeyed, and then returned it to me with a bow by way of thanks.

"You must not give it me back, fair Agatha, till you have had it washed."

She smiled, and gave it to her mother, glancing at me in a grateful manner, which I considered of good omen.

"May I have the pleasure of calling on you?" said I.

"I cannot receive you, sir, except in the presence of my landlady."

"This cursed restriction is general in Turin, then?"

"Yes, the superintendent uses everybody in the same way."

"Then I shall have the pleasure of seeing you again here?"

In the evening I had one of the best suppers I ever had in my life, if I except those I enjoyed during my stay at Turin. My cook was worthy of a place in the kitchen of Lucullus; but without detracting from his skill I must do justice to the products of the country. Everything is delicious; game, fish, birds, meat, vegetables, fruit, milk, and truffles—all are worthy of the table of the greatest *gourmets,* and the wines of the country yield to none. What a pity that strangers do not enjoy liberty at Turin! It is true that better society, and more politeness, such as are found in several French and Italian towns, are to be wished for.

The beauty of the women of Turin is no doubt due to the excellence of the air and diet.

I had not much trouble in extracting a promise from Madame Mazzoli and the two counts to sup with me every night, but the Chevalier de Raiberti would only promise to come whenever he could.

At the Carignan Theatre, where opera-bouffé was being played, I saw Redegonde, with whom I had failed at Florence. She saw me in the pit and gave me a smile, so I wrote to her, offering my services if the mother had changed her way of thinking. She answered that her mother was always the same, but that if I would ask the Corticelli she could come and sup with me, though the mother would doubtless have to be of the party. I gave her no answer, as the terms she named were by no means to my taste.

I had a letter from Madame du Rumain, enclosing one from M. de Choiseul to M. de Chauvelin, the French ambassador at Turin. It will be remembered that I had known this worthy nobleman at Soleure, and had been treated with great politeness by him, but I wished to have a more perfect title to his acquaintance; hence I asked Madame du Rumain to give me a letter.

M. de Chauvelin received me with the greatest cordiality; and reproaching me for having thought a letter of introduction necessary, introduced me to his charming wife, who was no less kind than her husband. Three or four days later he asked me to dine with him, and I met at his table M. Imberti, the Venetian ambassador, who said he was very sorry not to be able to present me at Court. On hearing the reason M. de Chauvelin offered to present me himself, but I thought it best to decline with thanks. No doubt it would have been a great honour, but the result would be that I should be more spied on than even in this town of spies, where the most indifferent actions do not pass unnoticed. My pleasures would have been interfered with.

Count Borromeo continued to honour me by coming every night to sup with me, preserving his dignity the while, for as he accompanied Madame Mazzoli it was not to be supposed that he came because he was in need of a meal. Count A—— B—— came more frankly, and I was pleased with him. He told me one day that the way I put up with his visits made him extremely grateful to Providence, for his wife could not send him any money, and he could not afford to pay for his dinner at the inn, so that if it were not for my kindness he would often be obliged to go hungry to bed. He shewed me his wife's letters; he had evidently a high opinion of her.

"I hope," he would say, "that you will come and stay with us at Milan, and that she will please you."

He had been in the service of Spain, and by what he said I judged his wife to be a pleasing brunette of twenty-five or twenty-six. The count had told her how I had lent him money several times, and of my goodness to him, and she replied, begging him to express her gratitude to me, and to make me promise to stay with them at Milan. She wrote wittily, and her letters interested me to such an extent that I gave a formal promise to journey to Milan, if it were only for the sake of seeing her.

I confess that in doing so I was overcome by my feelings of curiosity. I knew they were poor, and I should not have given a promise which would either bring them into difficulties or expose me to paying too dearly for my lodging. However, by way of excuse, I can only say that curiosity is near akin to love. I fancied the countess sensible like an Englishwoman, passionate like a Spaniard, caressing like a Frenchwoman, and as I had a good enough opinion of my own merit, I did not doubt for a moment that she would respond to my affection. With these pleasant delusions in my head, I counted on exciting the jealousy of all the ladies and gentlemen of Milan. I had plenty of money, and I longed for an opportunity of spending it.

Nevertheless, I went every day to rehearsal at Dupré's, and I soon got madly in love with Agatha. Madame Dupré won over by several presents I made her, received my confidences with kindness, and by asking Agatha and her mother to dinner procured me the pleasure of a more private meeting with my charmer. I profited by the opportunity to make known my feelings, and

I obtained some slight favours, but so slight were they that my flame only grew the fiercer.

Agatha kept on telling me that everybody knew that the Corticelli was my mistress, and that for all the gold in the world she would not have it said that she was my last shift, as I could not see the Corticelli in private. I swore to her that I did not love the Corticelli, and that I only kept her to prevent M. Raiberti being compromised; but all this was of no avail, she had formed her plans, and nothing would content her but a formal rupture which would give all Turin to understand that I loved her and her alone. On these conditions she promised me her heart, and everything which follows in such cases.

I loved her too well not to endeavour to satisfy her, since my satisfaction depended on hers. With this idea I got Dupré to give a ball at my expense in some house outside the town, and to invite all the dancers, male and female, who were engaged for the carnival at Turin. Every gentleman had the right to bring a lady to have supper and look on, as only the professional dancers were allowed to dance.

I told Dupré that I would look after the refreshment department, and that he might tell everybody that no expense was to be spared. I also provided carriages and sedan-chairs for the ladies, but nobody was to know that I was furnishing the money. Dupré saw that there was profit in store for him, and went about it at once. He found a suitable house, asked the lady dancers, and distributed about fifty tickets.

Agatha and her mother were the only persons who knew that the project was mine, and that I was responsible to a great extent for the expenses; but these facts were generally known the day after the ball.

Agatha had no dress that was good enough, so I charged Madame Dupré to provide one at my expense, and I was well served. It is well known that when this sort of people dip their fingers into other's purses they are not sparing, but that was just what I wanted. Agatha promised to dance all the quadrilles with me, and to return to Turin with Madame Dupré.

On the day fixed for the ball I stayed to dinner at the Dupré's to be present at Agatha's toilette. Her dress was a rich and newly-made Lyons silk, and the trimming was exquisite Alençon point lace, of which the girl did not know the value. Madame R——, who had arranged the dress, and Madame Dupré, had received instructions to say nothing about it to her.

When Agatha was ready to start, I told her that the ear-rings she was wearing were not good enough for her dress.

"That's true," said Madame Dupré, "and it's a great pity."

"Unfortunately," said the mother, "my poor girl hasn't got another pair."

"I have some pretty imitation pendants, which I could lend you," said I; "they are really very brilliant."

I had taken care to put the ear-rings which Madame d'Urfé had intended for the Countess Lascaris in my pocket. I drew them out, and they were greatly admired.

"One would swear they were real diamonds," said Madame Dupré.

I put them in Agatha's ears. She admired them very much, and said that all the other girls would be jealous, as they would certainly take them for real stones.

I went home and made an elaborate toilette, and on arriving at the ball I found Agatha dancing with Lord

Percy, a young fool, who was the son of the Duke of Northumberland, and an extravagant spendthrift.

I noticed several handsome ladies from Turin, who, being merely onlookers, might be thinking that the ball was given for their amusement, like the fly on the chariot wheel. All the ambassadors were present, and amongst others M. de Chauvelin, who told me that to make everything complete my pretty housekeeper at Soleure was wanting.

The Marquis and Marchioness de Prié were there also. The marquis did not care to dance, so was playing a little game of quinze with a rude gamester, who would not let the marquis's mistress look over his cards. She saw me, but pretended not to recognize me; the trick I had played her at Aix being probably enough to last her for some time.

The minuets came to an end, and Dupré announced the quadrilles, and I was glad to see the Chevalier Ville-Follet dancing with the Corticelli. My partner was Agatha, who had great difficulty in getting rid of Lord Percy, though she told him that she was fully engaged.

Minuets and quadrilles followed each other in succession, and refreshments began to make their appearance. I was delighted to see that the refreshment counter was furnished with the utmost liberality. The Piedmontese, who are great at calculations, estimated that Dupré must lose by it, the firing of champagne corks was continuous.

Feeling tired I asked Agatha to sit down, and I was telling her how I loved her when Madame de Chauvelin and another lady interrupted us. I rose to give them place, and Agatha imitated my example; but Madame de Chauvelin made her sit down beside her, and praised her dress, and above all the lace trimming. The other lady said how pretty her ear-rings were, and what a pity it was that those imitation stones would lose their brilliance in time. Madame de Chauvelin, who knew something about precious stones, said that they would never lose their brilliance, as they were diamonds of the first water.

"It is not so?" she added, to Agatha, who in the candour of her heart confessed that they were imitation, and that I had lent them to her.

At this Madame de Chauvelin burst out laughing, and said,——

"M. de Seingalt has deceived you, my dear child. A gentleman of his caste does not lend imitation jewellry to such a pretty girl as you are. Your ear-rings are set with magnificent diamonds."

She blushed, for my silence confirmed the lady's assertion, and she felt that the fact of my having lent her such stones was a palpable proof of the great esteem in which I held her.

Madame de Chauvelin asked me to dance a minuet with Agatha, and my partner executed the dance with wonderful grace. When it was over Madame de Chauvelin thanked me, and told me that she should always remember our dancing together at Soleure, and that she hoped I would dance again with her at her own house. A profound bow shewed her how flattered I felt by the compliment.

The ball did not come to an end till four o'clock in the morning, and I did not leave it till I saw Agatha going away in the company with Madame Dupré.

I was still in bed the next morning, when my man told me a pretty woman wanted to speak to me. I had her in and was delighted to find it was Agatha's mother. I made her sit down beside me, and gave her a cup of chocolate. As soon as we were alone she drew my ear-rings from her pocket, and said, with a smile, that she had just been shewing them to a jeweller, who had offered her a thousand sequins for them.

"The man's mad," said I, "you ought to have let him have them; they are not worth four sequins."

So saying, I drew her to my arms and gave her a kiss. Feeling that she had shared in the kiss, and that she seemed to like it, I went farther, and at last we spent a couple of hours in shewing what a high opinion we had of each other.

Afterwards we both looked rather astonished, and it was the beautiful mother who first broke the silence.

"Am I to tell my girl," said she, with a smile, "of the way in which you proved to me that you love her?"

"I leave that to your discretion, my dear," said I. "I have certainly proved that I love you, but it does not follow that I do not adore your daughter. In fact, I burn for her; and yet, if we are not careful to avoid being alone together, what has just happened between us will often happen again."

"It is hard to resist you, and it is possible that I may have occasion to speak to you again in private."

"You may be sure you will always be welcome, and all I ask of you is not to put any obstacles in the way of my suit with Agatha."

"I have also a favour to ask."

"If it is within my power, you may be sure I will grant it."

"Very good! Then tell me if these ear-rings are real, and what was your intention in putting them in my daughter's ears?"

"The diamonds are perfectly genuine, and my intention was that Agatha should keep them as a proof of my affection."

She heaved a sigh, and then told me that I might ask them to supper, with Dupré and his wife, whenever I pleased. I thanked her, gave her ten sequins, and sent her away happy.

On reflection I decided that I had never seen a more sensible woman than Agatha's mother. It would have been impossible to announce the success of my suit in a more delicate or more perspicuous manner.

My readers will no doubt guess that I seized the opportunity and brought this interesting affair to a conclusion. The same evening I asked Dupré and his wife, Agatha and her mother, to sup with me the next day, in addition to my usual company. But as I was leaving Dupré's I had an adventure.

My man, who was a great rascal, but who behaved well on this occasion, ran up to me panting for breath, and said triumphantly,——

"Sir, I have been looking for you to warn you that I have just seen the Chevalier de Ville-Follet slip into Madame Pacienza's house, and I suspect he is making an amorous call on the Corticelli."

I immediately walked to the abode of the worthy spy in high spirits, and hoping that my servant's guess had been correct. I walked in and found the landlady and the mother sitting together. Without noticing them, I was making my way towards the Corticelli's room when the two old ladies arrested my course, telling me that the signora was not well and wanted rest. I pushed them aside, and entered the room so swiftly and suddenly that I found the gentleman in a state of nature while the girl remained stretched on the bed as if petrified by my sudden apparition.

"Sir," said I, "I hope you will pardon me for coming in without knocking."

"Wait a moment, wait a moment."

Far from waiting I went away in high glee, and told the story to the Chevalier Raiberti, who enjoyed it as well as I did. I asked him to warn the Pacienza woman that from that day I would pay nothing for Corticelli, who had ceased to belong to me. He approved, and said,——

"I suppose you will not be going to complain to the Count d'Aglié?"

"It is only fools who complain, above all in circumstances like these."

This scandalous story would have been consigned to forgetfulness, if it had not been for the Chevalier de Ville-Follet's indiscretion. He felt angry at being interrupted in the middle of the business, and remembering he had seen my man just before fixed on him as the informer. Meeting him in the street the chevalier reproached him for spying, whereon the impudent rascal replied that he was only answerable to his master, and that it was his duty to serve me in all things. On this the chevalier caned him, and the man went to complain to the superintendent, who summoned Ville-Follet to appear before him and explain his conduct. Having nothing to fear, he told the whole story.

The Chevalier de Raiberti, too, was very ill received when he went to tell Madame Pacienza that neither he nor I were going to pay her anything more in future; but he would listen to no defence. The chevalier came to sup with me, and he informed me that on leaving the house he had met a police sergeant, whom he concluded had come to cite the landlady to appear before the Count d'Aglié.

The next day, just as I was going to M. de Chauvelin's ball, I received to my great surprise a note from the superintendent begging me to call on him as he had something to communicate to me. I immediately ordered my chairmen to take me to his residence.

M. de Aglié received me in private with great politeness, and after giving me a chair he began a long and pathetic discourse, the gist of which was that it was my duty to forgive this little slip of my mistress's.

"That's exactly what I am going to do," said I; "and for the rest of my days I never wish to see the Corticelli again, or to make or mar in her affairs, and for all this I am greatly obliged to the Chevalier de Ville-Follet."

"I see you are angry. Come, come! you must not abandon the girl for that. I will have the woman Pacienza punished in such a way as to satisfy you, and I will place the girl in a respectable family where you can go and see her in perfect liberty."

"I am greatly obliged to you for your kindness, indeed I am grateful; but I despise the Pacienza too heartily to wish for her punishment, and as to the Corticelli and her mother, they are two female swindlers, who have given me too much trouble already. I am well quit of them."

"You must confess, however, that you had no right to make a forcible entry into a room in a house which does not belong to you."

"I had not the right, I confess, but if I had not taken it I could never have had a certain proof of the perfidy of my mistress; and I should have been obliged to continue supporting her, though she entertained other lovers."

"The Corticelli pretends that you are her debtor, and not *vice versâ*. She says that the diamonds you have given another girl belong of right to her, and that Madame d'Urfé, whom I have the honour to know, presented her with them."

"She is a liar! And as you know Madame d'Urfé, kindly write to her (she is at Lyons); and if the marchioness replies that I owe the wretched girl anything, be sure that I will discharge the debt. I have a hundred thousand francs in good banks of this town, and the money will be a sufficient surety for the ear-rings I have disposed of."

"I am sorry that things have happened so."

"And I am very glad, as I have ridden myself of a burden that was hard to bear."

Thereupon we bowed politely to one another, and I left the office.

At the French ambassador's ball I heard so much talk of my adventure that at last I refused to reply to any more questions on the subject. The general opinion was that the whole affair was a trifle of which I could not honourably take any notice; but I thought myself the best judge of my own honour, and was determined to take no notice of the opinions of others. The Chevalier de Ville-Follet came up to me and said that if I abandoned the Corticelli for such a trifle, he should feel obliged to give me satisfaction. I shook his hand, saying,——

"My dear chevalier, it will be enough if you do not demand satisfaction of me."

He understood how the land lay, and said no more about it; but not so his sister, the Marchioness de Prié, who made a vigorous attack on me after we had danced together. She was handsome, and might have been victorious if she had liked, but luckily she did not think of exerting her power, and so gained nothing.

Three days after, Madame de St. Giles, a great power in Turin, and a kind of protecting deity to all actresses, summoned me to her presence by a liveried footman. Guessing what she wanted, I called on her unceremoniously in a morning coat. She received me politely, and began to talk of the Corticelli affair with great affability; but I did not like her, and replied dryly that I had had no hesitation in abandoning the girl to the protection of the 'gallant gentleman with whom I had surprised her *in flagrante delicto*. She told me I should be sorry for it, and that she would publish a little story which she had already read and which did not do me much credit. I replied that I never changed my mind, and that threats were of no avail with me. With that parting shot I left her.

I did not attach much importance to the town gossip, but a week after I received a manuscript containing an account—accurate in most respects—of my relations with the Corticelli and Madame d'Urfé, but so ill written and badly expressed that nobody could read it without weariness. It did not make the slightest impression on me, and I stayed a fortnight longer in Turin without its causing me the slightest annoyance. I saw the Corticelli again in Paris six months after, and will speak of our meeting in due time.

The day after M. de Chauvelin's ball I asked Agatha, her mother, the Duprés, and my usual company to supper. It was the mother's business to so arrange matters that the ear-rings should become Agatha's lawful property, so I left everything to her. I knew she would manage to introduce the subject, and while we were at supper she said that the common report of Turin was that I had given her daughter a pair of diamond ear-rings worth five hundred louis, which the Corticelli claimed as hers by right.

"I do not know," she added, "if they are real diamonds, or if they belong to the Corticelli, but I do know that my girl has received no such present from the gentleman."

"Well, well," said I, "we will have no more surmises in the matter;" and going up to Agatha I put the earrings on her, saying,——

"Dearest Agatha, I make you a present of them before this company, and my giving them to you now is a proof that hitherto they have belonged to me."

Everybody applauded, and I read in the girl's eyes that I should have no cause to regret my generosity.

We then fell to speaking of the affair of Ville-Follet and the Corticelli, and of the efforts that had been made to compel me to retain her. The Chevalier Raiberti said that in my place he would have offered Madame de St. Giles or the superintendent to continue paying for her board, but merely as an act of charity, and that I could have deposited money with either of them.

"I should be very glad to do so," said I; and the next day the worthy chevalier made the necessary arrangements with Madame de St. Giles, and I furnished the necessary moneys.

In spite of this charitable action, the wretched manuscript came out, but, as I have said, without doing me any harm. The superintendent made the Corticelli live in the same house with Redegonde, and Madame Pacienza was left in peace.

After supper, with the exception of the Chevalier Raiberti, we all masked, and went to the ball at the opera-house. I soon seized the opportunity of escaping with

Agatha, and she granted me all that love can desire. All constraint was banished; she was my titular mistress, and we were proud of belonging the one to the other, for we loved each other. The suppers I had given at my house had set me perfectly at liberty, and the superintendent could do nothing to thwart our love, though he was informed of it, so well are the spies of Turin organized.

Divine Providence made use of me as its instrument in making Agatha's fortune. It may be said that Providence might have chosen a more moral method, but are we to presume to limit the paths of Providence to the narrow circle of our prejudices and conventions? It has its own ways, which often appear dark to us because of our ignorance. At all events, if I am able to continue these Memoirs for six or seven years more, the reader will see that Agatha shewed herself grateful. But to return to our subject.

The happiness we enjoyed by day and night was so great, Agatha was so affectionate and I so amorous, that we should certainly have remained united for some time if it had not been for the event I am about to relate. It made me leave Turin much sooner than I had intended, for I had not purposed to visit the wonderful Spanish countess at Milan till Lent. The husband of the Spanish lady had finished his business and left Turin, thanking me with tears in his eyes; and if it had not been for me he would not have been able to quit the town, for I paid divers small debts he had incurred, and gave him the wherewithal for his journey. Often is vice thus found allied to virtue or masking in virtue's guise; but what matter? I allowed myself to be taken in, and did not wish to be disabused. I do not seek to conceal my faults. I have always led a profligate life, and have not always been very delicate in the choice of means to gratify my passions, but even amidst my vices I was always a passionate lover of virtue. Benevolence, especially, has always had a great charm for me, and I have never failed to exercise it unless when restrained by the desire of vengeance—a vice which has always had a controlling influence on my actions.

Lord Percy, as I have remarked, was deeply in love with my Agatha. He followed her about everywhere, was present at all the rehearsals, waited for her at the wings, and called on her every day, although her landlady, a duenna of the Pacienza school, would never let her see him alone. The principal methods of seduction —rich presents—had not been spared, but Agatha persistently refused them all, and forbade her duenna to take anything from the young nobleman. Agatha had no liking for him, and kept me well informed of all his actions, and we used to laugh at him together. I knew that I possessed her heart, and consequently Lord Percy's attempts neither made me angry or jealous— nay, they flattered my self-esteem, for his slighted love made my own happiness stand out in greater relief. Everybody knew that Agatha remained faithful to me, and at last Lord Percy was so convinced of the hopelessness of the attempt that he resolved on making a friend of me, and winning me over to his interests.

With the true Englishman's boldness and coolness he came to me one morning, and asked me to give him breakfast. I welcomed him in the French manner, that is, with combined cordiality and politeness, and he was soon completely at his ease.

With insular directness he went straight to the point at the first interview, declared his love for Agatha, and proposed an exchange, which amused, but did not offend me, as I knew that such bargains were common in England.

"I know," said he, "that you are in love with Redegonde, and have long tried vainly to obtain her; now I am willing to exchange her for Agatha, and all I want to know is what sum of money you want over and above?"

"You are very good, my dear lord, but to determine the excess of value would require a good mathematician. Redegonde is all very well, and inspires me with curiosity, but what is she compared to Agatha?"

"I know, I know, and I therefore offer you any sum you like to mention."

Percy was very rich, and very passionate. I am sure that if I had named twenty-five thousand guineas as overplus, or rather as exchange—for I did not care for Redegonde—he would have said *done*. However, I did not, and I am glad of it. Even now, when a hundred thousand francs would be a fortune to me, I never repent of my delicacy.

After we had breakfasted merrily together, I told him that I liked him well, but that in the first place it would be well to ascertain whether the two commodities would consent to change masters.

"I am sure of Redegonde's consent," said Lord Percy.

"But I am not at all sure of Agatha's," said I.

"Why not?"

"I have very strong grounds for supposing that she would not consent to the arrangement. What reasons have you for the contrary opinion?"

"She will shew her sense."

"But she loves me."

"Well, Redegonde loves me."

"I dare say; but does she love me?"

"I am sure I don't know, but she will love you."

"Have you consulted her upon the point?"

"No, but it is all the same. What I want to know now is whether you approve of my plan, and how much you want for the exchange, for your Agatha is worth much more than my Redegonde."

"I am delighted to hear you do my mistress justice. As for the money question, we will speak of that later. In the first place I will take Agatha's opinion, and will let you know the result to-morrow morning."

The plan amused me, and though I was passionately attached to Agatha I knew my inconstant nature well enough to be aware that another woman, may be not so fair as she, would soon make me forget her. I therefore resolved to push the matter through if I could do so in a manner that would be advantageous for her.

What surprised me was that the young nobleman had gained possession of Redegonde, whose mother appeared so intractable, but I knew what an influence caprice has on woman, and this explained the enigma.

Agatha came to supper as usual, and laughed heartily when I told her of Lord Percy's proposal.

"Tell me," said I, "if you would agree to the change?"

"I will do just as you like," said she; "and if the money he offers be acceptable to you, I advise you to close with him."

I could see by the tone of her voice that she was jesting, but her reply did not please me. I should have liked to have my vanity flattered by a peremptory refusal, and consequently I felt angry. My face grew grave, and Agatha became melancholy.

"We will see," said I, "how it all ends."

Next day I went to breakfast with the Englishman, and told him Agatha was willing, but that I must first hear what Redegonde had to say.

"Quite right," he observed.

"I should require to know how we are to live together."

"The four of us had better go masked to the first ball at the Carignan Theatre. We will sup at a house which belongs to me, and there the bargain can be struck."

The party took place according to agreement, and at the given signal we all left the ball-room. My lord's carriage was in waiting, and we all drove away and got down at a house I seemed to know. We entered the hall, and the first thing I saw was the Corticelli. This roused my choler, and taking Percy aside I told him that such a trick was unworthy of a gentleman. He laughed, and said he thought I should like her to be thrown in, and that two pretty women were surely worth as much as Agatha. This amusing answer made me less angry; but, calling him a madman, I took Agatha by the arm and went out without staying for any explanations. I would not make use of his carriage, and instead of returning to the ball we went home in sedan-chairs, and spent a delicious night in each other's arms.

CHAPTER XVIII

I Give up Agatha to Lord Percy—I Set out for Milan—
The Actress at Pavia—Countess A * * * B * * *—
Disappointment — Marquis Triulzi — Zenobia — The
Two Marchionesses Q * * *—The Venetian Barbaro

FAR from punishing the Corticelli by making her live
with Redegonde, the Count d'Aglié seemed to have
encouraged her; and I was not sorry for it, since as long
as she did not trouble me any more I did not care how
many lovers she had. She had become a great friend
of Redegonde's, and did exactly as she pleased, for
their duenna was much more easy going than the Pacienza.

Nobody knew of the trick which Lord Percy had
played me, and I took care to say nothing about it.
However, he did not give up his designs on Agatha, his
passion for her was too violent. He hit upon an ingenious method for carrying out his plans. I have already said that Percy was very rich, and spent his money
wildly, not caring at what expenditure he gratified his
passion. I was the last person to reproach him for his
extravagance, and in a country where money is always
scarce his guineas opened every door to him.

Four or five days after the ball night, Agatha came
to tell me that the manager of the Alexandria Theatre
had asked her if she would take the part of second
dancer throughout the carnival time.

"He offered me sixty sequins," she added, "and I told

him I would let him know by to-morrow. Do you advise me to accept his offer?"

"If you love me, dearest Agatha, you will prove it by refusing all engagements for a year. You know I will let you want for nothing. I will get you the best masters, and in that time you can perfect your dancing, and will be able to ask for a first-class appointment, with a salary of five hundred sequins a year."

"Mamma thinks that I should accept the offer, as the dancing on the stage will improve my style, and I can study under a good master all the same. I think myself that dancing in public would do me good."

"There is reason in what you say, but you do not need the sixty sequins. You will dishonour me by accepting such a poor offer, and you will do yourself harm too, as you will not be able to ask for a good salary after taking such a small one."

"But sixty sequins is not so bad for a carnival engagement."

"But you don't want sixty sequins; you can have them without dancing at all. If you love me, I repeat, you will tell the manager that you are going to rest for a year."

"I will do what you please, but it seems to me the best plan would be to ask an exorbitant sum."

"You are right; that is a good idea. Tell him you must be first dancer, and that your salary must be five hundred sequins."

"I will do so, and am only too happy to be able to prove that I love you."

Agatha had plenty of inborn common sense, which only needed development. With that and the beauty which Heaven had given her her future was assured.

She was eventually happy, and she deserved her happiness.

The next day she told me that the manager did not appear at all astonished at her demands.

"He reflected a few minutes," said she, "and told me he must think it over, and would see me again. It would be amusing if he took me at my word, would it not?"

"Yes, but we should then have to enquire whether he is a madman or a beggar on the verge of bankruptcy."

"And if he turns out to be a man of means?"

"In that case you would be obliged to accept."

"That is easily said and easily done, but have I sufficient talent? Where shall I find an actor to dance with me?"

"I will engage to find you one. As to talent, you have enough and to spare; but you will see that it will come to nothing."

All the time I felt a presentiment that she would be engaged, and I was right. The manager came to her the next day, and offered her the agreement for her signature. She was quite alarmed, and sent for me. I called at her house, and finding the manager there asked him what security he could give for the fulfilment of his part of the engagement.

He answered by naming M. Martin, a banker of my acquaintance, who would be his surety. I could make no objection to this, and the agreement was made out in duplicate in good form.

On leaving Agatha I went to M. Raiberti and told him the story. He shared my astonishment that M. Martin should become surety for the manager whom he knew, and whose financial position was by no means good; but the next day the problem was solved, for in spite of the secrecy that had been observed we found out that it was Lord Percy who was behind the manager. I might still bar the Englishman's way by continuing to keep Agatha, in spite of his five hundred sequins, but I was obliged to return to France after Easter to wait on Madame d'Urfé, and afterwards, peace having been concluded, I thought it would be a good opportunity for seeing England. I therefore determined to abandon Agatha, taking care to bind her new lover to provide for her, and I proceeded to make a friend of the nobleman. I was curious to see how he would win Agatha's good graces, for she did not love him, and physically he was not attractive.

In less than a week we had become intimate. We supped together every night either at his house or mine, and Agatha and her mother were always of the party. I concluded that his attentions would soon touch Agatha's heart, and that finding herself so beloved she would end by loving. This was enough to make me determine not to put any obstacles in their way, and I resolved to leave Turin earlier than I had intended. In consequence I spoke as follows to Lord Percy, while we were breakfasting together:

"My lord, you know that I love Agatha, and that she loves me, nevertheless I am your friend, and since you adore her I will do my best to hasten your bliss. I will leave you in possession of this treasure, but you must promise that when you abandon her you will give her two thousand guineas."

"My dear sir," said he, "I will give them her now if you like."

"No, my lord, I do not wish her to know anything about our agreement while you are living happily together."

"Then I will give you a bond binding myself to pay her the two thousand guineas when we separate."

"I don't want that, the word of an Englishman is enough; but since we cannot command the fates, and may die without having time to put our affairs in order, I wish you to take such steps as may seem convenient to you, whereby that sum would go to her after your death."

"I give you my word on it."

"That is enough; but I have one other condition to make."

"Say on."

"It is that you promise to say nothing to Agatha before my departure."

"I swear I will not."

"Very good; and on my part I promise to prepare her for the change."

The same day the Englishman, whose love grew hotter and hotter, made Agatha and her mother rich presents, which under any other circumstances I should not have allowed them to accept.

I lost no time in preparing Agatha and her mother for the impending change. They seemed affected, but I knew they would soon get reconciled to the situation. Far from giving me any cause for complaint, Agatha was more affectionate than ever. She listened attentively to my advice as to her conduct towards her new lover and the world in general, and promised to follow it. It was to this advice that she owed her happiness, for Percy made her fortune. However, she did not leave the theatre for some years, when we shall hear more of her.

I was not the man to take presents from my equals, and Percy no doubt being aware of that succeeded in making me a handsome present in a very singular way. I told him that I thought of paying a visit to England and requested him to give me a letter of introduction to the duchess, his mother, whereon he drew out a portrait of her set with magnificent diamonds, and gave it to me, saying,——

"This is the best letter I can give you. I will write and tell her that you will call and give her the portrait, unless, indeed, she likes to leave it in your hands."

"I hope my lady will think me worthy of such an honour."

There are certain ideas, it seems to me, which enter no head but an Englishman's.

I was invited by Count A—— B—— to Milan, and the countess wrote me a charming letter, begging me to get her two pieces of sarcenet, of which she enclosed the patterns.

After taking leave of all my friends and acquaintances I got a letter of credit on the banker, Greppi, and started for the capital of Lombardy.

My separation from Agatha cost me many tears, but not so many as those shed by her. Her mother wept also, for she loved me, and was grateful for all my kindness to her daughter. She said again and again that she could never have borne any rival but her own daughter, while the latter sobbed out that she wished she had not to part from me.

I did not like Passano, so I sent him to his family at Genoa, giving him the wherewithal to live till I came for him. As to my man, I dismissed him for good reasons and took another, as I was obliged to have somebody; but since I lost my Spaniard I have never felt confidence in any of my servants.

I travelled with a Chevalier de Rossignan, whose acquaintance I had made, and we went by Casal to see the opera-bouffé there.

Rossignan was a fine man, a good soldier, fond of wine and women, and, though he was not learned, he knew the whole of Dante's Divine Comedy by heart. This was his hobby-horse, and he was always quoting it, making the passage square with his momentary feelings. This made him insufferable in society, but he was an amusing companion for anyone who knew the sublime poet, and could appreciate his numerous and rare beauties. Nevertheless he made me privately give in my assent to the proverb, *Beware of the man of one book.* Otherwise he was intelligent, statesmanlike, and good-natured. He made himself known at Berlin by his services as ambassador to the King of Sardinia.

There was nothing interesting in the opera at Casal, so I went to Pavia, where, though utterly unknown, I was immediately welcomed by the Marchioness Corti, who received all strangers of any importance. In 1786 I made the acquaintance of her son, an admirable man, who honoured me with his friendship, and died quite young in Flanders with the rank of major-general. I wept bitterly for his loss, but tears, after all, are but an idle tribute to those who cause them to flow. His good qualities had endeared him to all his acquaintances, and if he had lived longer he would undoubtedly have risen to high command in the army.

I only stopped two days at Pavia, but it was decreed that I should get myself talked of, even in that short time.

At the second ballet at the opera an actress dressed in a tippet held out her cap to the boxes as if to beg an alms, while she was dancing a *pas de deux.* I was in the

Marchioness of Corti's box, and when the girl held out her cap to me I was moved by feelings of ostentation and benevolence to draw forth my purse and drop it in. It contained about twenty ducats. The girl took it, thanked me with a smile, and the pit applauded loudly. I asked the Marquis Belcredi, who was near me, if she had a lover.

"She has a penniless French officer, I believe," he replied; "there he is, in the pit."

I went back to my inn, and was supping with M. Basili, a Modenese colonel, when the ballet girl, her mother, and her younger sister came to thank me for my providential gift. "We are so poor," said the girl.

I had almost done supper, and I asked them all to sup with me after the performance the next day. This offer was quite a disinterested one, and it was accepted.

I was delighted to have made a woman happy at so little expense and without any ulterior objects, and I was giving orders to the landlord for the supper, when Clairmont, my man, told me that a French officer wanted to speak to me. I had him in, and asked what I could do for him.

"There are three courses before you, Mr. Venetian," said he, "and you can take which you like. Either countermand this supper, invite me to come to it, or come and measure swords with me now."

Clairmont, who was attending to the fire, did not give me time to reply, but seized a burning brand and rushed on the officer, who thought it best to escape. Luckily for him the door of my room was open. He made such a noise in running downstairs that the waiter came out and caught hold of him, thinking he had stolen something; but Clairmont, who was pursuing him with his firebrand, had him released.

This adventure became town talk directly. My servant, proud of his exploit and sure of my approval, came to tell me that I need not be afraid of going out, as the officer was only a braggart. He did not even draw his sword on the waiter who had caught hold of him, though the man only had a knife in his belt.

"At all events," he added, "I will go out with you."

I told him that he had done well this time, but that for the future he must not interfere in my affairs.

"Sir," he replied, "your affairs of this kind are mine too, I shall take care not to go beyond my duty."

With this speech, which I thought very sensible, though I did not tell him so, he took one of my pistols and saw to the priming, smiling at me significantly.

All good French servants are of the same stamp as Clairmont; they are devoted and intelligent, but they all think themselves cleverer than their masters, which indeed is often the case, and when they are sure of it they become the masters of their masters, tyrannize over them, and give them marks of contempt which the foolish gentlemen endeavour to conceal. But when the master knows how to make himself respected, the Clairmonts are excellent.

The landlord of my inn sent a report of the affair to the police, and the French officer was banished from the town the same day. At dinner Colonel Basili asked to hear the story, and said that no one but a French officer would think of attacking a man in his own room in such a foolish manner. I differed from him.

"The French are brave," I replied, "but generally they are perfectly polite and have wonderful tact. Wretchedness and love, joined to a false spirit of courage, makes a fool of a man all the world over."

At supper the ballet-girl thanked me for ridding her

of the poor devil, who (as she said) was always threatening to kill her, and wearied her besides. Though she was not beautiful, there was something captivating about this girl. She was graceful, well-mannered, and intelligent, her mouth was well-shaped, and her eyes large and expressive. I think I should have found her a good bargain, but as I wanted to get away from Pavia, and piqued myself on having been good-natured without ulterior motive, I bade her farewell after supper, with many thanks for her kindness in coming. My politeness seemed rather to confuse her, but she went away reiterating her gratitude.

Next day I dined at the celebrated Chartreuse, and in the evening I reached Milan, and got out at Count A——B——'s, who had not expected me till the following day.

The countess, of whom my fancy had made a perfect woman, disappointed me dreadfully. It is always so when passion gives reins to the imagination. The Countess was certainly pretty, though too small, and I might still have loved her, in spite of my disappointment, but at our meeting she greeted me with a gravity that was not to my taste, and which gave me a dislike to her.

After the usual compliments, I gave her the two pieces of sarcenet she had commissioned me to get. She thanked me, telling me that her confessor would reimburse me for my expenditure. The count then took me to my room, and left me there till supper. It was nicely furnished, but I felt ill at ease, and resolved to leave in a day or two if the countess remained immovable. Twenty-four hours was as much as I cared to give her.

We made a party of four at supper; the count talking all the time to draw me out, and to hide his wife's sulkiness. I answered in the same gay strain, speaking to his wife, however, in the hope of rousing her. It was all lost labour. The little woman only replied by faint smiles which vanished almost as they came, and by monosyllabic answers of the briefest description, without taking her eyes off the dishes which she thought tasteless; and it was to the priest, who was the fourth person present, that she addressed her complaints, almost speaking affably to him.

Although I liked the count very well, I could not help pronouncing his wife decidedly ungracious. I was looking at her to see if I could find any justification for her ill humour on her features, but as soon as she saw me she turned away in a very marked manner, and began to speak about nothing to the priest. This conduct offended me, and I laughed heartily at her contempt, or her designs on me, for as she had not fascinated me at all I was safe from her tyranny.

After supper the sarcenet was brought in; it was to be used for a dress with hoops, made after the extravagant fashion then prevailing.

The count was grieved to see her fall so short of the praises he had lavished on her, and came to my room with me, begging me to forgive her Spanish ways, and saying that she would be very pleasant when she knew me better.

The count was poor, his house was small, his furniture shabby, and his footman's livery threadbare; instead of plate he had china, and one of the countess's maids was chief cook. He had no carriages nor horses, not even a saddle horse of any kind. Clairmont gave me all this information, and added that he had to sleep in a little kitchen, and was to share his bed with the man who had waited at table.

I had only one room, and having three heavy trunks

found myself very uncomfortable, and I decided on seeking some other lodging more agreeable to my tastes.

The count came early in the morning to ask what I usually took for breakfast.

"My dear count," I replied, "I have enough fine Turin chocolate to go all round. Does the countess like it?"

"Very much, but she won't take it unless it is made by her woman."

"Here are six pounds; make her accept it, and tell her that if I hear anything about payment I shall take it back."

"I am sure she will accept it, and thank you too. Shall I have your carriage housed?"

"I shall be extremely obliged to you, and I shall be glad if you would get me a hired carriage, and a guide for whom you can answer."

"It shall be done."

The count was going out when the priest, who had supped with us the night before, came in to make his bow. He was a man of forty—one of the tribe of domestic chaplains who are so common in Italy—who, in return for keeping the accounts of the house, live with its master and mistress. In the morning this priest said mass in a neighbouring church, for the rest of the day he either occupied himself with the cares of the house, or was the lady's obedient servant.

As soon as we were alone he begged me to say that he had paid me the three hundred Milanese crowns for the sarcenet, if the countess asked me about it.

"Dear, dear, abbé!" said I, laughing, "this sort of thing is not exactly proper in a man of your sacred profession. How can you advise me to tell a lie? No, sir; if the countess asks me any such impertinent question, I shall tell her the truth."

"I am sure she will ask you, and if you answer like that I shall suffer for it."

"Well, sir, if you are in the wrong you deserve to suffer."

"But as it happens, I should be blamed for nothing."

"Well, go and tell her it's a present; and if she won't have that, tell her I am in no hurry to be paid."

"I see, sir, that you don't know the lady or the way in which this house is managed. I will speak to her husband."

In a quarter of an hour the count told me that he owed me a lot of money, which he hoped to pay back in the course of Lent, and that I must add the sarcenet to the account. I embraced him and said that he would have to keep the account himself, as I never noted down any of the moneys that I was only too happy to lend to my friends.

"If your wife asks me whether I have received the money, be sure I will answer in the affirmative."

He went out shedding grateful tears, while I felt indebted to him for having given me the opportunity of doing him a service; for I was very fond of him.

In the morning, the countess being invisible, I watched my man spreading out my suits over the chairs, amongst them being some handsome women's cloaks, and a rich red dress deeply trimmed with fur, which had been originally intended for the luckless Corticelli. I should no doubt have given it to Agatha, if I had continued to live with her, and I should have made a mistake, as such a dress was only fit for a lady of rank.

At one o'clock I received another visit from the count, who told me that the countess was going to introduce me to their best friend. This was the Marquis Triulzi, a man of about my own age, tall, well made, squinting slightly, and with all the manner of a nobleman. He told me that besides coming to have the honour of my acquaintance, he also came to enjoy the fire, "for," said he, "there's only one fireplace in the house and that's in your room."

As all the chairs were covered, the marquis drew the countess on to his knee and made her sit there like a baby; but she blushed, and escaped from his grasp. The marquis laughed heartily at her confusion, and she said,——

"Is it possible that a man of your years has not yet learnt to respect a woman?"

"Really, countess," said he, "I thought it would be very disrespectful to continue sitting while you were standing."

While Clairmont was taking the clothes off the chairs, the marquis noticed the mantles and the beautiful dress, and asked me if I were expecting a lady.

"No," said I, "but I hope to find someone at Milan who will be worthy of such presents." I added, "I know the Prince Triulzi, at Venice; I suppose he is of your family?"

"He says he is, and it may be so; but I am certainly not a member of his family."

This let me know that I should do well to say no more about the prince.

"You must stay to dinner, marquis," said Count A—— B——; "and as you only like dishes prepared by your own cook you had better send for them."

The marquis agreed, and we made good cheer. The table was covered with fair linen and handsome plate, the wine was good and plentiful, and the servants quick and well dressed. I could now understand the marquis's position in the house. It was his wit and mirth which kept the conversation going, and the countess came in for a share of his pleasantries, while she scolded him for his familiarity. I could see, however, that the marquis did not want to humiliate her; on the contrary, he was fond of her, and only wished to bring down her exaggerated pride. When he saw her on the point of bursting into tears of rage and shame, he quieted her down by saying that no one in Milan respected her charms and her high birth more than he.

After dinner the tailor who was to measure the countess for a domino for the ball was announced. On the marquis's praising the colours and the beauty of the materials, she told him that I had brought her the sarcenet from Turin, and this reminded her to ask me whether I had been paid.

"Your husband settled with me," said I, "but you have given me a lesson I can never forget."

"What lesson?" said the marquis.

"I had hoped that the countess would have deigned to receive this poor present at my hands."

"And she wouldn't take it? It's absurd, on my life."

"There is nothing to laugh at," said the countess, "but you laugh at everything."

While the man was measuring her, she complained of feeling cold, as she was in her stays, and her beautiful breast was exposed. Thereupon, the marquis put his hands on it, as if he were quite accustomed to use such familiarities. But the Spaniard, no doubt ashamed because of my presence, got into a rage, and abused him in the most awful manner, while he laughed pleasantly, as if he could calm the storm when he pleased. This was enough to inform me of the position in which they stood to one another, and of the part I ought to take.

We remained together till the evening, when the

countess and the marquis went to the opera, and the
count came with me to my room, till my carriage was
ready to take us there too. The opera had begun when
we got in, and the first person I noticed on the stage was
my dear Thérèse Palesi, whom I had left at Florence. It
was a pleasant surprise to me, and I foresaw that we
should renew our sweet interviews while I remained at
Milan I was discreet enough to say nothing to the count
about his wife's charms, or the way their house was
managed. I saw that the place was taken, and the odd
humours of the lady prevented my falling in love with
her. After the second act we went to the assembly
rooms, where five or six banks at faro were being held;
I staked and lost a hundred ducats as if to pay for my
welcome, and then rose from the table.

At supper the countess seemed to unbend a little, she
condoled with me on my loss, and I said that I was glad
of it as it made her speak so.

Just as I rang my bell the next morning, Clairmont
told me that a woman wanted to speak to me.

"Is she young?"

"Both young and pretty, sir."

"That will do nicely, shew her in."

I saw a simply dressed girl, who reminded me of Leah.
She was tall and beautiful, but had not as high pretensions as the Jewess, as she only wanted to know whether
she could do my washing for me. I was quite taken with
her. Clairmont had just brought me my chocolate, and
I asked her to sit down on the bed; but she answered
modestly that she did not want to trouble me, and would
come again when I was up.

"Do you live at any distance?"

"I live on the ground floor of this house."

"All by yourself?"

"No sir, I have my father and mother."

"And what is your name?"

"Zenobia."

"Your name is as pretty as you are. Will you give me your hand to kiss?"

"I can't," she replied, with a smile, "my hand is another's."

"You are engaged, are you?"

"Yes, to a tailor, and we are going to be married before the end of the carnival."

"Is he rich or handsome?"

"Neither the one nor the other."

"Then why are you going to marry him?"

"Because I want to have a house of my own."

"I like you, and will stand your friend. Go and fetch your tailor. I will give him some work to do."

As soon as she went out I got up and told Clairmont to put my linen on a table. I had scarcely finished dressing when she came back with her tailor. It was a striking contrast, for he was a little shrivelled-up man, whose appearance made one laugh.

"Well, master tailor," said I, "so you are going to marry this charming girl?"

"Yes, sir, the banns have been published already."

"You are a lucky fellow indeed to have so much happiness in store. When are you going to marry her?"

"In ten or twelve days."

"Why not to-morrow?"

"Your worship is in a great hurry."

"I think I should be, indeed," said I, laughing, "if I were in your place. I want you to make me a domino for the ball to-morrow."

"Certainly, sir; but your excellency must find me the stuff, for nobody in Milan would give me credit for it, and I couldn't afford to lay out so much money in advance."

"When you are married you will have money and credit too. In the meanwhile here are ten sequins for you."

He went away in high glee at such a windfall.

I gave Zenobia some lace to do up, and asked her if she was afraid of having a jealous husband.

"He is neither jealous nor amorous," she replied. "He is only marrying me because I earn more than he does."

"With your charms I should have thought you might have made a better match."

"I have waited long enough; I have got tired of maidenhood. Besides, he is sharp if he is not handsome, and perhaps a keen head is better than a handsome face."

"You are sharp enough yourself, anyhow. But why does he put off the wedding?"

"Because he hasn't got any money, and wants to have a fine wedding for his relations to come to. I should like it myself."

"I think you are right; but I can't see why you should not let an honest man kiss your hand."

"That was only a piece of slyness to let you know I was to be married. I have no silly prejudices myself."

"Ah, that's better! Tell your future husband that if he likes me to be the patron of the wedding I will pay for everything."

"Really?"

"Yes, really. I will give him twenty-five sequins on the condition that he spends it all on the wedding."

"Twenty-five sequins! That will make people talk; but what care we? I will give you an answer to-morrow."

"And a kiss now?"

"With all my heart."

Zenobia went away in great delight, and I went out to call on my banker and dear Thérèse.

When the door was opened the pretty maid recognized me, and taking me by the hand led me to her mistress, who was just going to get up. Her emotion at seeing me was so great that she could not utter a word, but only claps me to her breast.

Our natural transports over, Thérèse told me that she had got tired of her husband, and that for the last six months they had not been living together. She had made him an allowance to get rid of him, and he lived on it at Rome.

"And where is Cesarino?"

"In this town. You can see him whenever you like."

"Are you happy?"

"Quite. People say that I have a lover, but it is not true; and you can see me at any time with perfect liberty."

We spent two pleasant hours in telling each other of our experiences since our last meeting, and then, finding her as fresh and fair as in the season of our early loves, I asked her if she had vowed to be faithful to her husband.

"At Florence," she replied, "I was still in love with him; but now, if I am still pleasing in your eyes, we can renew our connection, and live together till we die."

"I will soon shew you, dearling, that I love you as well as ever."

She answered only by giving herself up to my embrace.

After action and contemplation I left her as amorous as she had been eighteen years before, but my passion found too many new objects to remain constant long.

Countess A—— B—— began to be more polite. "I know where you have been," said she, with a pleased air; "but if you love that person, you will not go and see her again, or else her lover will leave her."

"Then I would take his place, madam."

"You are right in amusing yourself with women who know how to earn your presents. I am aware that you never give anything till you have received evident proofs of their affection."

"That has always been my principle."

"It's an excellent way to avoid being duped. The lover of the person you have been with kept a lady in society for some time in great splendour, but all the rest of us despised her."

"Why so, if you please?"

"Because she lowered herself so terribly. Greppi is absolutely a man of no family whatever."

Without expressing my surprise at the name of Greppi, I replied that a man need not be well born to be an excellent lover.

"The only thing needful," said I, "is a fine physique and plenty of money, and those ladies who despised their friend were either ridiculously proud or abominably envious. I have not the slightest doubt that if they could find any more Greppis they would be willing enough to lower themselves."

She would doubtless have made a sharp reply, for what I had said had angered her; but the Marquis Triulzi arriving, she went out with him, while her husband and myself went to a place where there was a bank at faro, the banker only having a hundred sequins before him.

I took a card and staked small sums like the rest of

the company. After losing twenty ducats I left the place.

As we were going to the opera the poor count told me I had made him lose ten ducats on his word of honour, and that he did not know how he could pay it by the next day. I pitied him, and gave him the money without a word; for misery has always appealed strongly to me. Afterwards I lost two hundred ducats at the same bank to which I had lost money the evening before. The count was in the greatest distress. He did not know that Greppi, whom his proud wife considered so worthless, had a hundred thousand francs of my money, and that I possessed jewellery to an even greater amount.

The countess, who had seen me lose, asked me if I would sell my beautiful dress.

"They say it's worth a thousand sequins," said she.

"Yes, that is so; but I would sell everything I possess before parting with any of the articles which I intend for the fair sex."

"Marquis Triulzi wants it badly to present to someone."

"I am very sorry, but I cannot sell it to him."

She went away without a word, but I could see that she was exceedingly vexed at my refusal.

As I was leaving the opera-house I saw Thérèse getting into her sedan-chair. I went up to her, and told her that I was sure she was going to sup with her lover. She whispered in my ear that she was going to sup by herself, and that I might come if I dared. I gave her an agreeable surprise by accepting the invitation.

"I will expect you, then," she said.

I asked the count to ride home in my carriage, and taking a chair I reached Thérèse's house just as she was going in.

What a happy evening we had! We laughed heartily when we told each other our thoughts.

"I know you were in love with Countess A—— B——," said she, "and I felt sure you would not dare to come to supper with me."

"And I thought I should confound you by accepting your invitation, as I knew Greppi was your lover."

"He is my friend," she replied. "If he loves me in any other way than that of friendship, I pity him, for as yet he has not discovered the secret of seduction."

"Do you think he ever will?"

"No, I don't. I am rich."

"Yes, but he is richer than you."

"I know that, but I think he loves his money better than he loves me."

"I understand. You will make him happy if he loves you well enough to ruin himself."

"That is it, but it will never come to pass. But here we are, together again after a divorce of nearly twenty years. I don't think you will find any change in me."

"That is a privilege which nature grants to the fair sex only. You will find me changed, but you will be able to work miracles."

This was a piece of politeness, for she was hardly capable of working any miracle. However, after an excellent supper, we spent two hours in amorous raptures, and then Morpheus claimed us for his own. When we awoke I did not leave her before giving her a good day equal to the good night which had sent us to sleep.

When I got back I found the fair Zenobia, who said the tailor was ready to marry her next Sunday if my offer was not a joke.

"To convince you of the contrary," said I, "here are the twenty-five sequins."

Full of gratitude she let herself fall into my arms, and I covered her mouth and her beautiful bosom with my fiery kisses. Thérèse had exhausted me, so I did not go any further, but the girl no doubt attributed my self-restraint to the fact that the door was open. I dressed carefully, and made myself look less weary, and to freshen myself up I had a long drive in an open carriage.

When I returned, I found the Marquis of Triulzi teasing the countess as usual. On that day he furnished the dinner, and it was consequently, a very good one.

The conversation turned on the dress in my possession, and the countess told the marquis, like an idiot, that it was destined for the lady who would make me desirous and gratify my desire.

With exquisite politeness the marquis told me that I deserved to enjoy favours at a cheaper rate.

"I suppose you will be giving it to the person with whom you spent the night," said the countess.

"That's an impossibility," I answered, "for I spent the night in play."

Just then Clairmont came in, and told me an officer wanted to speak to me. I went to the door, and saw a handsome young fellow, who greeted me with an embrace. I recognized him as Barbaro, the son of a Venetian noble, and brother of the fair and famous Madame Gritti Sgombro, of whom I spoke ten years ago, whose husband had died in the citadel of Cattaro, where the State Inquisitors had imprisoned him. My young friend had also fallen into disgrace with the despotic Inquisitors. We had been good friends during the year before my imprisonment, but I had heard nothing of him since.

Barbaro told me the chief incidents in a life that had been adventurous enough, and informed me that he was now in the service of the Duke of Modena, the Governor of Milan.

"I saw you losing money at Canano's bank," said he, "and remembering our old friendship I want to communicate to you a sure way of winning money. All that is necessary is for me to introduce you to a club of young men who are very fond of play, and cannot possibly win."

"Where does this club meet?"

"In an extremely respectable house. If you agree I will keep the bank myself, and I am sure of winning. I want you to lend me capital, and I only ask a fourth of the profits."

"I suppose you can hold the cards well."

"You are right."

This was as much as to tell me that he was an adroit sharper, or, in other words, a skilful corrector of fortune's mistakes. He concluded by saying that I should find something worth looking at in the house he had mentioned.

"My dear sir," I replied, "I will give you my decision after seeing the club to which you want to introduce me."

"Will you be at the theatre coffee-house at three o'clock to-morrow?"

"Yes, but I hope to see you at the ball in the evening."

Zenobia's betrothed brought me my domino, and the countess had hers already. As the ball did not begin till the opera was over, I went to hear Thérèse's singing. In the interval between the acts I lost another two hundred sequins, and then went home to dress for the ball. The countess said that if I would be kind enough to take her to the ball in my carriage and fetch her home in it,

she would not send for the Marquis Triulzi's. I replied
that I was at her service.

Under the impression that the fair Spaniard had only
given me the preference to enable me to take liberties
with her, I told her I should be very glad to give her the
dress, and that the only condition was that I should spent
a night with her.

"You insult me cruelly," said she, "you must know my
character better than that."

"I know everything, my dear countess; but, after all,
the insult's nothing; you can easily forgive me if you
pluck up a little spirit; trample on a foolish prejudice;
get the dress, and make me happy for a whole night
long."

"That it all very well when one is in love, but you must
confess that your coarse way of speaking is more likely
to make me hate you than love you."

"I use that style, because I want to come to the point;
I have no time to waste. And you, countess, must confess in your turn, that you would be delighted to have me
sighing at your feet."

"It would be all the same to me, I don't think I could
love you."

"Then we are agreed on one point at all events, for
I love you no more than you love me."

"And yet you would spend a thousand sequins for the
pleasure of passing a night with me."

"Not at all, I don't want to sleep with you for the
sake of the pleasure, but to mortify your infernal pride,
which becomes you so ill."

God knows what the fierce Spaniard would have answered, but at that moment the carriage stopped at the
door of the theatre. We parted, and after I had got

tired of threading my way amidst the crowd I paid a
visit to the gaming-room, hoping to regain the money I
had lost. I had more than five hundred sequins about me
and a good credit at the bank, but I certainly did my
best to lose everything I had. I sat down at Canano's
bank, and noticing that the poor count, who followed me
wherever I went, was the only person who knew me, I
thought I should have a lucky evening. I only punted on
one card, and spent four hours without losing or gaining.
Towards the end, wishing to force fortune's favour, I lost
rapidly, and left all my money in the hands of the
banker. I went back to the ball-room, where the countess rejoined me, and we returned home.

When we were in the carriage, she said,——

"You lost an immense sum, and I am very glad of it.
The marquis will give you a thousand sequins, and the
money will bring you luck."

"And you, too, for I suppose you will have the dress?"

"Maybe."

"No, madam, you shall never have it in this way, and
you know the other. I despise a thousand sequins."

"And I despise you and your presents."

"You may despise me as much as you please, and you
may be sure I despise you."

With these polite expressions we reached the house.
When I got to my room I found the count there with a
long face, as if he wanted to pity me but dared not do
it. However, my good temper gave him the courage to
say,——

"Triulzi will give you a thousand sequins; that will fit
you up again."

"For the dress you mean?"

"Yes."

"I wanted to give it to your wife, but she said she would despise it, coming from my hands."

"You astonish me; she is mad after it. You must have wounded her haughty temper in some way or another. But sell it, and get the thousand sequins."

"I will let you know to-morrow."

I slept four or five hours, and then rose and went out in my great coat to call on Greppi, for I had no more money. I took a thousand sequins, begging him not to tell my affairs to anyone. He replied that my affairs were his own, and that I could count on his secrecy. He complimented me on the esteem in which Madame Palesi held me, and said he hoped to meet me at supper at her house one night.

"Such a meeting would give me the greatest pleasure," I replied.

On leaving him I called on Thérèse, but as there were some people with her I did not stay long. I was glad to see that she knew nothing about my losses or my affairs. She said that Greppi wanted to sup with me at her house, and that she would let me know when the day was fixed. When I got home I found the count in front of my fire.

"My wife is in a furious rage with you," said he, "and won't tell me why."

"The reason is, my dear count, that I won't let her accept the dress from any hand but mine. She told me that she should despise it as a gift from me, but she has nothing to be furious about that I know."

"It's some mad notion of hers, and I don't know what to make of it. But pray attend to what I am about to say to you. You despise a thousand sequins—good. I congratulate you. But if you are in a position to despise a sum which would make me happy, offer up a foolish

vanity on the shrine of friendship, take the thousand
sequins, and lend them to me, and let my wife have the
dress, for of course he will give it her."

This proposal made me roar with laughter, and
certainly it was of a nature to excite the hilarity of a
sufferer from confirmed melancholia, which I was far
from being. However, I stopped laughing when I saw
how the poor count blushed from shame. I kissed him
affectionately to calm him, but at last I was cruel enough
to say,——

"I will willingly assist you in this arrangement. I will
sell the dress to the marquis as soon as you please, but
I won't lend you the money. I'll give it to you in the
person of your wife at a private interview; but when she
receives me she must not only be polite and complaisant,
but as gentle as a lamb. Go and see if it can be arranged,
my dear count; 'tis absolutely my last word."

"I will see," said the poor husband; and with that he
went out.

Barbaro kept his appointment with exactitude. I made
him get into my carriage, and we alighted at a house at
the end of Milan. We went to the first floor, and there
I was introduced to a fine-looking old man, an amiable
lady of pleasing appearance, and then to two charming
cousins. He introduced me as a Venetian gentleman in
disgrace with the State Inquisitors, like himself, adding,
that as I was a rich bachelor their good or ill favour
made no difference to me.

He said I was rich, and I looked like it. My luxury
of attire was dazzling. My rings, my snuff-boxes, my
chains, my diamonds, my jewelled cross hanging on my
breast—all gave me the air of an important personage.
The cross belonged to the Order of the Spur the Pope
had given me, but as I had carefully taken the spur away

it was not known to what order I belonged. Those who might be curious did not dare to ask me, for one can no more enquire of a knight what order he belongs to, than one can say to a lady how old are you? I wore it till 1785, when the Prince Palatine of Russia told me in private that I would do well to get rid of the thing.

"It only serves to dazzle fools," said he, "and here you have none such to deal with."

I followed his advice, for he was a man of profound intelligence. Nevertheless, he removed the corner-stone of the kingdom of Poland. He ruined it by the same means by which he had made it greater.

The old man to whom Barbaro presented me was a marquis. He told me that he knew Venice, and as I was not a patrician I could live as pleasantly anywhere else. He told me to consider his house and all he possessed as mine.

The two young marchionesses had enchanted me; they were almost ideal beauties. I longed to enquire about them of some good authority, for I did not put much faith in Barbaro.

In half an hour the visitors commenced to come on foot and in carriages. Among the arrivals were several pretty and well-dressed girls, and numerous smart young men all vying with each other in their eagerness to pay court to the two cousins. There were twenty of us in all. We sat round a large table, and began to play a game called bankruptcy. After amusing myself for a couple of hours in losing sequins, I went out with Barbaro to the opera.

"The two young ladies are two incarnate angels," I said to my countryman. "I shall pay my duty to them, and shall find out in a few days whether they are for me. As for the gaming speculation, I will lend you two hundred sequins; but I don't want to lose the money, so you must give me good security."

"To that I agree willingly, but I am certain of giving it you back with good interest."

"You shall have a half share and not twenty-five per cent., and I must strongly insist that nobody shall know of my having anything to do with your bank. If I hear any rumours, I shall bet heavily on my own account."

"You may be sure I shall keep the secret; it is to my own interest to have it believed that I am my own capitalist."

"Very good. Come to me early to-morrow morning, and bring me good security, and you shall have the money."

He embraced me in the joy of his heart.

The picture of the two fair ladies was still in my brain, and I was thinking of enquiring of Greppi when I chanced to see Triulzi in the pit of the opera-house. He saw me at the same moment, and came up to me, saying gaily that he was sure I had had a bad dinner, and that I had much better dine with him every day.

"You make me blush, marquis, for not having called on you yet."

"No, no; there can be nothing of that kind between men of the world, who know the world's worth."

"We are agreed there, at all events."

"By the way, I hear you have decided on selling me that handsome dress of yours. I am really very much obliged to you, and will give you the fifteen thousand livres whenever you like."

"You can come and take it to-morrow morning."

He then proceeded to tell me about the various ladies I noticed in the theatre. Seizing the opportunity, I said,——

"When I was in church the other day I saw two exquisite beauties. A man at my side told me they were cousins, the Marchionesses Q—— and F——, I think he said. Do you know them? I am quite curious to hear about them."

"I know them. As you say, they are charming. It's not very difficult to obtain access to them; and I suppose they are good girls, as I have not heard their names in connection with any scandal. However, I know that Mdlle. F—— has a lover, but it is a great secret; he is the only son of one of the noblest of our families. Unfortunately, they are not rich; but if they are clever, as I am sure they are, they may make good matches. If you like I can get someone to introduce you there."

"I haven't made up my mind yet. I may be able to forget them easily only having seen them once. Nevertheless, I am infinitely obliged to you for your kind offer."

After the ballet I went into the assembly-room and I heard "there he is" several times repeated as I came in. The banker made me a bow, and offered me a place next to him. I sat down and he handed me a pack of cards. I punted, and with such inveterate bad luck that in less than an hour I lost seven hundred sequins. I should probably have lost all the money I had in my pocket if Canano had not been obliged to go away. He gave the cards to a man whose looks displeased me, and I rose and went home and got into bed directly, so as not to be obliged to conceal my ill temper.

In the morning Barbaro came to claim the two hundred sequins. He gave me the right to sequestrate his pay by way of surety. I do not think I should have had the heart to exercise my rights if things had gone wrong, but I liked to have some control over him. When I went out I called on Greppi, and took two thousand sequins in gold.

CHAPTER XIX

*Humiliation of The Countess—Zenobia's Wedding—Faro
—Conquest of The Fair Irene—Plan for a Masquerade*

ON MY return I found the count with one of the
marquis's servants, who gave me a note, begging me
to send the dress, which I did directly.

"The marquis will dine with us," said the count, "and,
no doubt, he will bring the money with him for this
treasure."

"You think it a treasure, then?"

"Yes, fit for a queen to wear."

"I wish the treasure had the virtue of giving you a
crown; one head-dress is as good as another."

The poor devil understood the allusion, and as I liked
him I reproached myself for having humiliated him un-
intentionally, but I could not resist the temptation to
jest. I hastened to smooth his brow by saying that as
soon as I got the money for the dress I would take it to
the countess.

"I have spoken to her about it," said he, "and your
proposal made her laugh; but I am sure she will make up
her mind when she finds herself in possession of the
dress."

It was a Friday. The marquis sent in an excellent
fish dinner, and came himself soon after with the dress
in a basket. The present was made with all ceremony,
and the proud countess was profuse in her expressions
of thanks, which the giver received coolly enough, as if
accustomed to that kind of thing. However, he ended by

the no means flattering remark that if she had any sense she would sell it, as everybody knew she was too poor to wear it. This suggestion by no means met with her approval. She abused him to her heart's content, and told him he must be a great fool to give her a dress which he considered unsuitable to her.

They were disputing warmly when the Marchioness Menafoglio was announced. As soon as she came in her eyes were attracted by the dress, which was stretched over a chair, and finding it superb she exclaimed,——

"I would gladly buy that dress."

"I did not buy it to sell again," said the countess, sharply.

"Excuse me," replied the marchioness, "I thought it was for sale, and I am sorry it is not."

The marquis, who was no lover of dissimulation, began to laugh, and the countess, fearing he would cover her with ridicule, hastened to change the conversation. But when the marchioness was gone the countess gave reins to her passion, and scolded the marquis bitterly for having laughed. However, he only replied by remarks which, though exquisitely polite, had a sting in them; and at last the lady said she was tired, and was going to lie down.

When she had left the room the marquis gave me the fifteen thousand francs, telling me that they would bring me good luck at Canano's.

"You are a great favourite of Canano's," he added, "and he wants you to come and dine with him. He can't ask you to supper, as he is obliged to spend his nights in the assembly-rooms."

"Tell him I will come any day he likes except the day after to-morrow, when I have to go to a wedding at the 'Apple Garden.'"

"I congratulate you," said the count and the marquis together, "it will no doubt be very pleasant."

"I expect to enjoy myself heartily there."

"Could not we come, too?"

"Do you really want to?"

"Certainly."

"Then I will get you an invitation from the fair bride herself on the condition that the countess comes as well. I must warn you that the company will consist of honest people of the lower classes, and I cannot have them humiliated in any way."

"I will persuade the countess," said Triulzi.

"To make your task an easier one, I may as well tell you that the wedding is that of the fair Zenobia."

"Bravo! I am sure the countess will come to that."

The count went out, and shortly reappeared with Zenobia. The marquis congratulated her, and encouraged her to ask the countess to the wedding. She seemed doubtful, so the marquis took her by the hand and let her into the proud Spaniard's room. In half an hour they returned informing us that my lady had deigned to accept the invitation.

When the marquis had gone, the count told me that I might go and keep his wife company, if I had nothing better to do, and that he would see to some business.

"I have the thousand sequins in my pocket," I remarked, "and if I find her reasonable, I will leave them with her."

"I will go and speak to her first."

"Do so."

While the count was out of the room, I exchanged the thousand sequins for the fifteen thousand francs in bank notes which Greppi had given me.

I was just shutting up my cash-box when Zenobia

came in with my lace cuffs. She asked me if I would
like to buy a piece of lace. I replied in the affirmative,
and she went out and brought it me.

I liked the lace, and bought it for eighteen sequins,
and said,——

"This lace is yours, dearest Zenobia, if you will content
me this moment."

"I love you well, but I should be glad if you would
wait till after my marriage."

"No, dearest, now or never. I cannot wait. I shall
die if you do not grant my prayer. Look! do you not
see what a state I am in?"

"I see it plainly enough, but it can't be done."

"Why not? Are you afraid of your husband noticing
the loss of your maidenhead?"

"Not I, and if he did I shouldn't care. I promise you
if he dared to reproach me, he should not have me at
all."

"Well said, for my leavings are too good for him.
Come quick!"

"But you will shut the door, at least?"

"No, the noise would be heard, and might give rise to
suspicion. Nobody will come in."

With these words I drew her towards me, and finding
her as gentle as a lamb and as loving as a dove, the
amorous sacrifice was offered with abundant libations
on both sides. After the first ecstacy was over, I proceeded to examine her beauties, and with my usual
amorous frenzy told her that she should send her tailor
out to graze and live with me. Fortunately she did not
believe in the constancy of my passion. After a second
assault I rested, greatly astonished that the count had
not interrupted our pleasures. I thought he must have
gone out, and I told Zenobia my opinion, whereon she

overwhelmed me with caresses. Feeling at my ease, I set her free from her troublesome clothes, and gave myself up to toying with her in a manner calculated to arouse the exhausted senses; and then for the third time we were clasped to each other's arms, while I made Zenobia put herself into the many attitudes which I knew from experience as most propitious to the voluptuous triumph.

We were occupied a whole hour in these pleasures, but Zenobia, in the flower of her age and a novice, poured forth many more libations than I.

Just as I lost life for the third time, and Zenobia for the fourteenth, I heard the count's voice. I told my sweetheart, who had heard it as well, and after we had dressed hastily I gave her the eighteen sequins, and she left the room.

A moment after the count came in laughing, and said,——

"I have been watching you all the time by this chink" (which he shewed me), "and I have found it very amusing."

"I am delighted to hear it, but keep it to youself."

"Of course, of course."

"My wife," said he, "will be very pleased to see you; and I," he added, "shall be very pleased as well."

"You are a philosophical husband," said I, "but I am afraid after the exercises you witnessed the countess will find me rather slow."

"Not at all, the recollection will make it all the pleasanter for you."

"Mentally perhaps, but in other respects . . ."

"Oh! you will manage to get out of it."

"My carriage is at your service, as I shall not be going out for the rest of the day."

I softly entered the countess's room and finding her in bed enquired affectionately after her health.

"I am very well," said she, smiling agreeably, "my husband has done me good."

I had seated myself quietly on the bed, and she had shewn no vexation; certainly a good omen.

"Aren't you going out any more to-day?" said she, "you have got your dressing-gown on."

"I fell asleep lying on my bed, and when I awoke I decided on keeping you company if you will be as good and gentle as you are pretty."

"If you behave well to me, you will always find me so."

"And will you love me?"

"That depends on you. So you are going to sacrifice Canano to me this evening."

"Yes, and with the greatest pleasure. He has won a lot from me already, and I foresee that he will win the fifteen thousand francs I have in my pocket to-morrow. This is the money the Marquis Triulzi gave me for the dress."

"It would be a pity to lose such a large sum."

"You are right, and I need not lose them if you will be complaisant, for they are meant for you. Allow me to shut the door."

"What for?"

"Because I am perishing with cold and desire, and intend warming myself in your bed."

"I will never allow that."

"I don't want to force you. Good-bye, countess, I will go and warm myself by my own fire, and to-morrow I will wage war on Canano's bank."

"You are certainly a sad dog. Stay here, I like your conversation."

Without more ado I locked the door, took off my clothes, and seeing that her back was turned to me, jumped into bed beside her. She had made up her mind, and let me do as I liked, but my combats with Zenobia had exhausted me. With closed eyes she let me place her in all the postures which lubricity could suggest, while her hands were not idle; but all was in vain, my torpor was complete, and nothing would give life to the instrument which was necessary to the operation.

Doubtless the Spaniard felt that my nullity was an insult to her charms; doubtless I must have tortured her by raising desires which I could not appease; for several times I felt my fingers drenched with a flow that shewed she was not passive in the matter; but she pretended all the while to be asleep. I was vexed at her being able to feign insensibility to such an extent, and I attached myself to her head; but her lips, which she abandoned to me, and which I abused disgracefully, produced no more effect than the rest of her body. I felt angry that I could not effect the miracle of resurrection, and I decided on leaving a stage where I had so wretched a part, but I was not generous to her, and put the finishing stroke to her humiliation by saying,——

" 'Tis not my fault, madam, that your charms have so little power over me. Here, take these fifteen thousand francs by way of consolation."

With this apostrophe I left her.

My readers, more especially my lady readers, if I ever have any, will no doubt pronounce me a detestable fellow after this. I understand their feelings, but beg them to suspend their judgment. They will see afterwards that my instinct served me wonderfully in the course I had taken.

Early the next day the count came into my room with a very pleased expression.

"My wife is very well," said he, "and told me to wish you good day."

I did not expect this, and I no doubt looked somewhat astonished.

"I am glad," he said, "that you gave her francs instead of the sequins you got from Triulzi, and I hope, as Triulzi said, you will have luck with it at the bank."

"I am not going to the opera," said I, "but to the masked ball, and I don't want anyone to recognize me."

I begged him to go and buy me a new domino, and not to come near me in the evening, so that none but he should know who I was. As soon as he had gone out I began to write letters. I had heavy arrears to make up in that direction.

The count brought me my domino at noon, and after hiding it we went to dine with the countess. Her affability, politeness, and gentleness astounded me. She looked so sweetly pretty that I repented having outraged her so scandalously. Her insensibility of the evening before seemed inconceivable, and I began to suspect that the signs I had noticed to the contrary were only due to the animal faculties which are specially active in sleep.

"Was she really asleep," said I to myself, "when I was outraging her so shamefully?"

I hoped it had been so. When her husband left us alone, I said, humbly and tenderly, that I knew I was a monster, and that she must detest me.

"You a monster?" said she. "On the contrary I owe much to you, and there is nothing I can think of for which I have cause to reproach you."

I took her hand, tenderly, and would have carried it to my lips, but she drew it away gently and gave me a kiss. My repentance brought a deep blush to my face.

When I got back to my room I sealed my letters and went to the ball. I was absolutely unrecognizable. Nobody had ever seen my watches or my snuff-boxes before, and I had even changed my purses for fear of anybody recognizing me by them.

Thus armed against the glances of the curious, I sat down at Canano's table and commenced to play in quite a different fashion. I had a hundred Spanish pieces in my pocket worth seven hundred Venetian sequins. I had got this Spanish money from Greppi, and I took care not to use what Triulzi had given me for fear he should know me.

I emptied my purse on the table, and in less than an hour it was all gone. I rose from the table and everybody thought I was going to beat a retreat, but I took out another purse and put a hundred sequins on one card, going second, with paroli, seven, and the va. The stroke was successful and Canano gave me back my hundred Spanish pieces, on which I sat down again by the banker, and recommenced regular play. Canano was looking at me hard. My snuff-box was the one which the Elector of Cologne had given me, with the prince's portrait on the lid. I took a pinch of snuff and he gave me to undestand that he would like one too, and the box was subjected to a general examination. A lady whom I did not know said the portrait represented the Elector of Cologne in his robes as Grand Master of the Teutonic Order. The box was returned to me and I saw that it had made me respected, so small a thing imposes on people. I then put fifty sequins on one card, going paroli and paix de paroli, and at daybreak I had broken the bank. Canano said politely that if I liked to be spared the trouble of carrying all that gold he would have it weighed and give me a cheque. A pair of scales was brought, and it was found that I had thirty-four pounds weight in gold, amounting to two thousand eight hundred and fifty-six sequins. Canano wrote me a cheque, and I slowly returned to the ball-room.

Barbaro had recognized me with the keenness of a Venetian. He accosted me and congratulated me on my luck, but I gave him no answer, and seeing that I wished to remain incognito he left me.

A lady in a Greek dress richly adorned with diamonds came up to me, and said in a falsetto voice that she would like to dance with me. I made a sign of assent, and as she took off her glove I saw a finely-shaped hand as white as alabaster, one of the fingers bearing an exquisite diamond ring. It was evidently no ordinary person, and though I puzzled my head I could not guess who she could be.

She danced admirably, in the style of a woman of fashion, and I too exerted myself to the utmost. By the time the dance was over I was covered with perspiration.

"You look hot," said my partner, in her falsetto voice, "come and rest in my box."

My heart leaped with joy, and I followed her with great delight; but as I saw Greppi in the box to which she took me, I had no doubt that it must be Thérèse, which did not please me quite so well. In short, the lady took off her mask; it was Thérèse, and I complimented her on her disguise.

"But how did you recognize me, dearest?"

"By your snuff-box. I knew it, otherwise I should never have found you out."

"Then you think that nobody has recognized me?"

"Nobody, unless in the same way as I did."

"None of the people here have seen my snuff-box."

I took the opportunity of handing over to Greppi Canano's cheque, and he gave me a receipt for it. Thérèse asked us to supper for the ensuing evening, and said,——

"There will be four of us in all."

Greppi seemed curious to know who the fourth person could be, but I right guessed it would be my dear son Cesarino.

As I went down once more to the ball-room two pretty female dominos attacked me right and left, telling me that *Messer-Grande* was waiting for me outside. They then asked me for some snuff, and I gave them a box ornamented with an indecent picture. I had the impudence to touch the spring and shew it them, and after inspecting it they exclaimed,——

"Fie, fie! your punishment is never to know who we are."

I was sorry to have displeased the two fair masquers, who seemed worth knowing, so I followed them, and meeting Barbaro, who knew everybody, I pointed them out to him, and heard to my delight that they were the two Marchionesses Q—— and F——. I promised Barbaro to go and see them. He said that everybody in the ball-room knew me, and that our bank was doing very well, though, of course, that was a trifle to me.

Towards the end of the ball, when it was already full daylight, a masquer, dressed as a Venetian gondolier, was accosted by a lady masquer, also in Venetian costume. She challenged the gondolier to prove himself a Venetian by dancing the *forlana* with her. The gondolier accepted, and the music struck up, but the boatman, who was apparently a Milanese, was hooted, while the lady danced exquisitely. I was very fond of the dance, and I asked the unknown Venetian lady to dance it again with me. She agreed, and a ring was formed round us, and we were so applauded that we had to dance it over again. This would have sufficed if a very pretty shepherdess without a mask had not begged me to dance it with her. I could not refuse her, and she danced exquisitely; going round and round the circle three times, and seeming to hover in the air. I was quite out of breath. When it was finished, she came up to me and whispered my name in my ear. I was astonished, and feeling the charm of the situation demanded her name.

"You shall know," said she, in Venetian, "if you will come to the 'Three Kings.'"

"Are you alone?"

"No, my father and mother, who are old friends of yours, are with me."

"I will call on Monday."

What a number of adventures to have in one night! I went home wearily, and went to bed, but I was only allowed to sleep for two hours. I was roused and begged to dress myself. The countess, the marquis, and the count, all ready for Zenobia's wedding, teased me till I was ready, telling me it was not polite to keep a bride waiting. Then they all congratulated me on my breaking the bank and the run of luck against me. I told the marquis that it was his money that had brought me luck, but he replied by saying that he knew what had become of his money.

This indiscretion either on the count's part or the countess's surprised me greatly; it seemed to me contrary to all the principles in intrigue.

"Canano knew you," said the marquis, "by the way you opened your snuff-box, and he hopes to see us to dinner before long. He says he hopes you will win a hundred pounds weight of gold; he has a fancy for you."

"Canano," said I, "has keen eyes, and plays faro admirably. I have not the slightest wish to win his money from him."

We then started for the "Apple Garden," where we found a score of honest folks and the bride and bridegroom, who overwhelmed us with compliments. We soon put the company at their ease. At first our presence overawed them, but a little familiarity soon restored the general hilarity. We sat down to dinner, and among the guests were some very pretty girls, but my head was too full of Zenobia to care about them. The dinner lasted three hours. It was an abundant repast, and the foreign wines were so exquisite that it was easy to see that the sum I had furnished had been exceeded. Good fellowship prevailed, and after the first bumper had passed round everybody proposed somebody else's health, and as each tried to say something different to his neighbour the most fearful nonsense prevailed. Then everybody thought himself bound to sing, and they were not at all first-rate vocalists by any means. We laughed heartily and also caused laughter, for our speeches and songs were as bad as those of our humble friends.

When we rose from the table kissing became general, and the countess could not resist laughing when she found herself obliged to hold out her cheeks for the salute of the tailor, who thought her laughter a special mark of favour.

Strains of sweet music were heard, and the ball was duly opened by the newly-married couple. Zenobia danced, if not exactly well, at least gracefully; but the tailor, who had never put his legs to any other use besides crossing them, cut such a ridiculous figure that the countess had much ado to restrain her laughter. But in spite of that I led out Zenobia for the next minuet, and the proud countess was obliged to dance with the wretched tailor.

When the minuets stopped the square dances began, and refreshments were liberally handed round. *Confetti,* a kind of sweetmeat, even better than that made at Verdun, were very plentiful.

When we were just going I congratulated the husband and offered to bring Zenobia home in my carriage, which he was pleased to style a very honourable offer. I gave my hand to Zenobia, and helped her into the carriage, and having told the coachman to go slowly I put her on my knee, extinguisher fashion, and kept her there all the time. Zenobia was the first to get down, and noticing that my breeches of grey velvet were spoiled, I told her that I would be with her in a few minutes. In two minutes I put on a pair of black satin breeches, and I rejoined the lady before her husband came in. She asked what I had been doing, and on my telling her that our exploits in the carriage had left very evident marks on my trousers, she gave me a kiss, and thanked me for my forethought.

Before long the husband and his sister arrived. He thanked me, calling me his gossip, and then noticing the change in my dress he asked me how I had contrived to make the alteration so quickly.

"I went to my room, leaving your wife at your house, for which I beg your pardon."

"Didn't you see that the gentleman had spilt a cup of coffee over his handsome breeches?" said Zenobia.

"My dear wife," said the crafty tailor, "I don't see

everything, nor is it necessary that I should do so, but you should have accompanied the gentleman to his room."

Then turning to me with a laugh, he asked me how I had enjoyed the wedding.

"Immensely, and my friends have done the same; but you must let me pay you, dear gossip, for what you spent over and above the twenty-four sequins. You can tell me how much it is."

"Very little, a mere trifle; Zenobia shall bring you the bill."

I went home feeling vexed with myself for not having foreseen that the rogue would notice my change of dress, and guess the reason. However, I consoled myself with the thought that the tailor was no fool, and that it was plain that he was content to play the part we had assigned to him. So after wishing good night to the count, the countess and the marquis, who all thanked me for the happy day they had spent, I went to bed.

As soon as I was awake, I thought of the shepherdess who had danced the *forlana* so well at the ball, and I resolved to pay her a visit. I was not more interested in her beauty than to find out who her father and mother, "old friends of mine," could be. I dressed and walked to the "Three Kings," and on walking into the room which the shepherdess had indicated to me, what was my astonishment to find myself face to face with the Countess Rinaldi, whom Zavoisky had introduced me to at the *locanda* of Castelletto sixteen years ago. The reader will remember how M. de Bragadin paid her husband the money he won from me at play.

Madame Rinaldi had aged somewhat, but I knew her directly. However, as I had never had more than a passing fancy for her, we did not go back to days which did neither of us any honour.

"I am delighted to see you again," said I; "are you still living with your husband?"

"You will see him in half an hour, and he will be glad to present his respects to you."

"I should not at all care for it myself, madam; there are old quarrels between us which I do not want to renew, so, madam, farewell."

"No, no, don't go yet, sit down."

"Pardon me."

"Irene, don't let the gentleman go."

At these words Irene ran and barred the way—not like a fierce mastiff, but like an angel, entreating me to stay with that mingled look of innocence, fear, and hope, of which girls know the effect so well. I felt I could not go.

"Let me through, fair Irene," said I, "we may see each other somewhere else."

"Pray do not go before you have seen my father."

The words were spoken so tenderly that our lips met. Irene was victorious. How can one resist a pretty girl who implores with a kiss? I took a chair, and Irene, proud of her victory, sat on my knee and covered me with kisses.

I took it into my head to task the countess where and when Irene was born.

"At Mantua," said she, "three months after I left Venice."

"And when did you leave Venice?"

"Six months after I met you."

"That is a curious coincidence, and if we had been tenderly acquainted you might say that Irene was my

daughter, and I should believe you, and think that my
affection for her was purely paternal."

"Your memory is not very good, sir, I wonder at
that."

"I may tell you, that I never forget certain things.
But I guess your meaning. You want me to subdue my
liking for Irene. I am willing to do so, but she will be
the loser."

This conversation had silenced Irene, but she soon
took courage, and said she was like me.

"No, no," I answered, "if you were like me you would
not be so pretty."

"I don't think so; I think you are very handsome."

"You flatter me."

"Stay to dinner with us."

"No, if I stayed I might fall in love with you, and
that would be a pity, as your mother says I am your
father."

"I was joking," said the countess, "you may love Irene
with a good conscience."

"We will see what can be done."

When Irene had left the room, I said to the
mother,——

"I like your daughter, but I won't be long sighing
for her, and you mustn't take me for a dupe."

"Speak to my husband about it. We are very poor,
and we want to go to Cremona."

"I suppose Irene has a lover?"

"No."

"But she has had one, of course?"

"Never anything serious."

"I can't believe it."

"It's true, nevertheless. Irene is intact."

Just then Irene came in with her father, who had aged

to such an extent that I should never have known him in the street. He came up to me and embraced me, begging me to forget the past. "It is only you," he added, "who can furnish me with funds to go to Cremona. I have several debts here, and am in some danger of imprisonment. Nobody of any consequence comes to see me. My dear daughter is the only thing of value which I still possess. I have just been trying to sell this pinchbeck watch, and though I asked only six sequins, which is half what it is worth, they would not give me more than two. When a man gets unfortunate, everything is against him."

I took the watch, and gave the father six sequins for it, and then handed it to Irene. She said with a smile that she could not thank me, as I only gave her back her own, but she thanked me for the present I had made her father.

"Here," said she seriously to the old man, "you can sell it again now."

This made me laugh. I gave the count ten sequins in addition, embraced Irene, and said I must be gone, but that I would see them again in three or four days.

Irene escorted me to the bottom of the stairs, and as she allowed me to assure myself that she still possessed the rose of virginity, I gave her another ten sequins, and told her that the first time she went alone to the ball with me I would give her a hundred sequins. She said she would consult her father.

Feeling sure that the poor devil would hand over Irene to me, and having no apartment in which I could enjoy her in freedom, I stopped to read a bill in a pastrycook's window. It announced a room to let. I went in, and the pastrycook told me that the house belonged to him, and his pretty wife, who was suckling a baby, begged me to come upstairs and see the room. The street was a lonely one, and had a pleasing air of mystery about it. I climbed to the third floor, but the rooms there were wretched garrets of no use to me.

"The first floor," said the woman, "consists of a suite of four nice rooms, but we only let them together."

"Let us go and see them. Good! they will do. What is the rent?"

"You must settle that with my husband."

"And can't I settle anything with you, my dear?"

So saying I gave her a kiss which she took very kindly, but she smelt of nursing, which I detested, so I did not go any farther despite her radiant beauty.

I made my bargain with the landlord, and paid a month's rent in advance for which he gave me a receipt. It was agreed that I should come and go as I pleased, and that he should provide me with food. I gave him a name so common as to tell him nothing whatever about me, but he seemed to care very little about that.

As I had agreed with Barbaro to visit the fair marchionesses, I dressed carefully, and after a slight repast with the countess, who was pleasant but did not quite please me, I met my fellow-countryman and we called on the two cousins.

"I have come," said I, "to beg your pardons for having revealed to you the secret of the snuff-box."

They blushed, and scolded Barbaro, thinking that he had betrayed them. On examining them I found them far superior to Irene, my present flame, but their manner, the respect they seemed to require, frightened me. I was not at all disposed to dance attendance on them. Irene, on the contrary, was an easy prey. I had only to do her parents a service, and she was in my power; while the two cousins had their full share of aristocratic

pride, which debases the nobility to the level of the
vilest of the people, and only imposes upon fools, who
after all are in the majority everywhere. Further I was
no longer at that brilliant age which fears nothing, and
I was afraid that my appearance would hardly overcome
them. It is true that Barbaro had made me hope that
presents would be of some use, but after what the Marquis Triulzi had said, I feared that Barbaro had only
spoken on supposition.

When the company was sufficiently numerous, the
card-tables were brought in. I sat down by Mdlle.
Q——, and disposed myself to play for small stakes. I
was introduced by the aunt, the mistress of the house,
to a young gentleman in Austrian uniform who sat beside me.

My dear countryman played like a true sharper, much
to my displeasure. My fair neighbour, at the end of
the game, which lasted four hours, found herself the
gainer of a few sequins, but the officer, who had played
on his word of honour, after losing all the money in his
pockets, owed ten louis. The bank was the winner of
fifty sequins, including the officer's debt. As the young
man lived at some distance he honoured me by coming
in my carriage.

On the way, Barbaro told us he would introduce us
to a girl who had just come from Venice. The officer
caught fire at this, and begged that we should go and
see her directly, and we accordingly went. The girl
was well enough looking, but neither I nor the officer
cared much about her. While they were making some
coffee for us, and Barbaro was entertaining the young
lady, I took a pack of cards, and had not much difficulty
in inducing the officer to risk twenty sequins against the
twenty I put on the table. While we were playing I

spoke to him of the passion with which the young marchioness inspired me.

"She's my sister," said he.

I knew as much, but pretended to be astonished, and I went on playing. Taking the opportunity I told him that I knew of no one who could let the marchioness know of my affection better than he. I made him laugh, and as he thought I was jesting he only gave vague answers; but seeing that while I talked of my passion I forgot my card, he soon won the twenty sequins from me, and immediately paid them to Barbaro. In the excess of his joy he embraced me as if I had given him the money; and when we parted he promised to give me some good news of his sister at our next meeting.

I had to go to supper with Thérèse, Greppi, and my son, but having some spare time before me I went to the opera-house. The third act was going on, and I accordingly visited the cardroom, and there lost two hundred sequins at a single deal. I left the room almost as if I was flying from an enemy. Canano shook me by the hand, and told me he expected me and the marquis to dinner every day, and I promised we would come at the earliest opportunity.

I went to Thérèse's, and found Greppi there before me. Thérèse and Don Cesarino, whom I covered with kisses, came in a quarter of an hour afterwards. The banker stared at him in speechless wonder. He could not make out whether he was my son or my brother. Seeing his amazement, Thérèse told him Cesarino was her brother. This stupefied the worthy man still more. At last he asked me if I had known Thérèse's mother pretty well, and on my answering in the affirmative he seemed more at ease.

The meal was excellent, but all my attention went to my son. He had all the advantages of a good disposition and an excellent education. He had grown a great deal since I had seen him at Florence, and his mental powers had developed proportionately. His presence made the party grave, but sweet. The innocence of youth throws around it an ineffable charm; it demands respect and restraint. An hour after midnight we left Thérèse, and I went to bed, well pleased with my day's work, for the loss of two hundred sequins did not trouble me much.

When I got up I received a note from Irene, begging me to call on her. Her father had given her permission to go to the next ball with me, and she had a domino, but she wanted to speak to me. I wrote and told her I would see her in the course of the day. I had written to tell the Marquis Triulzi that I was going to dine with Canano, and he replied that he would be there.

We found this skilled gamester in a fine house, richly furnished, and shewing traces on every side of the wealth and taste of its owner. Canano introduced me to two handsome women, one of whom was his mistress, and to five or six marquises; for at Milan no noble who is not a marquis is thought anything of, just as in the same way they are all counts at Vicenza. The dinner was magnificent and the conversation highly intellectual. In a mirthful moment Canano said he had known me for seventeen years, his acquaintance dating from the time I had juggled a professional gamester, calling himself Count Celi, out of a pretty ballet-girl whom I had taken to Mantua. I confessed the deed and amused the company by the story of what had happened at Mantua with Oreilan, and how I had found Count Celi at Cesena metamorphosed into Count Alfani. Somebody mentioned the ball which was to be held the next day, and when I said I was not going they laughed.

"I bet I know you," said Canano, "if you come to the bank."

"I am not going to play any more," said I.

"All the better for me," answered Canano; "for though your punting is unlucky, you don't leave off till you have won my money. But that's only my joke; try again, and I protest I would see you win half my fortune gladly."

Count Canano had a ring on his finger with a stone not unlike one of mine; it had cost him two thousand sequins, while mine was worth three thousand. He proposed that we should stake them against each other after having them unmounted and valued.

"When?" said I.

"Before going to the opera."

"Very good; but on two turns of the cards, and a deal to each."

"No, I never punt."

"Then we must equalise the game."

"How do you mean?"

"By leaving doubles and the last two cards out of account."

"Then you would have the advantage."

"If you can prove that I will pay you a hundred sequins. Indeed, I would bet anything you like that the game would still be to the advantage of the banker."

"Can you prove it?"

"Yes; and I will name the Marquis Triulzi as judge."

I was asked to prove my point without any question of a bet.

"The advantages of the banker," said I, "are two. The first and the smaller is that all he has got to attend

to is not to deal wrongly, which is a very small matter
to an habitual player; and all the time the punter has
to rack his brains on the chances of one card or another
coming out. The other advantage is one of time. The
banker draws his card at least a second before the
punter, and this again gives him a purchase."

No one replied; but after some thought the Marquis
Triulzi said that to make the chances perfectly equal
the players would have to be equal, which was almost
out of the question.

"All that is too sublime for me," said Canano; "I
don't understand it." But, after all, there was not much
to understand.

After dinner I went to the "Three Kings" to find out
what Irene had to say to me, and to enjoy her presence.
When she saw me she ran up to me, threw her arms
round my neck, and kissed me, but with too much eagerness for me to lay much value on the salute. However,
I have always known that if one wants to enjoy pleasure
one must not philosophise about it, or one runs a risk
of losing half the enjoyment. If Irene had struck me
in dancing the *forlana,* why should not I have pleased
her in spite of my superiority in age? It was not impossible, and that should be enough for me, as I did not
intend to make her my wife.

The father and mother received me as their preserver,
and they may have been sincere. The count begged
me to come out of the room for a moment
with him, and when we were on the other side of the
door, said,——

"Forgive an old and unfortunate man, forgive a father,
if I ask you whether it is true that you promised Irene
a hundred sequins if I would let her go to the ball with
you."

"It is quite true, but of course you know what the consequences will be."

At these words the poor old rascal took hold of me in a way which would have frightened me if I had not possessed twice his strength, but it was only to embrace me.

We went back to the room, he in tears and I laughing. He ran and told his wife, who had not been able to believe in such luck any more than her husband, and Irene added a comic element to the scene by saying,——

"You must not think me a liar, or that my parents suspected that I was imposing on them; they only thought you said fifty instead of a hundred, as if I were not worth such a sum."

"You are worth a thousand, my dear Irene; your courage in barring the way pleased me extremely. But you must come to the ball in a domino."

"Oh! you will be pleased with my dress."

"Are those the shoes and buckles you are going to wear? Have you no other stockings? Where are your gloves?"

"Good heavens! I have nothing."

"Quick! Send for the tradesmen. We will choose what we want, and I will pay."

Rinaldi went out to summon a jeweller, a shoemaker, a stocking-maker, and a perfumer. I spent thirty sequins in what I considered necessary, but then I noticed that there was no English point on her mask, and burst out again. The father brought in a milliner, who adorned the mask with an ell of lace for which I paid twelve sequins. Irene was in great delight, but her father and mother would have preferred to have the money in their pockets, and at bottom they were right.

When Irene put on her fine clothes I thought her delicious, and I saw what an essential thing dress is to a woman.

"Be ready," said I, "before the time for the opera to-morrow, for before going to the ball we will sup together in a room which belongs to me, where we shall be quite at our ease. You know what to expect," I added, embracing her. She answered me with an ardent kiss.

As I took leave of her father, he asked me where I was going after leaving Milan.

"To Marseilles, then to Paris, and then to London, at which place I intend stopping a year."

"Your flight from The Leads was wonderfully lucky."

"Yes, but I risked my life."

"You have certainly deserved all your good fortune."

"Do you think so? I have only used my fortune in subservience to my pleasures."

"I wonder you do not have a regular mistress."

"The reason is, that I like to be my own master. A mistress at my coat-tails would be more troublesome than a wife; she would be an obstacle to the numerous pleasant adventures I encounter at every town. For example, if I had a mistress I should not be able to take the charming Irene to the ball to-morrow."

"You speak like a wise man."

"Yes, though my wisdom is by no means of the austere kind."

In the evening I went to the opera, and should no doubt have gone to the card-table if I had not seen Cesarino in the pit. I spent two delightful hours with him. He opened his heart to me, and begged me to plead for him with his sister to get her consent to his going to sea, for which he had a great longing. He said that he might make a large fortune by a judicious course of trading.

After a temperate supper with my dear boy, I went to bed. The next morning the fine young officer, the Marchioness of Q——'s brother, came and asked me to give him a breakfast. He said he had communicated my proposal to his sister, and that she had replied that I must be making a fool of him, as it was not likely that a man who lived as I did would be thinking of marrying.

"I did not tell you that I aspired to the honour of marrying her."

"No, and I did not say anything about marriage; but that's what the girls are always aiming at."

"I must go and disabuse her of the notion."

"That's a good idea; principals are always the best in these affairs. Come at two o'clock, I shall be dining there, and as I have got to speak to her cousin you will be at liberty to say what you like."

This arrangement suited me exactly. I noticed that my future brother-in-law admired a little gold case on my night-table, so I begged him to accept it as a souvenir of our friendship. He embraced me, and put it in his pocket, saying he would keep it till his dying day.

"You mean till the day when it advances your suit with a lady," said I.

I was sure of having a good supper with Irene, so I resolved to take no dinner. As the count had gone to St. Angelo, fifteen miles from Milan, the day before, I felt obliged to wait on the countess in her room, to beg her to excuse my presence at dinner. She was very polite, and told me by no means to trouble myself. I suspected that she was trying to impose on me, but I wanted her to think she was doing so successfully. In my character of dupe I told her that in Lent I would make amends for the dissipation which prevented me paying my court to her. "Happily," I added, "Lent is not far off."

"I hope it will be so," said the deceitful woman with an enchanting smile, of which only a woman with poison in her heart is capable. With these words she took a pinch of snuff, and offered me her box.

"But what is this, my dear countess, it isn't snuff?"

"No," she replied, "it makes the nose bleed, and is an excellent thing for the head-ache."

I was sorry that I had taken it, but said with a laugh, that I had not got a head-ache, and did not like my nose to bleed.

"It won't bleed much," said she, with a smile, "and it is really beneficial."

As she spoke, we both began to sneeze, and I should have felt very angry if I had not seen her smile.

Knowing something about these sneezing powders, I did not think we should bleed, but I was mistaken. Directly after, I felt a drop of blood, and she took a silver basin from her night-table.

"Come here," said she, "I am beginning to bleed too."

There we were, bleeding into the same basin, facing each other in the most ridiculous position. After about thirty drops had fallen from each of us, the bleeding ceased. She was laughing all the time, and I thought the best thing I could do was to imitate her example. We washed ourselves in fair water in another basin.

"This admixture of our blood," said she, still smiling, "will create a sweet sympathy between us, which will only end *with the death of one or the other.*"

I could make no sense of this, but the reader will

soon see that the wretched woman did not mean our friendship to last very long. I asked her to give me some of the powder, but she refused; and on my enquiring the name of it, she replied that she did not know, as a lady friend had given it to her.

I was a good deal puzzled by the effects of this powder, never having heard of the like before, and as soon as I left the countess I went to an apothecary to enquire about it, but Mr. Drench was no wiser than I. He certainly said that euphorbia sometimes produced bleeding of the nose, but it was not a case of sometimes but always. This small adventure made me think seriously. The lady was Spanish, and she must hate me; and these two facts gave an importance to our blood-letting which it would not otherwise possess.

I went to see the two charming cousins, and I found the young officer with Mdlle. F—— in the room by the garden. The lady was writing, and on the pretext of not disturbing her I went after Mdlle. Q——, who was in the garden. I greeted her politely, and said I had come to apologize for a stupid blunder which must have given her a very poor opinion of me.

"I guess what you mean, but please to understand that my brother gave me your message in perfect innocence. Let him believe what he likes. Do you think I really believed you capable of taking such a step, when we barely knew each other?"

"I am glad to hear you say so."

"I thought the best thing would be to give a matrimonial turn to your gallantry. Otherwise my brother, who is quite a young man, might have interpreted it in an unfavourable sense."

"That was cleverly done, and of course I have nothing more to say. Nevertheless, I am grateful to your brother for having given you to understand that your charms have produced a vivid impression on me. I would do anything to convince you of my affection."

"That is all very well, but it would have been wiser to conceal your feelings from my brother, and, allow me to add, from myself as well. You might have loved me without telling me, and then, though I should have perceived the state of your affections, I could have pretended not to do so. Then I should have been at my ease, but as circumstances now stand I shall have to be careful. Do you see?"

"Really, marchioness, you astonish me. I was never so clearly convinced that I have done a foolish thing. And what is still more surprising, is that I was aware of all you have told me. But you have made me lose my head. I hope you will not punish me too severely?"

"Pray inform me how it lies in my power to punish you."

"By not loving me."

"Ah! loving and not loving; that is out of one's power. Of a sudden we know that we are in love, and our fate is sealed."

I interpreted these last words to my own advantage, and turned the conversation. I asked her if she was going to the ball.

"No."

"Perhaps you are going incognito?"

"We should like to, but it is an impossibility; there is always someone who knows us."

"If you would take me into your service, I would wager anything that you would not be recognized."

"You would not care to trouble yourself about us."

"I like you to be a little sceptical, but put me to the proof. If you could manage to slip out unobserved, I would engage to disguise you in such a manner that no one would know you."

"We could leave the house with my brother and a young lady with whom he is in love. I am sure he would keep our counsel."

"I shall be delighted, but it must be for the ball on Sunday. I will talk it over with your brother. Kindly warn him not to let Barbaro know anything about it. You will be able to put on your disguise in a place I know of. However, we can settle about that again. I shall carry the matter through, you may be sure, with great secrecy. Permit me to kiss your hand."

She gave it me, and after imprinting a gentle kiss I held it to my heart, and had the happiness of feeling a soft pressure. I had no particular disguise in my head, but feeling sure of hitting on something I put off the consideration of it till the next day; the present belonged to Irene. I put on my domino, and went to the "Three Kings," where I found Irene waiting for me at the door. She had run down as soon as she had seen my carriage, and I was flattered by this mark of her eagerness. We went to my rooms, and I ordered the confectioner to get me a choice supper by midnight. We had six hours before us, but the reader will excuse my describing the manner in which they were spent. The opening was made with the usual fracture, which Irene bore with a smile, for she was naturally voluptuous. We got up at midnight, pleasantly surprised to find ourselves famishing with hunger, and a delicious supper waiting for us.

Irene told me that her father had taught her to deal in such a manner that she could not lose. I was curious to see how it was done, and on my giving her a pack of cards she proceeded to distract my attention by talking

to me, and in a few minutes the thing was done. I gave
her the hundred sequins I had promised her, and told
her to go on with her play.

"If you only play on a single card," said she, "you
are sure to lose."

"Never mind; go ahead."

She did so, and I was forced to confess that if I had
not been warned I should never have detected the trick.
I saw what a treasure she must be to the old rascal
Rinaldi. With her air of innocence and gaiety, she
would have imposed on the most experienced sharpers.
She said in a mortified manner that she never had any
opportunity of turning her talents to account, as their
associates were always a beggarly lot. She added tenderly that if I would take her with me she would leave
her parents there and win treasures for me.

"When I am not playing against sharpers," she said,
"I can also punt very well."

"Then you can come to Canano's bank and risk the
hundred sequins I have given you. Put twenty sequins
on a card, and if you win go paroli, seven, and the va,
and leave the game when they turn up. If you can't
make the three cards come out second, you will lose,
but I will reimburse you."

At this she embraced me, and asked if I would take
half the profits.

"No," said I, "you shall have it all."

I thought she would have gone mad with joy.

We went off in sedan-chairs, and the ball not having
commenced we went to the assembly-rooms. Canano
had not yet done anything, and he opened a pack of
cards and pretended not to recognize me, but he smiled
to see the pretty masker, my companion, sit down and
play instead of me. Irene made him a profound bow

as he made room for her by his side, and putting the hundred sequins before her she began by winning a hundred and twenty-five, as instead of going seven and the va, she only went the paix de paroli. I was pleased to see her thus careful, and I let her go on. In the following deal she lost on three cards in succession, and then won another paix de paroli. She then bowed to the banker, pocketed her winnings, and left the table, but just as we were going out I heard somebody sobbing, and on my turning to her she said,——

"I am sure it is my father weeping for joy."

She had three hundred and sixty sequins which she took to him after amusing herself for a few hours. I only danced one minuet with her, for my amorous exploits and the heavy supper I had taken had tired me, and I longed for rest. I let Irene dance with whom she liked, and going into a corner fell asleep. I woke up with a start and saw Irene standing before me. I had been asleep for three hours. I took her back to the "Three Kings," and left her in the charge of her father and mother. The poor man was quite alarmed to see so much gold on the table, and told me to wish him a pleasant journey, as he was starting in a few hours. I could make no opposition and I did not wish to do so, but Irene was furious.

"I won't go," she cried; "I want to stay with my lover. You are the ruin of my life. Whenever anybody takes a liking to me, you snatch me away. I belong to this gentleman, and I won't leave him."

However, she saw that I did not back her up, and began to weep, then kissed me again and again, and just as she was going to sit down, worn out with fatigue and despair, I went off, wishing them a pleasant journey, and telling Irene we should meet again. The reader will learn in due time when and how I saw them again. After all the fatigue I had gone through I was glad to go to bed.

It was eight o'clock when the young lieutenant awoke me.

"My sister has told me about the masquerade," said he, "but I have a great secret to confide in you."

"Say on, and count on my keeping your secret."

"One of the finest noblemen of the town, my friend and my cousin's lover, who has to be very careful of his actions on account of his exalted position, would like to be of the party if you have no objection. My sister and my cousin would like him to come very much."

"Of course he shall. I have been making my calculations for a party of five, and now it will be a party of six, that is all."

"You really are a splendid fellow."

"On Sunday evening you must be at a certain place, of which I will tell you. First of all we will have supper, then put on our disguises, and then go to the ball. To-morrow at five o'clock we shall meet at your sister's. All I want to know is what is the height of your mistress and of the young nobleman."

"My sweetheart is two inches shorter than my sister, and a little thinner; my friend is just about the same make as you are, and if you were dressed alike you would be mistaken for each other."

"That will do. Let me think it over, and leave me alone now; there's a Capuchin waiting for me, and I am curious to learn his business."

A Capuchin had called on me and I had told Clairmont to give him an alms, but he had said he wanted to speak to me in private. I was puzzled, for what could a Capuchin have to say to me?

He came in, and I was at once impressed by his grave
and reverend appearance. I made him a profound bow
and offered him a seat, but he remained standing, and
said,——

"Sir, listen attentively to what I am about to tell
you, and beware of despising my advice, for it might
cost you your life. You would repent when it was too
late. After hearing me, follow my advice immediately;
but ask no questions, for I can answer none. You may
guess, perhaps, that what silences me is a reason in-
cumbent on all Christians—the sacred seal of the confessional. You may be sure that my word is above suspicion; I have no interests of my own to serve. I am
acting in obedience to an inspiration; I think it must be
your guardian angel speaking with my voice. God will
not abandon you to the malice of your enemies. Tell
me if I have touched your heart, and if you feel disposed to follow the counsels I am going to give you."

"I have listened to you, father, with attention and
respect. Speak freely and advise me; what you have
said has not only moved me, but has almost frightened
me. I promise to do as you tell me if it is nothing
against honour or the light of reason."

"Very good. A feeling of charity will prevent your
doing anything to compromise me, whatever may be the
end of the affair. You will not speak of me to anyone,
or say either that you know me or do not know me?"

"I swear to you I will not on my faith as a Christian.
But speak, I entreat you. Your long preface has made
me burn with impatience."

"This day, before noon, go by yourself to —— Square,
No. ——, on the second floor, and ring at the bell on
your left. Tell the person who opens the door that you
want to speak to Madame ——. You will be taken to

her room without any difficulty; I am sure your name will not be asked, but if they do ask you, give an imaginary name. When you are face to face with the woman, beg her to hear you, and ask her for her secret, and to inspire confidence put a sequin or two in her hand. She is poor, and I am sure that your generosity will make her your friend. She will shut her door, and tell you to say on.

"You must then look grave, and tell her that you are not going to leave her house before she gives you the little bottle that a servant brought her yesterday with a note. If she resists, remain firm, but make no noise; do not let her leave the room or call anybody. Finally, tell her that you will give her double the money she may lose by giving you the bottle and all that depends on it. Remember these words: *and all that depends on it.* She will do whatever you want. It will not cost you much, but even if it did, your life is worth more than all the gold of Peru. I can say no more, but before I go, promise me that you will follow my advice."

"Yes, reverend father, I will follow the inspiration of the angel who led you here."

"May God give you His blessing."

When the good priest went out I did not feel at all disposed to laugh. Reason, certainly, bade me despise the warning, but my inherent superstition was too strong for reason. Besides, I liked the Capuchin. He looked like a good man, and I felt bound by the promise I had given him. He had persuaded me, and my reason told me that a man should never go against his persuasion; in fine, I had made up my mind. I took the piece of paper on which I had written the words I had to use, I put a pair of pistols in my pocket, and I told Clairmont to wait for me in the square. This latter, I thought, was a precaution that could do no harm.

Everything happened as the good Capuchin had said. The awful old creature took courage at the sight of the two sequins, and bolted her door. She began by laughing and saying that she knew I was amorous, and that it was my fault if I were not happy, but that she would do my business for me. I saw by these words that I had to do with a pretended sorceress. The famous Mother Bontemps had spoken in the same way to me at Paris. But when I told her that I was not going to leave the room till I had got the mysterious bottle, and all that depended on it, her face became fearful; she trembled, and would have escaped from the room; but I stood before her with an open knife, and would not suffer her to pass. But on my telling her that I would give her double the sum she was to be paid for her witchcraft, and that thus she would be the gainer and not a loser in complying with my demands, she became calm once more.

"I shall lose six sequins," said she, "but you will gladly pay double when I shew you what I have got; I know who you are."

"Who am I?"

"Giacomo Casanova, the Venetian."

It was then I drew the ten sequins from my purse. The old woman was softened at the sight of the money, and said,——

"I would not have killed you outright, certainly, but I would have made you amorous and wretched."

"Explain what you mean."

"Follow me."

I went after her into a closet, and was greatly amazed at seeing numerous articles about which my common sense could tell me nothing. There were phials of all shapes and sizes, stones of different colours, metals, minerals, big nails and small nails, pincers, crucibles, misshapen images, and the like.

"Here is the bottle," said the old woman.

"What does it contain?"

"Your blood and the countess's, as you will see in this letter."

I understood everything then, and now I wonder I did not burst out laughing. But as a matter of fact my hair stood on end, as I reflected on the awful wickedness of which the Spaniard was capable. A cold sweat burst out all over my body.

"What would you have done with this blood?"

"I should have plastered you with it."

"What do you mean by 'plastered'? I don't understand you."

"I will shew you."

As I trembled with fear the old woman opened a casket, a cubit long, containing a waxen statue of a man lying on his back. My name was written on it, and though it was badly moulded, my features were recognizable. The image bore my cross of the Order of the Golden Spur, and the generative organs were made of an enormous size. At this I burst into a fit of hysterical laughter, and had to sit down in an arm-chair till it was over.

As soon as I had got back my breath the sorceress said——

"You laugh, do you? Woe to you if I had bathed you in the bath of blood mingled according to my art, and more woe still if, after I had bathed you, I had thrown your image on a burning coal."

"Is this all?"

"Yes."

"All the apparatus is to become mine for twelve sequins; here they are. And now, quick! light me a fire that I may melt this monster, and as for the blood I think I will throw it out of the window." This was no sooner said than done.

The old woman had been afraid that I should take the bottle and the image home with me, and use them to her ruin; and she was delighted to see me melt the image. She told me that I was an angel of goodness, and begged me not to tell anyone of what had passed between us. I swore I would keep my own counsel, even with the countess. I was astonished when she calmly offered to make the countess madly in love with me for another twelve sequins, but I politely refused and advised her to abandon her fearful trade if she did not want to be burnt alive.

I found Clairmont at his post, and I sent him home. In spite of all I had gone through, I was not sorry to have acquired the information, and to have followed the advice of the good Capuchin who really believed me to be in deadly peril. He had doubtless heard of it in the confessional from the woman who had carried the blood to the witch. Auricular confession often works miracles of this kind.

I was determined never to let the countess suspect that I had discovered her criminal project, and I resolved to behave towards her so as to appease her anger, and to make her forget the cruel insult to which I had subjected her. It was lucky for me that she believed in sorcery; otherwise she would have had me assassinated.

As soon as I got in, I chose the better of the two cloaks I had, and presented her with it. She accepted

the gift with exquisite grace, and asked me why I gave
it her.

"I dreamt," said I, "that you were so angry with me
that you were going to have me assassinated."

She blushed, and answered that she had not gone mad.
I left her absorbed in a sombre reverie. Nevertheless,
whether she forgot and forgave, or whether she could
hit upon no other way of taking vengeance, she was
perfectly agreeable to me during the rest of my stay in
Milan.

The count came back from his estate, and said that
we must really go and see the place at the beginning of
Lent. I promised I would come, but the countess said
she could not be of the party. I pretended to be mortified, but in reality her determination was an extremely
pleasant one to me.

CHAPTER XX

The Masquerade—My Amour with the Fair Marchion-
ess—The Deserted Girl; I Become Her Deliverer—
My Departure for St. Angelo

A S I had engaged myself to provide an absolutely
impenetrable disguise, I wanted to invent a costume remarkable at once for its originality and its rich-
ness. I tortured my brains so to speak, and my readers
shall see if they think my invention was a good one.

I wanted someone on whom I could rely, and above
all, a tailor. It may be imagined that my worthy gossip
was the tailor I immediately thought of. Zenobia would
be as serviceable as her husband; she could do some of
the work, and wait on the young ladies whom I was
going to dress up.

I walked to my gossip, and told him to take me to
the best second-hand clothes dealer in Milan.

When we got to the shop I said to the man——

"I want to look at your very finest costumes, both
for ladies and gentlemen."

"Would you like something that has never been
worn?"

"Certainly, if you have got such a thing."

"I have a very rich assortment of new clothes."

"Get me, then, in the first place, a handsome velvet
suit, all in one piece, which nobody in Milan will be
able to recognize."

Instead of one he shewed me a dozen such suits, all

in excellent condition. I chose a blue velvet lined with white satin. The tailor conducted the bargaining, and it was laid on one side; this was for the pretty cousin's lover. Another suit, in smooth sulphur-coloured velvet throughout, I put aside for the young officer. I also took two handsome pairs of trousers in smooth velvet, and two superb silk vests.

I then chose two dresses, one flame-coloured and the other purple, and a third dress in shot silk. This was for the officer's mistress. Then came lace shirts, two for men, and three for women, then lace handkerchiefs, and finally scraps of velvet, satin, shot silk, etc., all of different colours.

I paid two hundred gold ducats for the lot, but on the condition that if anybody came to know that I had bought them by any indiscretion of his he should give me the money and take back the materials in whatever condition they might be in. The agreement was written out and signed, and I returned with the tailor, who carried the whole bundle to my rooms over the pastry-cook's.

When it was all spread out on the table I told the tailor that I would blow out his brains if he told anybody about it, and then taking a stiletto I proceeded to cut and slash the coats, vests, and trousers all over, to the astonishment of the tailor, who thought I must be mad to treat such beautiful clothes in this manner.

After this operation, which makes me laugh to this day when I remember it, I took the scraps I had bought and said to the tailor——

"Now, gossip, it is your turn; I want you to sew in these pieces into the holes I have made, and I hope your tailoring genius will aid you to produce some pretty contrasts. You see that you have got your work cut out

for you and no time to lose. I will see that your meals
are properly served in an adjoining chamber, but you
must not leave the house till the work is finished. I will
go for your wife, who will help you, and you can sleep
together."

"For God's sake, sir! you don't want the ladies'
dresses treated like the coats and trousers?"

"Just the same."

"What a pity! it will make my wife cry."

"I will console her."

On my way to Zenobia's I bought five pairs of white
silk stockings, men's and women's gloves, two fine castor
hats, two burlesque men's masks, and three graceful-
looking female masks. I also bought two pretty china
plates, and I carried them all to Zenobia's in a sedan-
chair.

I found that charming woman engaged in her toilet.
Her beautiful tresses hung about her neck, and her full
breast was concealed by no kerchief. Such charms
called for my homage, and to begin with I devoured her
with kisses. I spent half an hour with her, and my
readers will guess that it was well employed. I then
helped her to finish her toilette, and we went off in the
sedan-chair.

We found the tailor engaged in picking out the scraps
and cutting them to fit the holes I had made. Zenobia
looked on in a kind of stupor, and when she saw me
begin to slash the dresses she turned pale and made an
involuntary motion to stay my hand, for not knowing
my intentions she thought I must be beside myself.
Her husband had got hardened, and reassured her, and
when she heard my explanation she became calm, though
the idea struck her as a very odd one.

When it is a question of an affair of the heart, of the passions, or of pleasure, a woman's fancy moves much faster than a man's. When Zenobia knew that these dresses were meant for three beautiful women, whom I wished to make a centre of attraction to the whole assembly, she improved on my cuts and slashes, and arranged the rents in such a manner that they would inspire passion without wounding modesty. The dresses were slashed especially at the breast, the shoulders, and the sleeves, so that the lace shift could be seen, and in its turn the shift was cut open here and there, and the sleeves were so arranged that half the arms could be seen. I saw sure that she understood what I wanted, and that she would keep her husband right; and I left them, encouraging them to work their best and quickest. But I looked in three or four times in the day, and was more satisfied every time with my idea and their execution.

The work was not finished till the Saturday afternoon. I gave the tailor six sequins and dismissed him, but I kept Zenobia to attend on the ladies. I took care to place powder, pomade, combs, pins, and everything that a lady needs, on the table, not forgetting ribbons and pack-thread.

The next day I found play going on in a very spirited manner, but the two cousins were not at the tables, so I went after them. They told me they had given up playing as Barbaro always won.

"You have been losing, then?"

"Yes, but my brother has won something," said the amiable Q——.

"I hope luck will declare itself on your side also."

"No, we are not lucky."

When their aunt left the room, they asked me if the lieutenant had told me that a lady friend of theirs was coming to the ball with them.

"I know all," I answered, "and I hope you will enjoy yourselves, but you will not do so more than I. I want to speak to the gallant lieutenant to-morrow morning."

"Tell us about our disguises."

"You will be disguised in such a manner that nobody will recognize you."

"But how shall we be dressed?"

"Very handsomely."

"But what costume have you given us?"

"That is my secret, ladies. However much I should like to please you, I shall say nothing till the time for you to dress comes round. Don't ask me anything more, as I have promised myself the enjoyment of your surprise. I am very fond of dramatic situations. You shall know all after supper."

"Are we to have supper, then?"

"Certainly, if you would like it. I am a great eater myself and I hope you will not let me eat alone."

"Then we will have some supper to please you. We will take care not to eat much dinner, so as to be able to vie with you in the evening. The only thing I am sorry about," added Mdlle. Q——, "is that you should be put to such expense."

"It is a pleasure; and when I leave Milan I shall console myself with the thought that I have supped with the two handsomest ladies in the town."

"How is fortune treating you?"

"Canano wins two hundred sequins from me every day."

"But you won two thousand from him in one night."

"You will break his bank on Sunday. We will bring you luck."

"Would you like to look on?"

"We should be delighted, but my brother says you don't want to go with us."

"Quite so, the reason is that I should be recognized. But I believe the gentleman who will accompany you is of the same figure as myself."

"Exactly the same," said the cousin; "except that he is fair."

"All the better," said I, "the fair always conquer the dark with ease."

"Not always," said the other. "But tell us, at any rate, whether we are to wear men's dresses."

"Fie! fie! I should be angry with myself if I had entertained such a thought."

"That's curious; why so?"

"I'll tell you. If the disguise is complete I am disgusted, for the shape of a woman is much more marked than that of a man, and consequently a woman in man's dress, who looks like a man, cannot have a good figure."

"But when a woman shews her shape well?"

"Then I am angry with her for shewing too much, for I like to see the face and the general outlines of the form and to guess the rest."

"But the imagination is often deceptive."

"Yes, but it is with the face that I always fall in love, and that never deceives me as far as it is concerned. Then if I have the good fortune to see anything more I am always in a lenient mood and disposed to pass over small faults. You are laughing?"

"I am smiling at your impassioned arguments."

"Would you like to be dressed like a man?"

"I was expecting something of the kind, but after you have said we can make no more objections." •

"I can imagine what you would say; I should certainly not take you for men, but I will say no more."

They looked at each other, and blushed and smiled as they saw my gaze fixed on two pre-eminences which one would never expect to see in any man. We began to talk of other things, and for two hours I enjoyed their lively and cultured conversation.

When I left them I went off to my apartments, then to the opera, where I lost two hundred sequins, and finally supped with the countess, who had become quite amiable. However, she soon fell back into her old ways when she found that my politeness was merely external, and that I had no intentions whatever of troubling her in her bedroom again.

On the Saturday morning the young officer came to see me, and I told him that there was only one thing that I wanted him to do, but that it must be done exactly according to my instructions. He promised to follow them to the letter, and I proceeded——

"You must get a carriage and four, and as soon as the five of you are in it tell the coachman to drive as fast as his horses can gallop out of Milan, and to bring you back again by another road to the house. There you must get down, send the carriage away, after enjoining silence on the coachman, and come in. After the ball you will undress in the same house, and then go home in sedan-chairs. Thus we shall be able to baffle the inquisitive, who will be pretty numerous, I warn you."

"My friend the marquis will see to all that," said he, "and I promise you he will do it well, for he is longing to make your acquaintance."

"I shall expect you, then, at seven o'clock to-morrow.

Warn your friend that it is important the coachman should not be known, and do not let anybody bring a servant."

All these arrangements being made, I determined to disguise myself as Pierrot. There's no disguise more perfect; for, besides concealing the features and the shape of the body, it does not even let the colour of the skin remain recognizable. My readers may remember what happened to me in this disguise ten years before. I made the tailor get me a new Pierrot costume, which I placed with the others, and with two new purses, in each of which I placed five hundred sequins, I repaired to the pastrycook's before seven o'clock. I found the table spread, and the supper ready. I shut up Zenobia in the room where the ladies were to make their toilette, and at five minutes past seven the joyous company arrived.

The marquis was delighted to make my acquaintance, and I welcomed him as he deserved. He was a perfect gentleman in every respect, handsome, rich, and young, very much in love with the pretty cousin whom he treated with great respect. The lieutenant's mistress was a delightful little lady and madly fond of her lover.

As they were all aware that I did not want them to know their costumes till after supper, nothing was said about it, and we sat down to table. The supper was excellent; I had ordered it in accordance with my own tastes; that is to say, everything was of the best, and there was plenty of everything. When we had eaten and drunk well, I said——

"As I am not going to appear with you, I may as well tell you the parts you are to play. You are to be five beggars, two men and three women, all rags and tatters."

The long faces they pulled at this announcement were a pleasant sight to see.

"You will each carry a plate in your hands to solicit alms, and you must walk together about the ball-room as a band of mendicants. But now follow me and take possession of your ragged robes."

Although I had much ado to refrain from laughing at the vexation and disappointment which appeared on all their faces, I succeeded in preserving my serious air. They did not seem in any kind of hurry to get their clothes, and I was obliged to tell them that they were keeping me waiting. They rose from the table and I threw the door open, and all were struck with Zenobia's beauty as she stood up by the table on which the rich though tattered robes were displayed, bowing to the company with much grace.

"Here, ladies," said I to the cousins, "are your dresses, and here is yours, mademoiselle—a little smaller. Here are your shifts, your handkerchiefs and your stockings, and I think you will find everything you require on this table. Here are masks, the faces of which shew so poorly beside your own, and here are three plates to crave alms. If anybody looks as high as your garters, they will see how wretched you are, and the holes in the stockings will let people know that you have not the wherewithal to buy silk to mend them. This packthread must serve you for buckles, and we must take care that there are holes in your shoes and also in your gloves, and as everything must match, as soon as you have put on your chemises you must tear the lace round the neck."

While I was going through this explanation I saw surprise and delight efface the disappointment and vexation which had been there a moment before. They saw what a rich disguise I had provided for them, and they could not find it in their hearts to say, "What a pity!"

"Here, gentlemen, are your beggar-clothes. I forgot to lacerate your beaver hats, but that is soon done. Well, what do you think of the costume?"

"Now, ladies, we must leave you; shut the door fast, for it is a case of changing your shifts. Now, gentlemen, leave the room."

The marquis was enthusiastic.

"What a sensation we shall create!" said he, "nothing could be better."

In half an hour we were ready. The stockings in holes, the worn-out shoes, the lace in rags, the straggling hair, the sad masks, the notched plates—all made a picture of sumptuous misery hard to be described.

The ladies took more time on account of their hair, which floated on their shoulders in fine disorder. Mdlle. Q——'s hair was especially fine, it extended almost to her knees.

When they were ready the door was opened, and we saw everything which could excite desire without wounding decency. I admired Zenobia's adroitness. The rents in dresses and chemises disclosed parts of their shoulders, their breasts, and their arms, and their white legs shone through the holes in the stockings.

I shewed them how to walk, and to sway their heads to and fro, to excite compassion, and yet be graceful, and how to use their handkerchiefs to shew people the tears in them and the fineness of the lace. They were delighted, and longed to be at the ball, but I wanted to be there first to have the pleasure of seeing them come in. I put on my mask, told Zenobia to go to bed, as we would not be back till daybreak, and set out on my way.

I entered the ball-room, and as there were a score of Pierrots nobody noticed me. Five minutes after there was a rush to see some maskers who were coming in, and I stood so as to have a good view. The marquis came in first between the two cousins. Their slow, pitiful step matched the part wonderfully. Mdlle. Q—— with her flame-coloured dress, her splendid hair, and her fine shape, drew all eyes towards her. The astonished and inquisitive crowd kept silence for a quarter of an hour after they had come in, and then I heard on every side, "What a disguise!" "It's wonderful!" "Who are they?" "Who can they be?" "I don't know." "I'll find out."

I enjoyed the results of my inventiveness.

The music struck up, and three fine dominos went up to the three beggar-girls to ask them to dance a minuet, but they excused themselves by pointing to their dilapidated shoes. I was delighted; it shewed that they had entered into the spirit of the part.

I followed them about for a quarter of an hour, and the curiosity about them only increased, and then I paid a visit to Canano's table, where play was running high. A masquer dressed in the Venetian style was punting on a single card, going fifty sequins paroli and paix de paroli, in my fashion. He lost three hundred sequins, and as he was a man of about the same size as myself people said it was Casanova, but Canano would not agree. In order that I might be able to stay at the table, I took up the cards and punted three or four ducats like a beginner. The next deal the Venetian masquer had a run of luck, and going paroli, paix de paroli and the va, won back all the money he had lost.

The next deal was also in his favour, and he collected his winnings and left the table.

I sat down in the chair he had occupied, and a lady said——

"That's the Chevalier de Seingalt."

"No," said another. "I saw him a little while ago in the ball-room disguised as a beggar, with four other masquers whom nobody knows."

"How do you mean, dressed as a beggar?" said Canano.

"Why, in rags, and the four others, too; but in spite of that the dresses are splendid and the effect is very good. They are asking for alms."

"They ought to be turned out," said another.

I was delighted to have attained my object, for the recognition of me was a mere guess. I began putting sequins on one card, and I lost five or six times running. Canano studied me, but I saw he could not make me out. I heard whispers running round the table.

"It isn't Seingalt; he doesn't play like that; besides, he is at the ball."

The luck turned; three deals were in my favour, and brought me back more than I had lost. I continued playing with a heap of gold before me, and on my putting a fistfull of sequins on a card it came out, and I went paroli and paix de paroli. I won again, and seeing that the bank was at a low ebb I stopped playing. Canano paid me, and told his cashier to get a thousand sequins, and as he was shuffling the cards I heard a cry of, "Here come the beggars."

The beggars came in and stood by the table, and Canano, catching the marquis's eye, asked him for a pinch of snuff. My delight may be imagined when I saw him modestly presenting a common horn snuffbox to the banker. I had not thought of this detail, which made everybody laugh immensely. Mdlle. Q—— stretched out her plate to ask an alms of Canano, who said——

"I don't pity you with that fine hair of yours, and if you like to put it on a card I will allow you a thousand sequins for it."

She gave no answer to this polite speech, and held out her plate to me, and I put a handful of sequins on it, treating the other beggars in the same way.

"Pierrot seems to like beggars," said Canano, with a smile.

The three mendicants bowed gratefully to me and left the room.

The Marquis Triulzi who sat near Canano, said——

"The beggar in the straw-coloured dress is certainly Casanova."

"I recognized him directly," replied the banker, "but who are the others?"

"We shall find out in due time."

"A dearer costume could not be imagined; all the dresses are quite new."

The thousand sequins came in, and I carried them all off in two deals.

"Would you like to go on playing?" said Canano.

I shook my head, and indicating with a sign of my hand that I would take a cheque, he weighed my winnings and gave me a cheque for twenty-nine pounds of gold, amounting to two thousand, five hundred sequins. I put away the cheque, and after shaking him by the hand, I got up and rolled away in true Pierrot fashion, and after making the tour of the ball-room I went to a box on the third tier of which I had given the key to the young officer, and there I found my beggars.

We took off our masks and congratulated each other on our success, and told our adventures. We had nothing to fear from inquisitive eyes, for the boxes on each side of us were empty. I had taken them myself, and the keys were in my pocket.

The fair beggars talked of returning me the alms I had given them, but I replied in such a way that they said no more about it.

"I am taken for you, sir," said the marquis, "and it may cause some annoyance to our fair friends here."

"I have foreseen that," I replied, " and I shall unmask before the end of the ball. This will falsify all suppositions, and nobody will succeed in identifying you."

"Our pockets are full of sweetmeats," said Mdlle. Q——. "Everybody wanted to fill our plates."

"Yes," said the cousin, "everybody admired us; the ladies came down from their boxes to have a closer view of us, and everyone said that no richer disguise could be imagined."

"You have enjoyed yourselves, then?"

"Yes, indeed."

"And I too. I feel quite boastful at having invented a costume which has drawn all eyes upon you, and yet has concealed your identity."

"You have made us all happy," said the lieutenant's little mistress. "I never thought I should have such a pleasant evening."

"*Finis coronat opus,*" I replied, "and I hope the end will be even better than the beginning."

So saying I gave my sweetheart's hand a gentle pressure, and whether she understood me or not I felt her hand tremble in mine.

"We will go down now," said she.

"So will I, for I want to dance, and I am sure I shall make you laugh as Pierrot."

"Do you know how much money you gave each of us?"

"I cannot say precisely, but I believe I gave each an equal share."

"That is so. I think it is wonderful how you could do it."

"I have done it a thousand times. When I lose a paroli of ten sequins I put three fingers into my purse, and am certain to bring up thirty sequins. I would bet I gave you each from thirty-eight to forty sequins."

"Forty exactly. It's wonderful. We shall remember this masqued ball."

"I don't think anybody will imitate us," said the marquis.

"No," said the cousin, "and we would not dare to wear the same dresses again."

We put on our masks, and I was the first to go out. After numerous little jocularities with the harlequins, especially the female ones, I recognized Thérèse in a domino, and walking up to her as awkwardly as I could I asked her to dance with me.

"You are the Pierrot who broke the bank?" she said.

I answered the question in the affirmative by a nod.

I danced like a madman, always on the point of falling to the ground and never actually doing so.

When the dance was over, I offered her my arm and took her back to her box, where Greppi was sitting by himself. She let me come in, and their surprise was great when I took off my mask. They had thought I was one of the beggars. I gave M. Greppi Canano's cheque, and as soon as he had handed me an acknowledgment I went down to the ball-room again with my mask off, much to the astonishment of the inquisitive, who had made sure that the marquis was I.

Towards the end of the ball I went away in a sedan-chair, which I stopped near the door of an hotel, and a little further on I took another which brought me to the door of the pastrycook's. I found Zenobia in bed. She said she was sure I would come back by myself. I undressed as quickly as I could, and got into bed with this Venus of a woman. She was absolute perfection. I am sure that if Praxiteles had had her for a model, he would not have required several Greek beauties from which to compose his Venus. What a pity that such an exquisite figure should be the property of a sorry tailor! I stripped her naked, and after due contemplation I made her feel how much I loved her. She was pleased with my admiration, and gave me back as much as she got. I had her entirely to myself for the first time. When we heard the trot of four horses we rose and put on our clothes in a twinkling.

When the charming beggars came in, I told them that I should be able to help in their toilette as they had not to change their chemises, and they did not make many objections.

My gaze was fixed all the while on Mdlle. Q——. I admired her charms, and I was delighted to see that she was not miserly in their display. After Zenobia had done her hair she left her to me, and went to attend on the others. She allowed me to put on her dress, and did not forbid my eyes wandering towards a large rent in her chemise, which let me see almost the whole of one of her beautiful breasts.

"What are you going to do with this chemise?"

"You will laugh at our silliness. We have determined

to keep everything as a memorial of the splendid evening we have had. My brother will bring it all to the house. Are you coming to see us this evening?"

"If I were wise I should avoid you."

"And if I were wise I shouldn't ask you to come."

"That is fairly answered! Of course I will come; but before we part may I ask one kiss?"

"Say two."

Her brother and the marquis left the room, and two sedan-chairs I had summoned took off the cousins.

As soon as the marquis was alone with me he asked me very politely to let him share in the expenses.

"I guessed you were going to humiliate me."

"Such was not my intention, and I do not insist; but then you know I shall be humiliated."

"Not at all; I reckon on your good sense. It really costs me nothing. Besides, I give you my word to let you pay for all the parties of pleasure we enjoy together during the carnival. We will sup here when you like; you shall invite the company, and I will leave you to pay the bill."

"That arrangement will suit me admirably. We must be friends. I leave you with this charming attendant. I did not think that such a beauty could exist in Milan unknown to all but you."

"She is a townswoman, who knows how to keep a secret. Do you not?"

"I would rather die than tell anyone that this gentleman is the Marquis of F——."

"That's right; always keep your word, and take this trifle as a souvenir of me."

It was a pretty ring, which Zenobia received with much grace; it might be worth about fifty sequins.

When the marquis was gone, Zenobia undressed me and did my hair for the night, and as I got into bed I gave her twenty-four sequins, and told her she might go and comfort her husband.

"He won't be uneasy," said she, "he is a philosopher."

"He need be with such a pretty wife. Kiss me again, Zenobia, and then we must part."

She threw herself upon me, covering me with kisses, and calling me her happiness and her providence. Her fiery kisses produced their natural effect, and after I had given her a fresh proof of the power of her charms, she left me and I went to sleep.

It was two o'clock when I awoke ravenously hungry. I had an excellent dinner, and then I dressed to call on the charming Mdlle. Q——, whom I did not expect to find too hard on me, after what she had said. Everybody was playing cards with the exception of herself. She was standing by a window reading so attentively that she did not hear me come into the room, but when she saw me near her, she blushed, shut up the book, and put it in her pocket.

"I will not betray you," said I, "or tell anyone that I surprised you reading a prayer-book."

"No, don't; for my reputation would be gone if I were thought to be a devotee."

"Has there been any talk of the masqued ball or of the mysterious masquers?"

"People talk of nothing else, and condole with us for not having been to the ball, but no one can guess who the beggars were. It seems that an unknown carriage and four that sped like the wind took them as far as the first stage, and where they went next God alone knows! It is said that my hair was false, and I have longed to let it down and thus give them the lie. It is also said that you must know who the beggars were, as you loaded them with ducats."

"One must let people say and believe what they like and not betray ourselves."

"You are right; and after all we had a delightful evening. If you acquit yourself of all commissions in the same way, you must be a wonderful man."

"But it is only you who could give me such a commission."

"I to-day, and another to-morrow."

"I see you think I am inconstant, but believe me if I find favour in your eyes your face will ever dwell in my memory."

"I am certain you have told a thousand girls the same story, and after they have admitted you to their favour you have despised them."

"Pray do not use the word 'despise,' or I shall suppose you think me a monster. Beauty seduces me. I aspire to its possession, and it is only when it is given me from other motives than love that I despise it. How should I despise one who loved me? I should first be compelled to despise myself. You are beautiful and I worship you, but you are mistaken if you think that I should be content for you to surrender yourself to me out of mere kindness."

"Ah! I see it is my heart you want."

"Exactly."

"To make me wretched at the end of a fortnight."

"To love you till death, and to obey your slightest wishes."

"My slightest wishes?"

"Yes, for to me they would be inviolable laws."

"Would you settle in Milan?"

"Certainly, if you made that a condition of my happiness."

"What amuses me in all this is that you are deceiving me without knowing it, if indeed you really love me."

"Deceiving you without knowing it! That is something new. If I am not aware of it, I am innocent of deceit."

"I am willing to admit your innocency, but you are deceiving me none the less, for after you had ceased to love me no power of yours could bring love back again."

"That, of course, might happen, but I don't choose to entertain such unpleasant thoughts; I prefer to think of myself as loving you to all eternity. It is certain at all events that no other woman in Milan has attracted me."

"Not the pretty girl who waited on us, and whose arms you have possibly left an hour or two ago?"

"What are you saying? She is the wife of the tailor who made your clothes. She left directly after you, and her husband would not have allowed her to come at all if he was not aware that she would be wanted to wait on the ladies whose dresses he had made."

"She is wonderfully pretty. Is it possible that you are not in love with her?"

"How could one love a woman who is at the disposal of a low, ugly fellow? The only pleasure she gave me was by talking of you this morning."

"Of me?"

"Yes. You will excuse me if I confess to having asked her which of the ladies she waited on looked handsomest without her chemise."

"That was a libertine's question. Well, what did she say?"

"That the lady with the beautiful hair was perfect in every respect."

"I don't believe a word of it. I have learnt how to change my chemise with decency, and so as not to shew anything I might not shew a man. She only wished to flatter your impertinent curiosity. If I had a maid like that, she should soon go about her business."

"You are angry with me."

"No."

"It's no good saying no, your soul flashed forth in your denunciation. I am sorry to have spoken."

"Oh! it's of no consequence. I know men ask chamber-maids questions of that kind, and they all give answers like your sweetheart, who perhaps wanted to make you curious about herself."

"But how could she hope to do that by extolling your charms above those of the other ladies? And how could she know that I preferred you?"

"If she did not know it, I have made a mistake; but for all that, she lied to you."

"She may have invented the tale, but I do not think she lied. You are smiling again! I am delighted."

"I like to let you believe what pleases you."

"Then you will allow me to believe that you do not hate me."

"Hate you? What an ugly word! If I hated you, should I see you at all? But let's talk of something else. I want you to do me a favour. Here are two sequins; I want you to put them on an *ambe* in the lottery. You can bring me the ticket when you call again, or still better, you can send it me, but don't tell anybody."

"You shall have the ticket without fail, but why should I not bring it?"

"Because, perhaps, you are tired of coming to see me."

"Do I look like that? If so I am very unfortunate. But what numbers will you have?"

"Three and forty; you gave them me yourself."

"How did I give them you?"

"You put your hand three times on the board, and took up forty sequins each time. I am superstitious, and you will laugh at me, I daresay, but it seems to me that you must have come to Milan to make me happy."

"Now you make me happy indeed. You say you are superstitious, but if these numbers don't win you mustn't draw the conclusion that I don't love you; that would be a dreadful fallacy."

"I am not superstitious as all that, nor so vile a logician."

"Do you believe I love you?"

"Yes."

"May I tell you so a hundred times?"

"Yes."

"And prove it in every way?"

"I must enquire into your methods before I consent to that, for it is possible that what you would call a very efficacious method might strike me as quite useless."

"I see you are going to make me sigh after you for a long time."

"As long as I can."

"And when you have no strength left?"

"I will surrender. Does that satisfy you?"

"Certainly, but I shall exert all my strength to abate yours."

"Do so; I shall like it."

"And will you help me to succeed?"

"Perhaps."

"Ah, dear marchioness; you need only speak to make a man happy. You have made me really so, and I am leaving you full of ardour."

On leaving this charming conversationalist I went to the theatre and then to the faro-table, where I saw the masquer who had won three hundred sequins the evening before. This night he was very unlucky. He had lost two thousand sequins, and in the course of the next hour his losses had doubled. Canano threw down his cards and rose, saying, "That will do." The masquer left the table. He was a Genoese named Spinola.

"The bank is prosperous," I remarked to Canano.

"Yes," he replied, "but it is not always so. Pierrot was very lucky the other night."

"You did not recognize me in the least?"

"No, I was so firmly persuaded that the beggar was you. You know who he is?"

"I haven't an idea. I never saw him before that day." In this last particular I did not lie.

"It is said that they are Venetians, and that they went to Bergamo."

"It may be so, but I know nothing about them. I left the ball before they did."

In the evening I supped with the countess, her husband, and Triulzi. They were of the same opinion as Canano. Triulzi said that I had let the cat out of the bag by giving the beggars handfuls of sequins.

"That is a mistake," I answered. "When the luck is in my favour I never refuse anyone who asks me for money, for I have a superstition that I should lose if I did. I had won thirty pounds weight of gold, and I could afford to let fools talk."

The next day I got the lottery ticket and took it to the marchioness. I felt madly in love with her because I knew she was in love with me. Neither of them were playing, and I spent two hours in their company, talking of love all the while and enjoying their conversation immensely, for they were exceedingly intelligent. I left them with the conviction that if the cousin, and not Mdlle. Q——, had been thrown in my way, I should have fallen in love with her in just the same manner.

Although the carnival is four days longer at Milan than at any other town, it was now drawing to a close. There were three more balls. I played every day, and every day I lost two or three hundred sequins. My prudence caused even more surprise than my bad fortune. I went every day to the fair cousins and made love, but I was still at the same point; I hoped, but could get nothing tangible. The fair marchioness sometimes gave me a kiss, but this was not enough for me. It is true that so far I had not dared to ask her to meet me alone. As it was I felt my love might die for want of food, and three days before the ball I asked her if she, her two friends, the marquis, and the lieutenant, would come and sup with me.

"My brother," she said, "will call on you to-morrow to see what can be arranged."

This was a good omen. The next day the lieutenant came. I had just received the drawings at the lottery, and what was my surprise and delight to see the two numbers three and forty. I said nothing to the young marquis, as his sister had forbidden me, but I foresaw that this event would be favourable to my suit.

"The Marquis of F——," said the worthy ambassador, "asks you to supper in your own rooms with all the band of beggars. He wishes to give us a surprise, and would be obliged if you would lend him the room to have a set of disguises made, and to ensure secrecy he wants you to let have the same waiting-maid."

"With pleasure; tell the marquis that all shall be according to his pleasure."

"Get the girl to come there at three o'clock to-day, and let the pastrycook know that the marquis has full powers to do what he likes in the place."

"Everything shall be done as you suggest."

I guessed at once that the marquis wanted to have a taste of Zenobia; but this seemed to me so natural that, far from being angry, I felt disposed to do all in my power to favour his plans. Live and let live has always been my maxim, and it will be so to my dying day, though now I do but live a life of memories.

As soon as I was dressed I went out, and having told the pastrycook to consider the gentleman who was coming as myself, I called on the tailor, who was delighted at my getting his wife work. He knew by experience that she was none the worse for these little absences.

"I don't want you," said I to the tailor, "as it is only women's dresses that have to be done. My good gossip here will be sufficient."

"At three o'clock she may go, and I shall not expect to see her again for three days."

After I had dined I called as usual on the fair marchioness, and found her in a transport of delight. Her lottery ticket had got her five hundred sequins.

"And that makes you happy, does it?" said I.

"It does, not because of the gain in money, though I am by no means rich, but for the beauty of the idea and for the thought that I owe it all to you. These two things speak volumes in your favour."

"What do they say?"

"That you deserve to be loved."

"And also that you love me?"

"No, but my heart tells me as much."

"You make me happy, but does not your heart also tell you that you should prove your love?"

"Dearest, can you doubt it?"

With these words she gave me her hand to kiss for the first time.

"My first idea," she added, "was to put the whole forty sequins on the *ambe*."

"You hadn't sufficient courage?"

"It wasn't that, I felt ashamed to do it. I was afraid that you might have a thought you would not tell me of—namely, that if I gave you the forty sequins to risk on the lottery, you would think I despised your present. This would have been wrong, and if you had encouraged me I should have risked all the money."

"I am so sorry not to have thought of it. You would have had ten thousand sequins, and I should be a happy man."

"We will say no more about it."

"Your brother tells me that we are going to the masqued ball under the direction of the marquis, and I leave you to imagine how glad I feel at the thought of spending a whole night with you. But one thought troubles me."

"What is that?"

"I am afraid it will not go off so well as before."

"Don't be afraid, the marquis is a man of much ingenuity, and loves my cousin's honour as herself. He is sure to get us disguises in which we shall not be recognized."

"I hope so. He wants to pay for everything, including the supper."

"He cannot do better than imitate your example in that respect."

On the evening of the ball I went at an early hour to the pastrycook's, where I found the marquis well pleased with the progress that had been made. The dressing-room was shut. I asked him in a suggestive manner if he was satisfied with Zenobia.

"Yes, with her work," he answered; "I did not ask her to do anything else for me."

"Oh! of course I believe it, but I am afraid your sweetheart will be rather sceptical."

"She knows that I cannot love anyone besides herself."

"Well, well, we will say no more about it."

When the guests came the marquis said that as the costumes would amuse us we had better put them on before supper.

We followed him into the next room, and he pointed out two thick bundles.

"Here, ladies, are your disguises," said he; "and here is your maid who will help you while we dress in another room."

He took the larger of the two bundles, and when we were shut up in our room he undid the string, and gave us our dresses, saying——

"Let us be as quick as we can."

We burst out laughing to see a set of women's clothes. Nothing was wanting, chemises, embroidered shoes with high heels, superb garters, and, to relieve us of the trouble of having our hair done, exquisite caps with rich lace coming over the forehead. I was surprised to find that my shoes fitted me perfectly, but I heard afterwards that he employed the same bootmaker as I did. Corsets, petticoats, gowns, kerchief, fans, work-bags, rouge-boxes, masks, gloves—all were there. We only helped each other with our hair, but when it was done we looked intensely stupid, with the exception of the young officer, who really might have been taken for a pretty woman; he had concealed his deficiency in feminine characteristics by false breasts and a bustle.

We took off our breeches one after the other.

"Your fine garters," said I, to the marquis, "make me want to wear some too."

"Exactly," said the marquis; "but the worst of it is nobody will take the trouble to find out whether we have garters or not, for two young ladies five feet ten in height will not inspire very ardent desires."

I had guessed that the girls would be dressed like men, and I was not mistaken. They were ready before us, and when we opened the door we saw them standing with their backs to the fireplace.

They looked three young pages minus their impudence, for though they endeavoured to seem quite at their ease they were rather confused.

We advanced with the modesty of the fair sex, and imitating the air of shy reserve which the part demanded. The girls of course thought themselves obliged to mimic the airs of men, and they did not accost us like young men accustomed to behave respectfully to ladies. They were dressed as running footmen, with tight breeches, well-fitting waistcoats, open throats, garters with a silver fringe, laced waistbands, and pretty caps trimmed with silver lace, and a coat of arms emblazoned in gold. Their lace shirts were ornamented with an immense frill of Alençon point. In this dress, which displayed their beautiful shapes under a veil which was almost transparent, they would have stirred the sense of a paralytic, and we had no symptoms of that disease. However, we loved them too well to frighten them.

After the silly remarks usual on such occasions had been passed, we began to talk naturally while we were waiting for supper. The ladies said that as this was the first time they had dressed as men they were afraid of being recognized.

"Supposing somebody knew us," cried the cousin, "we should be undone!"

They were right; but our part was to reassure them, though I at any rate would have preferred to stay where we were.

We sat down to supper, each next to his sweetheart, and to my surprise the lieutenant's mistress was the first to begin the fun. Thinking that she could not pretend to be a man without being impudent, she began to toy with the lady-lieutenant, who defended himself like a prudish miss. The two cousins, not to be outdone, began to caress us in a manner that was rather free. Zenobia, who was waiting on us at table could not help laughing when Mdlle. Q—— reproached her for having made my dress too tight in the neck. She stretched out her hand as if to toy with me, whereupon I gave her a slight box on the ear, and imitating the manner of a repentant cavalier she kissed my hand and begged my pardon.

The marquis said he felt cold, and his mistress asked him if he had his breeches on, and put her hand under his dress to see, but she speedily drew it back with a blush. We all burst out laughing, and she joined in, and proceeded with her part of hardy lover.

The supper was admirable; everything was choice and abundant. Warm with love and wine, we rose from the table at which we had been for two hours, but as we got up sadness disfigured the faces of the two pretty cousins. They did not dare to go to the ball in a costume that would put them at the mercy of all the libertines there. The marquis and I felt that they were right.

"We must make up our minds," said the lieutenant, "shall we go to the ball or go home?"

"Neither," said the marquis, "we will dance here."

"Where are the violins" asked his mistress, "you could not get them to-night for their weight in gold."

"Well," said I, "we will do without them. We will have some punch, laugh, and be merry, and we shall enjoy ourselves better than at the ball, and when we are tired we can go to sleep. We have three beds here."

"Two would be enough," said the cousin.

"True, but we can't have too much of a good thing."

Zenobia had gone to sup with the pastrycook's wife, but she was ready to come up again when she should be summoned.

After two hours spent in amorous trifling, the lieutenant's mistress, feeling a little dizzy, went into an adjoining room and lay down on the bed. Her lover was soon beside her.

Mdlle. Q——, who was in the same case, told me that she would like to rest, so I took her into a room where she could sleep the night, and advised her to do so.

"I don't think I need fear its going any farther," I said, "we will leave the marquis with your cousin then, and I will watch over you while you sleep."

"No, no, you shall sleep too." So saying, she went into the dressing-room, and asked me to get her cloak. I brought it to her, and when she came in she said,——

"I breathe again. Those dreadful trousers were too tight; they hurt me." She threw herself on the bed, with nothing on besides her cloak.

"Where did the breeches hurt you?" said I.

"I can't tell you, but I should think you must find them dreadfully uncomfortable."

"But, dearest, our anatomy is different, and breeches do not trouble us at all where they hurt you."

As I spoke I held her to my breast and let myself fall gently beside her on the bed. We remained thus a quarter of an hour without speaking, our lips glued together in one long kiss. I left her a moment by herself, and when I returned she was between the sheets. She said she had undressed to be able to sleep better, and, shutting her eyes, turned away. I knew that the happy hour had come, and taking off my woman's clothes in a twinkling, I gently glided into the bed beside her, for the last struggles of modesty must be tenderly respected. I clasped her in my arms and a gentle pressure soon aroused her passions, and turning towards me she surrendered to me all her charms.

After the first sacrifice I proposed a wash, for though I could not exactly flatter myself that I had been the first to break open the lock, the victim had left some traces on the bed, which looked as if it were so. The offer was received with delight, and when the operation was over she allowed me to gaze on all her charms, which I covered with kisses. Growing bolder, she made me grant her the same privilege.

"What a difference there is," said she, "between nature and art!"

"But of course you think that art is the better?"

"No, certainly not."

"But there may be imperfections in nature, whereas art is perfect."

"I do not know whether there be any imperfection in what I behold, but I do know that I have never seen anything so beautiful."

In fact she had the instrument of love before her eyes in all its majesty, and I soon made her feel its power. She did not remain still a moment, and I have known few women so ardent and flexible in their movements.

"If we were wise," said she, "instead of going to the ball again we would come here and enjoy ourselves."

I kissed the mouth which told me so plainly that I was to be happy, and I convinced her by my transports that no man could love her as ardently as I did. I had no need to keep her awake, she shewed no inclination for sleep. We were either in action or contemplation, or engaged in amorous discourse, the whole time. I cheated her now and then, but to her own advantage, for a young woman is always more vigorous than a man, and we did not stop till the day began to break. There was no need for concealment, for each had enjoyed his sweetheart in peace and happiness, and it was only modesty which silenced our congratulations. By this silence we did not proclaim our happiness, but neither did we deny it.

When we were ready I thanked the marquis, and asked him to supper for the next ball night without any pretence of our going to the masquerade, if the ladies had no objection. The lieutenant answered for them in the affirmative, and his mistress threw her arms round his neck, reproaching him for having slept all night. The marquis confessed to the same fault, and I repeated the words like an article of faith, while the ladies kissed us, and thanked us for our kindness to them. We parted in the same way as before, except that this time the marquis remained with Zenobia.

I went to bed as soon as I got home, and slept till three o'clock. When I got up I found the house was empty, so I went to dine at the pastrycook's, where I found Zenobia and her husband, who had come to enjoy the leavings of our supper. He told me that I had made his fortune, as the marquis had given his wife twenty-four sequins and the woman's dress he had worn. I gave her mine as well. I told my gossip that I should like some dinner, and the tailor went away in a grateful mood.

As soon as I was alone with Zenobia I asked her if she were satisfied with the marquis.

"He paid me well," she answered, a slight blush mounting on her cheeks.

"That is enough," said I, "no one can see you without loving you, or love you without desiring to possess your charms."

"The marquis did not go so far as that."

"It may be so, but I am surprised to hear it."

When I had dined, I hastened to call on the fair marchioness, whom I loved more than ever after the delicious night she had given me. I wanted to see what effect she would have on me, after making me so happy. She looked prettier than ever. She received me in a way becoming in a mistress who is glad to have acquired some rights over her lover.

"I was sure," said she, "that you would come and see me; "and though her cousin was there she kissed me so often and so ardently that there was no room for doubt as to the manner in which we had spent our night together. I passed five hours with her, which went by all too quickly, for we talked of love, and love is an inexhaustible subject. This five hours' visit on the day after our bridal shewed me that I was madly in love with my new conquest, while it must have convinced her that I was worthy of her affection.

Countess A—— B—— had sent me a note asking me to sup with her, her husband, and the Marquis Triulzi, and other friends. This engagement prevented my paying a visit to Canano, who had won a thousand sequins of me since my great victory as Pierrot. I knew that he boasted that he was sure of me, but in my own mind I had determined to gain the mastery. At supper the countess waged war on me. I slept out at night. I was rarely visible. She tried hard to steal my secret from me, and to get some information as to my amorous adventures. It was known that I sometimes supped at Thérèse's with Greppi, who was laughed at because he had been silly enough to say that he had nothing to dread from my power. The better to conceal my game, I said he was quite right.

The next day Barbaro, who was as honest as most professional sharpers are, brought me the two hundred sequins I had lent him, with a profit of two hundred more. He told me that he had had a slight difference with the lieutenant, and was not going to play any more. I thanked him for having presented me to the fair marchioness, telling him that I was quite in love with her and in hopes of overcoming her scruples. He smiled, and praised my discretion, letting me understand that I did not take him in; but it was enough for me not to confess to anything.

About three o'clock I called on my sweetheart, and spent five hours with her as before. As Barbaro was not playing, the servants had been ordered to say that no one was at home. As I was the declared lover of the marchioness, her cousin treated me as an intimate friend. She begged me to stay at Milan as long as possible, not only to make her cousin happy, but for her sake as well, since without me she could not enjoy the marquis's society in private, and while her father was alive he would never dare to come openly to the house. She thought she would certainly become his wife as soon as her old father was dead, but she hoped vainly, for soon after the marquis fell into evil ways and was ruined.

Next evening we all assembled at supper, and instead of going to the ball gave ourselves up to pleasure. We spent a delicious night, but it was saddened by the reflection that the carnival was drawing to a close, and with it our mutual pleasures would be over.

On the eve of Shrove Tuesday as there was no ball I sat down to play, and not being able once to hit on three winning cards, I lost all the gold I had about me. I should have left the table as usual if a woman disguised as a man had not given me a card, and urged me by signs to play it. I risked a hundred sequins on it, giving my word for the payment. I lost, and in my endeavours to get back my money I lost a thousand sequins, which I paid the next day.

I was just going out to console myself with the company of my dear marchioness, when I saw the evil-omened masquer approaching, accompanied by a man, also in disguise, who shook me by the hand and begged me to come at ten o'clock to the "Three Kings" at such a number, if the honour of an old friend was dear to me.

"What friend is that?"

"Myself."

"What is your name?"

"I cannot tell you."

"Then you need not tell me to come, for if you were a true friend of mine you would tell me your name."

I went out and he followed me, begging me to come with him to the end of the arcades. When we got there he took off his mask, and I recognized Croce, whom my readers may remember.

I knew he was banished from Milan, and understood why he did not care to give his name in public, but I was exceedingly glad I had refused to go to his inn.

"I am surprised to see you here," said I.

"I dare say your are. I have come here in this carnival season, when one can wear a mask, to compel my relations to give me what they owe me; but they put me off from one day to another, as they are sure I shall be obliged to go when Lent begins."

"And will you do so?"

"I shall be obliged to, but as you will not come and see me, give me twenty sequins, which will enable me to leave Milan. My cousin owes me ten thousand livres, and will not pay me a tenth even. I will kill him before I go."

"I haven't a farthing, and that mask of yours has made me lose a thousand sequins, which I do not know how to pay."

"I know. I am an unlucky man, and bring bad luck to all my friends. It was I who told her to give you a card, in the hope that it would change the run against you."

"Is she a Milanese girl?"

"No, she comes from Marseilles, and is the daughter of a rich agent. I fell in love with her, seduced her, and carried her off to her unhappiness. I had plenty of money then, but, wretch that I am, I lost it all at Genoa, where I had to sell all my possessions to enable me to come here. I have been a week in Milan. Pray give me the wherewithal to escape."

I was touched with compassion, and I borrowed twenty sequins from Canano, and gave them to the poor wretch, telling him to write to me.

This alms-giving did me good; it made me forget my losses, and I spent a delightful evening with the marchioness.

The next day we supped together at my rooms, and spent the rest of the night in amorous pleasures. It was the Saturday, the last day of the carnival at Milan, and

I spent the whole of the Sunday in bed, for the marchioness had exhausted me, and I knew that a long sleep would restore my strength.

Early on Monday morning Clairmont brought me a letter which had been left by a servant. It had no signature, and ran as follows:

"Have compassion, sir, on the most wretched creature breathing. M. de la Croix has gone away in despair. He has left me here in the inn, where he has paid for nothing. Good God! what will become of me? I conjure you to come and see me, be it only to give me your advice."

I did not hesitate for a moment, and it was not from any impulses of love or profligacy that I went, but from pure compassion. I put on my great coat, and in the same room in which I had seen Irene I saw a young and pretty girl, about whose face there was something peculiarly noble and attractive. I saw in her innocence and modesty oppressed and persecuted. As soon as I came in she humbly apologized for having dared to trouble me, and she asked me to tell a woman who was in the room to leave it, as she did not speak Italian.

"She has been tiring me for more than an hour. I cannot understand what she says, but I can make out that she wants to do me a service. However, I do not feel inclined to accept her assistance."

"Who told you to come and see this young lady?" said I, to the woman.

"One of the servants of the inn told me that a young lady from foreign parts had been left alone here, and that she was much to be pitied. My feelings of humanity made me come and see if I could be useful to her; but I see she is in good hands, and I am very glad of it for her sake, poor dear!"

I saw that the woman was a procuress, and I only replied with a smile of contempt.

The poor girl then told me briefly what I had already heard, and added that Croce, who called himself De St. Croix, had gone to the gaming-table as soon as he had got my twenty sequins, and that he had then taken her back to the inn, where he had spent the next day in a state of despair, as he did not dare to shew himself abroad in the daytime. In the evening he put on his mask and went out, not returning till the next morning.

"Soon after he put on his great coat and got ready to go out, telling me that if he did not return he would communicate with me by you, at the same time giving me your address, of which I have made use as you know. He has not come back, and if you have not seen him I am sure he has gone off on foot without a penny in his pocket. The landlord wants to be paid, and by selling all I have I could satisfy his claims; but, good God! what is to become of me, then?"

"Dare you return to your father?"

"Yes, sir, I dare return to him. He will forgive me when on my knees and with tears in my eyes I tell him that I am ready to bury myself in a nunnery."

"Very good! then I will take you to Marseilles myself, and in the meanwhile I will find you a lodging with some honest people. Till then, shut yourself up in your room, do not admit anyone to see you, and be sure I will have a care for you."

I summoned the landlord and paid the bill, which was a very small one, and I told him to take care of the lady till my return. The poor girl was dumb with surprise and gratitude. I said good-bye kindly and left her without even taking her hand. It was not altogether a case

of the devil turning monk; I always had a respect for
distress.

I had already thought of Zenobia in connection with
the poor girl's lodging, and I went to see her on the spot.
In her husband's presence I told her what I wanted, and
asked if she could find a corner for my new friend.

"She shall have my place," cried the worthy tailor, "if
she won't mind sleeping with my wife. I will hire a
small room hard by, and will sleep there as long as the
young lady stays."

"That's a good idea, gossip, but your wife will lose by
the exchange."

"Not much," said Zenobia; and the tailor burst out
laughing.

"As for her meals," he added, "she must arrange that
herself."

"That's a very simple matter," said I, "Zenobia will
get them and I will pay for them."

I wrote the girl a short note, telling her of the arrangements I had made, and charged Zenobia to take her the
letter. The next day I found her in the poor lodging
with these worthy folks, looking pleased and ravishingly
pretty. I felt that I could behave well for the present,
but I sighed at the thought of the journey. I should
have to put a strong restraint on myself.

I had nothing more to do at Milan, but the count had
made me promise to spend a fortnight at St. Angelo.
This was an estate belonging to him, fifteen miles from
Milan, and the count spoke most enthusiastically of it.
If I had gone away without seeing St. Angelo, he would
have been exceedingly mortified. A married brother of
his lived there, and the count often said that his brother
was longing to know me. When we returned he would
no doubt let me depart in peace.

I had made up my mind to shew my gratitude to the worthy man for his hospitality, so on the fourth day of Lent I took leave of Thérèse, Greppi, and the affectionate marchioness, for two weeks, and we set out on our way.

To my great delight the countess did not care to come. She much preferred staying in Milan with Triulzi, who did not let her lack for anything.

We got to St. Angelo at three o'clock, and found that we were expected to dinner.

CHAPTER XXI

*An Ancient Castle—Clementine—The Fair Penitent—
Lodi—A Mutual Passion*

THE manorial castle of the little town of St. Angelo
is a vast and ancient building, dating back at least
eight centuries, but devoid of regularity, and not indicating the date of its erection by the style of its architec-
ture. The ground floor consists of innumerable small
rooms, a few large and lofty apartments, and an immense hall. The walls, which are full of chinks and
crannies, are of that immense thickness which proves
that our ancestors built for their remote descendants,
and not in our modern fashion; for we are beginning to
build in the English style, that is, barely for one generation. The stone stairs had been trodden by so many
feet that one had to be very careful in going up or down.
The floor was all of bricks, and as it had been renewed at
various epochs with bricks of divers colours it formed a
kind of mosaic, not very pleasant to look upon. The
windows were of a piece with the rest; they had no glass
in them, and the sashes having in many instances given
way they were always open; shutters were utterly unknown there. Happily the want of glass was not much
felt in the genial climate of the country. The ceilings
were conspicuous by their absence, but there were heavy
beams, the haunts of bats, owls, and other birds, and
light ornament was supplied by the numerous spiders'
webs.

In this great Gothic palace—for palace it was rather than castle, for it had no towers or other attributes of feudalism, except the enormous coat-of-arms which crowned the gateway—in this palace, I say, the memorial of the ancient glories of the Counts A—— B——, which they loved better than the finest modern house, there were three sets of rooms better kept than the rest. Here dwelt the masters, of whom there were three; the Count A—— B——, my friend, Count Ambrose, who always lived there, and a third, an officer in the Spanish Walloon Guards. I occupied the apartment of the last named. But I must describe the welcome I received.

Count Ambrose received me at the gate of the castle as if I had been some high and puissant prince. The door stood wide open on both sides, but I did not take too much pride to myself on this account, as they were so old that it was impossible to shut them.

The noble count who held his cap in his hand, and was decently but negligently dressed, though he was only forty years old, told me with high-born modesty that his brother had done wrong to bring me here to see their miserable place, where I should find none of those luxuries to which I had been accustomed, but he promised me a good old-fashioned Milanese welcome instead. This is a phrase of which the Milanese are very fond, but as they put it into practice it becomes them well. They are generally most worthy and hospitable people, and contrast favourably with the Piedmontese and Genoese.

The worthy Ambrose introduced me to his countess and his two sisters-in-law, one of whom was an exquisite beauty, rather deficient in manner, but this was no doubt due to the fact that they saw no polished company whatever. The other was a thoroughly ordinary woman, neither pretty nor ugly, of a type which is plentiful all the world over. The countess looked like a Madonna; her features had something angelic about them in their dignity and openness. She came from Lodi, and had only been married two years. The three sisters were very young, very noble, and very poor. While we were at dinner Count Ambrose told me that he had married a poor woman because he thought more of goodness than riches.

"She makes me happy," he added; "and though she brought me no dower, I seem to be a richer man, for she has taught me to look on everything we don't possess as a superfluity."

"There, indeed," said I, "you have the true philosophy of an honest man."

The countess, delighted at her husband's praise and my approval, smiled lovingly at him, and took a pretty baby from the nurse's arms and offered it her alabaster breast. This is the privilege of a nursing mother; nature tells her that by doing so she does nothing against modesty. Her bosom, feeding the helpless, arouses no other feelings than those of respect. I confess, however, that the sight might have produced a tenderer sentiment in me; it was exquisitely beautiful, and I am sure that if Raphael had beheld it his Madonna would have been still more lovely.

The dinner was excellent, with the exception of the made dishes, which were detestable. Soup, beef, fresh salted pork, sausages, mortadella, milk dishes, vegetables, game, mascarpon cheese, preserved fruits—all were delicious; but the count having told his brother that I was a great gourmand, the worthy Ambrose had felt it his duty to give me some ragouts, which were as bad as can well be imagined. I had to taste them, out of politeness; but I made up my mind that I would do so no more. After dinner I took my host apart, and shewed him that with ten plain courses his table would be delicate and excellent, and that he had no need of introducing any ragouts. From that time I had a choice dinner every day.

There were six of us at table, and we all talked and laughed with the exception of the fair Clementine. This was the young countess who had already made an impression on me. She only spoke when she was obliged to do so, and her words were always accompanied with a blush; but as I had no other way of getting a sight of her beautiful eyes, I asked her a good many questions. However, she blushed so terribly that I thought I must be distressing her, and I left her in peace, hoping to become better acquainted with her.

At last I was taken to my apartment and left there. The windows were glazed and curtained as in the dining-room, but Clairmont came and told me that he could not unpack my trunks as there were no locks to anything and should not care to take the responsibility. I thought he was right, and I went to ask my friend about it.

"There's not a lock or a key," said he, " in the whole castle, except in the cellar, but everything is safe for all that. There are no robbers at St. Angelo, and if there were they would not dare to come here."

"I daresay, my dear count, but you know it is my business to suppose robbers everywhere. My own valet might take the opportunity of robbing me, and you see I should have to keep silence if I were robbed."

"Quite so, I feel the force of your argument. Tomorrow morning a locksmith shall put locks and keys to your doors, and you will be the only person in the castle who is proof against thieves."

I might have replied in the words of Juvenal, *Cantabit vacuus coram latrone viator,* but I should have mortified him. I told Clairmont to leave my trunks alone till next day, and I went out with Count A—— B—— and his sisters-in-law to take a walk in the town. Count Ambrose and his better-half stayed in the castle; the good mother would never leave her nursling. Clementine was eighteen, her married sister being four years older. She took my arm, and my friend offered his to Eleanore.

"We will go and see the beautiful penitent," said the count.

I asked him who the beautiful penitent was, and he answered, without troubling himself about his sisters-in-law,——

"She was once a Lais of Milan, and enjoyed such a reputation for beauty that not only all the flower of Milan but people from the neighbouring towns were at her feet. Her hall-door was opened and shut a hundred times in a day, and even then she was not able to satisfy the desires aroused. At last an end came to what the old and the devout called a scandal. Count Firmian, a man of learning and wit, went to Vienna, and on his departure received orders to have her shut up in a convent. Our august Marie Thérèse cannot pardon mercenary beauty, and the count had no choice but to have the fair sinner imprisoned. She was told that she had done amiss, and dealt wickedly; she was obliged to make a general confession, and was condemned to a life-long penance in this convent. She was absolved by Cardinal Pozzobonelli, Archbishop of Milan, and he then confirmed her, changing the name of Thérèse, which she had received at the baptismal font, to Mary Magdalen, thus shewing her how she should save her soul by following the example of her new patroness, whose wantonness had hitherto been her pattern.

"Our family are the patrons of this convent, which is devoted to penitents. It is situated in an inaccessible spot, and the inmates are in the charge of a kind mother-superior, who does her best to soften the manifold austerities of their existences. They only work and pray, and see no one besides their confessor, who says mass every day. We are the only persons whom the superioress would admit, as long as some of our family are present she always let them bring whom they like."

This story touched me and brought tears to my eyes. Poor Mary Magdalen! Cruel empress! I think I have noted in another passage the source of her austere virtue.

When we were announced the mother-superior came to meet us, and took us into a large hall, where I soon made out the famous penitent amongst five or six other girls, who were penitents like herself, but I presume for trifling offences, as they were all ugly. As soon as the poor women saw us they ceased working, and stood up respectfully. In spite of the severe simplicity of her dress, Thérèse made a great impression on me. What beauty! What majesty brought low! With my profane eyes, instead of looking to the enormity of the offences for which she was suffering so cruelly, I saw before me a picture of innocence—a humbled Venus. Her fine eyes were fixed on the ground, but what was my surprise, when, suddenly looking at me, she exclaimed,——

"O my God! what do I see? Holy Mary, come to my aid! Begone, dreadful sinner, though thou deservest to be here more than I. Scoundrel!"

I did not feel inclined to laugh. Her unfortunate position, and the singular apostrophe she had addressed to me, pierced me to the heart. The mother-superior hastened to say,——

"Do not be offended, sir, the poor girl has become mad, and unless she really has recognized you. . . ."

"That is impossible, madam, I have never seen her before."

"Of course not, but you must forgive her, as she has lost the use of her reason."

"Maybe the Lord has made her thus in mercy."

As a matter of fact, I saw more sense than madness in this outburst, for it must have been very grievous for the poor girl to have to encounter my idle curiosity in the place of her penitence. I was deeply moved, and in spite of myself a big tear rolled down my face. The count, who had known her, laughed, but I begged him to restrain himself.

A moment after, the poor wretch began again. She raved against me madly, and begged the mother-superior to send me away, as I had come there to damn her.

The good lady chid her with all a true mother's gentleness, and told her to leave the room, adding that all who came there only desired that she should be saved eternally. She was stern enough, however, to add, that no one had been a greater sinner than she, and the poor Magdalen went out weeping bitterly.

If it had been my fortune to enter Milan at the head of a victorious army, the first thing I should have done would be he setting free of this poor captive, and if the abbess had resisted she would have felt the weight of my whip.

When Magdalen was gone, the mother-superior told us that the poor girl had many good qualities, and if God willed that she should keep some particle of sense she did not doubt her becoming a saint like her patroness.

"She has begged me," she added, "to take down the pictures of St. Louis de Gonzaga and St. Antony from the chapel wall because she says they distract her fearfully. I have thought it my duty to yield to her request, in spite of our confessor, who says it's all nonsense."

The confessor was a rude churl. I did not exactly tell the abbess that, but I said enough for a clever woman as she was to grasp my meaning.

We left the sorrowful place in sadness and silence, cursing the sovereign who had made such ill use of her power.

If, as our holy religion maintains, there is a future life before us all, Marie Thérèse certainly deserves damnation, if only the oppressions she has used towards those poor women whose life is wretched enough at the best. Poor Mary Magdalen had gone mad and suffered the torments of the damned because nature had given her two of her best gifts—beauty, and an excellent heart. You will say she had abused them, but for a fault which is only a crime before God, should a fellow-creature and a greater sinner have condemned her to such a fearful doom? I defy any reasonable man to answer in the affirmative.

On our way back to the castle Clementine, who was on my arm, laughed to herself once or twice. I felt curious to know what she was laughing at, and said,——

"May I ask you, fair countess, why you laugh thus to yourself?"

"Forgive me; I was not amused at the poor girl's recognizing you, for that must have been a mistake, but I cannot help laughing when I think of your face at her words 'You are more deserving of imprisonment than I.'"

"Perhaps you think she was right."

"I? Not at all. But how is it that she attacked you and not my brother-in-law?"

"Probably because she thought I looked a greater sinner than he."

"That, I suppose, must have been the reason. One should never heed the talk of mad people."

"You are sarcastic, but I take it all in good part. Perhaps I am as great a sinner as I look; but beauty should be merciful to me, for it is by beauty that I am led astray."

"I wonder the empress does not shut up men as well as women."

"Perhaps she hopes to see them all at her feet when there are no more girls left to amuse them."

"That is a jest. You should rather say that she cannot forgive her own sex the lack of a virtue which she exercises so eminently, and which is so easily observed."

"I have nothing to allege against the empress's virtue, but with your leave I beg to entertain very strong doubts as to the possibility of the general exercise of that virtue which we call continence."

"No doubt everyone thinks by his own standard. A man may be praised for temperance in whom temperance is no merit. What is easy to you may be hard to me, and *vice versâ*.. Both of us may be right."

This interesting conversation made me compare Clementine to the fair marchioness at Milan, but there was this difference between them: Mdlle. Q—— spoke with an air of gravity and importance, whereas Clementine expounded her system with great simplicity and an utter indifference of manner. I thought her observations so acute and her utterance so perfect and artistic, that I felt ashamed of having misjudged her at dinner. Her silence, and the blush which mounted to her face when anyone asked her a question, had made me suspect both confusion and poverty in her ideas, for timidity is often another word for stupidity; but the conversation I have just reported made me feel that I had made a great mistake. The marchioness, being older and having seen more of the world, was more skilled in argument; but Clementine had twice eluded my questions with the utmost skill, and I felt obliged to award her the palm.

When we got back to the castle we found a lady with her son and daughter, and another relation of the count's, a young abbé, whom I found most objectionable.

He was a pitiless talker, and on the pretence of having seen me at Milan he took the opportunity of flattering me in a disgusting manner. Besides, he made sheep's eyes at Clementine, and I did not like the idea of having a fellow like that for a rival. I said very dryly that I did not remember him at all; but he was not a man of delicate feeling, and this did not disconcert him in the least. He sat down beside Clementine, and taking her hand told her that she must add me to the long catalogue of her victims. She could do nothing else but laugh at silly talk of this kind; I knew it, but that laugh of hers displeased me. I would have had her say—I do not know what, but something biting and sarcastic. Not at all; the impertinent fellow whispered something in her ear, and she answered in the same way. This was more than I could bear. Some question or other was being discussed, and the abbé asked for my opinion. I do not remember what I answered, but I know that I gave him a bitter reply in the hope of putting him in a bad temper and reducing him to silence. But he was a battle charger, and used to trumpet, fife, and gun; nothing put him out. He appealed to Clementine, and I had the mortification of hearing her opinion given, though

with a blush, in his favour. The fop was satisfied, and
kissed the young countess's hand with an air of fatuous
happiness. This was too much; and I cursed the abbé
and Clementine, too. I rose from my seat and went to
the window.

The window is a great blessing to an impatient man,
whom the rules of politeness in some degree constrain.
He can turn his back on bores, without their being able
to charge him with direct rudeness; but people know
what he means, and that soothes his feelings.

I have noted this trifling circumstance only to point
out how bad temper blinds its victims. The poor abbé
vexed me because he made himself agreeable to Clementine, with whom I was already in love without knowing
it. I saw in him a rival, but far from endeavouring to
offend me, he had done his best to please me; and I
should have taken account of his good will. But under
such circumstances I always gave way to ill humour,
and now I am too old to begin curing myself. I don't
think I need do so, for if I am ill tempered the company
politely pass me over. My misfortune obliges me to
submit.

Clementine had conquered me in the space of a few
hours. True, I was an inflammable subject, but hitherto
no beauty had committed such ravages upon me in so
short a time. I did not doubt of success, and I confess
that there was a certain amount of vanity in this assurance; but at the same time I was modest, for I knew
that at the slightest slip the enterprise would miscarry.
Thus I regarded the abbé as a wasp to be crushed as
speedily as possible. I was also a victim to that most
horrible of passions, jealousy; it seemed to me that if
Clementine was not in love with this man-monkey, she
was extremely indulgent to him; and with this idea I

conceived a horrible plan of revenging my wrongs on her. Love is the god of nature, but this god is, after all, only a spoilt child. We know all his follies and frailties, but we still adore him.

My friend the count, who was surprised, I suppose, to see me contemplating the prospect for such a long time, came up to me and asked me if I wanted anything.

"I am thinking some matter over," said I, " and I must go and write one or two letters in my room till it is time for supper."

"You won't leave us surely?" said he.

"Clementine, help me to keep M. de Seingalt; you must make him postpone his letter-writing."

"But my dear brother," said the charming girl, "if M. de Seingalt has business to do, it would be rude of me to try and prevent his doing it."

Though what she said was perfectly reasonable, it stung me to the quick; when one is in an ill humour, everything is fuel for the fire. But the abbé said pleasantly that I had much better come and make a bank at faro, and as everything echoed this suggestion I had to give in.

The cards were brought in, and various coloured counters handed round, and I sat down putting thirty ducats before me. This was a very large sum for a company who only played for amusement's sake; fifteen counters were valued only at a sequin. Countess Ambrose sat at my right hand, and the abbé at my left. As if they had laid a plot to vex and annoy me, Clementine had made room for him. I took a mere accident for a studied impertinence, and told the poor man that I never dealt unless I had a lady on each side of me, and never by any chance with a priest beside me.

"Do you think it would bring you ill luck?"

"I don't like birds of ill omen."

At this he got up, and Clementine took his place.

At the end of three hours, supper was announced. Everybody had won from me except the abbé; the poor devil had lost counters to the extent of twenty sequins.

As a relation the abbé stayed to supper, but the lady and her children were asked in vain to do so.

The abbé looked wretched, which made me in a good temper, and inclined me to be pleasant. I proceeded to flirt with Clementine, and by making her reply to the numerous questions I asked, I gave her an opportunity of displaying her wit, and I could see that she was grateful. I was once more myself, and I took pity of the abbé, and spoke to him politely, asking him his opinion on some topic.

"I was not listening," said he, "but I hope you will give me my revenge after supper."

"After supper I shall be going to bed, but you shall have your revenge, and as much as you like of it, to-morrow, provided that our charming hostesses like playing. I hope the luck will be in your favour."

After supper the poor abbé went sadly away, and the count took me to my room, telling me that I could sleep securely in spite of the lack of keys for his sisters-in-law who were lodged close by were no better off.

I was astonished and delighted at the trust he put in me, and at the really magnificent hospitality (it must be remembered all things are relative) with which I had been treated in the castle.

I told Clairmont to be quick about putting my hair in curl-papers, for I was tired and in need of rest, but he was only half-way through the operation when I was agreeably surprised by the apparition of Clementine.

"Sir," said she, " as we haven't got a maid to look after

your linen, I have come to beg you to let me undertake that office."

"You! my dear countess?"

"Yes, I, sir, and I hope you will make no objection. It will be a pleasure to me, and I hope to you as well. Let me have the shirt you are going to wear to-morrow, and say no more about it."

"Very good, it shall be as you please."

I helped Clairmont to carry my linen trunk into her room, and added,——

"Every day I want a shirt, a collar, a front, a pair of drawers, a pair of stocking, and two handkerchiefs; but I don't mind which you take, and leave the choice to you as the mistress, as I wish you were in deed and truth. I shall sleep a happier sleep than Jove himself. Farewell, dear Hebe!"

Her sister Eleanore was already in bed, and begged pardon for her position. I told Clairmont to go to the count directly, and inform him that I had changed my mind about the locks. Should I be afraid for my poor properties when these living treasures were confined to me so frankly? I should have been afraid of offending them.

I had an excellent bed, and I slept wonderfully. Clairmont was doing my hair when my youthful Hebe presented herself with a basket in her hands. She wished me good day and said she hoped I would be contented with her handiwork. I gazed at her delightedly, no trace of false shame appeared on her features. The blush on her cheeks was a witness of the pleasure she experienced in being useful—a pleasure which is unkown to those whose curse is their pride, the characteristic of fools and upstarts. I kissed her hand and told her that I had never seen linen so nicely done.

Just then the count came in and thanked Clementine for attending on me. I approved of that, but he accompanied his thanks with a kiss which was well received, and this I did not approve of at all. But you will say they were brother-in-law and sister-in-law? Just so, but I was jealous all the same. Nature is all-wise, and it was nature that made me jealous. When one loves and has not as yet gained possession, jealousy is inevitable; the heart must fear lest that which it longs for so be carried away by another.

The count took a note from his pocket and begged me to read it. It came from his cousin the abbé, who begged the count to apologize to me for him if he was unable to pay the twenty sequins he had lost to me in the proper time, but that he would discharge his debt in the course of the week.

"Very good! Tell him that he can pay when he likes, but warn him not to play this evening. I will not take his bets."

"But you would have no objection to his punting with ready money."

"Certainly I should, unless he pays me first, otherwise he would be punting with my money. Of course it's a mere trifle, and I hope he won't trouble himself in the least or put himself to any inconvenience to pay it."

"I am afraid he will be mortified."

"So much the better," said Clementine; "what did he play for, when he knew that he could not pay his debts if he incurred any? It will be a lesson to him."

This outburst was balm to my heart. Such is man—a mere selfish egotist, when passion moves him.

The count made no reply, but left us alone.

"My dear Clementine, tell me frankly whether the rather uncivil way in which I have treated the abbé has

pained you. I am going to give you twenty sequins, do
you send them to him, and to-night he can pay me
honourably, and make a good figure. I promise you no
one shall know about it."

"Thank you, but the honour of the abbé is not dear
enough to me for me to accept your offer. The lesson
will do him good. A little shame will teach him that
he must mend his ways."

"You will see he won't come this evening."

"That may be, but do you think I shall care?"

"Well—yes, I did think so."

"Because we joked together, I suppose. He is a
hare-brained fellow, to whom I do not give two thoughts
in the year."

"I pity him, as heartily as I congratulate anyone of
whom you do think."

"Maybe there is no such person."

"What! You have not yet met a man worthy of your
regard?"

"Many worthy of regard, but none of love."

"Then you have never been in love?"

"Never,."

"Your heart is empty?"

"You make me laugh. Is it happiness, is it unhappiness? Who can say. If it be happiness, I am glad, and
if it be unhappiness, I do not care, for I do not feel it to
be so."

"Nevertheless, it is a misfortune, and you will know
it to have been so on the day in which you love."

"And if I become unhappy through love, shall I not
pronounce my emptiness of heart to have been happiness?"

"I confess you would be right, but I am sure love
would make you happy."

"I do not know. To be happy one must live in perfect agreement; that is no easy matter, and I believe it to be harder still when the bond is lifelong."

"I agree, but God sent us into the world that we might run the risk."

"To a man it may be a necessity and a delight, but a girl is bound by stricter laws."

"In nature the necessity is the same though the results are different, and the laws you speak of are laid down by society."

The count came in at this point and was astonished to see us both together.

"I wish you would fall in love with one another," said he.

"You wish to see us unhappy, do you?" said she.

"What do you mean by that?" I cried.

"I should be unhappy with an inconstant lover, and you would be unhappy too, for you would feel bitter remorse for having destroyed my peace of mind."

After this she discreetly fled.

I remained still as if she had petrified me, but the count who never wearied himself with too much thinking, exclaimed,——

"Clementine is rather too romantic; she will get over it, however; she is young yet."

We went to bid good day to the countess, whom we found suckling her baby.

"Do you know, my dear sister," said the count, "that the chevalier here is in love with Clementine, and she seems inclined to pay him back in his own coin?"

The countess smiled and said,——

"I hope a suitable match like that may make us relations."

There is something magical about the word "marriage."

What the countess said pleased me extremely, and I replied with a bow of the most gracious character.

We went to pay a call on the lady who had come to the castle the day before. There was a canon regular there, who after a great many polite speeches in praise of my country, which he knew only from books, asked me of what order was the cross I carried on my breast.

I replied, with a kind of boastful modesty, that it was a peculiar mark of the favour of the Holy Father, the Pope, who had freely made me a knight of the Order of St. John Lateran, and a prothonotary-apostolic.

This monk had stayed at home far from the world, or else he would not have asked me such a question. However, far from thinking he was offending me, he thought he was honouring me by giving me an opportunity of talking of my own merit.

At London, the greatest possible rudeness is to ask anyone what his religion is, and it is something the same in Germany; an Anabaptist is by no means ready to confess his creed. And in fact the best plan is never to ask any questions whatever, not even if a man has change for a louis.

Clementine was delightful at dinner. She replied wittily and gracefully to all the questions which were addressed to her. True, what she said was lost on the majority of her auditors—for wit cannot stand before stupidity—but I enjoyed her talk immensely. As she kept filling up my glass I reproached her, and this gave rise to the following little dialogue which completed my conquest.

"You have no right to complain," said she, "Hebe's duty is to keep the cup of the chief of the gods always full."

"Very good; but you know Jupiter sent her away."

"Yes, but I know why. I will take care not to stumble in the same way; and no Ganymede shall take my place for a like cause."

"You are very wise. Jupiter was wrong, and henceforth I will be Hercules. Will that please you, fair Hebe?"

"No; because he did not marry her till after her death."

"True, again. I will be Iolas then, for . . ."

"Be quiet. Iolas was old."

"True; but so was I yesterday. You have made me young again."

"I am very glad, dear Iolas; but remember what I did when he left me."

"And what did you do? I do not remember."

"I did not believe a word he said."

"You can believe."

"I took away the gift I had made."

At these words this charming girl's face was suffered with blushes. If I had touched her with my hand, sure it would have been on fire; but the rays that darted from her eyes froze my heart.

Philosophers, be not angry if I talk of freezing rays. It is no miracle, but a very natural phenomenon, which is happening every day. A great love, which elevates a man's whole nature, is a strong flame born out of a great cold, such as I then felt for a moment; it would have killed me if it had lasted longer.

The superior manner in which Clementine had applied the story of Hebe convinced me not only that she had a profound knowledge of mythology, but also that she had a keen and far-reaching intellect. She had given me more than a glimpse of her learning; she had let me guess that I interested her, and that she thought of me.

These ideas, entering a heart which is already warm, speedily set all the senses in flames. In a moment all doubt was laid to rest; Clementine loved me, and I was sure that we should be happy.

Clementine slipped away from the table to calm herself, and thus I had time to escape from my astonishment.

"Pray where was that young lady educated?" I said to the countess.

"In the country. She was always present when my brother had his lessons, but the tutor, Sardini, never took any notice of her, and it was only she who gained anything; my brother only yawned. Clementine used to make my mother laugh, and puzzle the old tutor sadly sometimes."

"Sardini wrote and published some poems which are not bad; but nobody reads them, because they are so full of mythology."

"Quite so. Clementine possesses a manuscript with which he presented her, containing a number of mythological tales verified. Try and make her shew you her books and the verses she used to write; she won't shew them to any of us."

I was in a great state of admiration. When she returned I complimented her upon her acquirements, and said that as I was a great lover of literature myself I should be delighted if she would shew me her verses.

"I should be ashamed. I had to give over my studies two years ago, when my sister married and we came to live here, where we only see honest folks who talk about the stable, the harvest, and the weather. You are the first person I have seen who has talked to me about literature. If our old Sardini had come with us I should have gone on learning, but my sister did not care to have him here."

"But my dear Clementine," said the countess, "what do you think my husband could have done with an old man of eighty whose sole accomplishments are weighing the wind, writing verses, and talking mythology?"

"He would have been useful enough," said the husband, "if he could have managed the estate, but the honest old man will not believe in the existence of rascals. He is so learned that he is quite stupid."

"Good heavens!" cried Clementine. "Sardini stupid? It is certainly easy to deceive him, but that is because he is so noble. I love a man who is easily deceived, but they call me silly."

"Not at all, my dear sister," said the countess. "On the contrary, there is wisdom in all you say, but it is wisdom out of place in a woman; the mistress of a household does not want to know anything about literature, poetry, or philosophy, and when it comes to marrying you I am very much afraid that your taste for this kind of thing will stand in your way."

"I know it, and I am expecting to die a maid; not that it is much compliment to the men."

To know all that such a dialogue meant for me, the reader must imagine himself most passionately in love. I thought myself unfortunate. I could have given her a hundred thousand crowns, and I would have married her that moment. She told me that Sardini was at Milan, very old and ill.

"Have you been to see him?" I asked.

"I have never been to Milan."

"Is it possible? It is not far from here."

"Distance is relative, you know."

This was beautifully expressed. It told me without

any false shame that she could not afford to go, and I was pleased by her frankness. But in the state of mind I was in I should have been pleased with anything she chose to do. There are moments in a man's life when the woman he loves can make anything of him.

I spoke to her in a manner that affected her so that she took me into a closet next to her room to shew me her books. There were only thirty in all, but they were chosen, although somewhat elementary. A woman like Clementine needed something more.

"Do you know, my dear Hebe, that you want more books?"

"I have often suspected it, dear Iolas, without being able to say exactly what I want."

After spending an hour in glancing over Sardini's works, I begged her to shew me her own.

"No," said she, "they are too bad."

"I expect so; but the good will outweigh the bad."

"I don't think so."

"Oh, yes! you needn't be afraid. I will forgive the bad grammar, bad style, absurd images, faulty method, and even the verses that won't scan."

"That's too much, Iolas; Hebe doesn't need so vast a pardon as all that. Here, sir, these are my scribblings; sift the faults and the defaults. Read what you will."

I was delighted that my scheme of wounding her vanity had succeeded, and I began by reading aloud an anacreontic, adding to its beauties by the modulation of my voice, and keenly enjoying her pleasure at finding her work so fair. When I improved a line by some trifling change she noticed it, for she followed me with her eyes; but far from being humiliated, she was pleased with my corrections. The picture was still hers, she thought, though with my skilled brush I brought out the lights and darkened the shadows, and she was charmed to see that my pleasure was as great or greater than hers. The reading continued for two hours. It was a spiritual and pure, but a most intensely voluptuous, enjoyment. Happy, and thrice happy, if we had gone no farther; but love is a traitor who laughs at us when we think to play with him without falling into his nets. Shall a man touch hot coals and escape the burning?

The countess interrupted us, and begged us to join the company. Clementine hastened to put everything back, and thanked me for the happiness I had given her. The pleasure she felt shewed itself in her blushes, and when she came into the drawing-room she was asked if she had been fighting, which made her blush still more.

The faro-table was ready, but before sitting down I told Clairmont to get me four good horses for the following day. I wanted to go to Lodi and back by dinner-time.

Everybody played as before, the abbé excepted, and he, to my huge delight, did not put in an appearance at all, but his place was supplied by a canon, who punted a ducat at a time and had a pile of ducats before him. This made me increase my bank, and when the game was over, I was glad to see that everybody had won except the canon, but his losses had not spoilt his temper.

Next day I started for Lodi at day-break without telling anybody where I was going, and bought all the books I judged necessary for Clementine, who only knew Italian. I bought numerous translation, which I was surprised to find at Lodi, which hitherto had been only famous in my mind for its cheese, usually called Parmesan. This cheese is made at Lodi and not at Parma, and I did not fail to make an entry to that effect under the article "Parmesan" in my "Dictionary of Cheeses," a work which I was obliged to abandon as beyond my powers, as Rousseau was obliged to abandon his "Dictionary of Botany." This great but eccentric individual was then known under the pseudonym of Renaud, the Botanist. *Quisque histrioniam exercet.* But Rousseau, great man though he was, was totally deficient in humour.

I conceived the idea of giving a banquet at Lodi the day after next, and a project of this kind not calling for much deliberation I went forthwith to the best hotel to make the necessary arrangements. I ordered a choice dinner for twelve, paid the earnest money, and made the host promise that everything should be of the best.

When I got back to St. Angelo, I had a sackfull of books carried into Clementine's room. She was petrified. There were more than one hundred volumes, poets, historians, geographers, philosophers, scientists—nothing was forgotten. I had also selected some good novels, translated from the Spanish, English, and French, for we have no good novels in Italian.

This admission does not prove by any means that Italian literature is surpassed by that of any other country. Italy has little to envy in other literatures, and has numerous masterpieces, which are unequalled the whole world over. Where will you find a worthy companion to the *Orlando Furioso?* There is none, and this great work is incapable of transalation. The finest and truest panegyric of Ariosto was written by Voltaire when he was sixty. If he had not made this apology for the rash judgement of his youthful days, he would not have enjoyed, in Italy at all events, that immortality which is so justly his due. Thirty-six years ago I told him as much, and he took me at my word. He was afraid, and he acted wisely.

If I have any readers, I ask their pardon for these digressions. They must remember that these Memoirs were written in my old age, and the old are always garrulous. The time will come to them also, and then they will understand that if the aged repeat themselves, it is because they live in a world of memories, without a present and without a future.

I will now return to my narrative, which I have kept steadily in view.

Clementine gazed from me to the books, and from the books to me. She wondered and admired, and could scarcely believe this treasure belonged to her. At last she collected herself, and said in a tone full of gratitude,——

"You have come to St. Angelo to make me happy."

Such a saying makes a man into a god. He is sure that she who speaks thus will do all in her power to make a return for the happiness which she has been given.

There is something supremely lovely in the expression of gratefulness on the face of the being one loves. If you have not experienced the feelings I describe, dear reader, I pity you, and am forced to conclude that you must have been either awkward or miserly, and therefore unworthy of love.

Clementine ate scarcely anything at dinner, and afterwards retired to her room where I soon joined her. We amused ourselves by putting the books in order, and she sent for a carpenter to make a bookcase with a lock and key.

"It will be my pleasure to read these books," said she, "when you have left us."

In the evening she was lucky with the cards, and in delightful spirits. I asked them all to dine with me at

Lodi, but as the dinner was for twelve the Countess Ambrose said she would be able to find the two guests who were wanted at Lodi, and the canon said he would take the lady friend with her two children.

The next day was one of happy quiet, and I spent it without leaving the castle, being engaged in instructing my Hebe on the nature of the sphere, and in preparing her for the beauties of Wolf. I presented her with my case of mathematical instruments, which seemed to her invaluable.

I burned with passion for this charming girl; but would I have done so if her taste for literature and science had not been backed up by her personal charms? I suspect not. I like a dish pleasing to the palate, but if it is not pleasing to the eye as well, I do not taste it but put down as bad. The surface is always the first to interest, close examination comes afterwards. The man who confines himself to superficial charms, is superficial himself, but with them all love begins, except that which rises in the realm of fancy, and this nearly always falls before the reality.

When I went to bed, still thinking of Clementine, I began to reflect seriously, and I was astonished to find that during all the hours we had spent together she had not caused the slightest sensual feeling to arise in me. Nevertheless, I could not assign the reason to fear, nor to shyness which is unknown to me, nor to false shame, nor to what is called a feeling of duty. It was certainly not virtue, for I do not carry virtue so far as that. Then what was it? I did not tire myself by pursuing the question. I felt quite sure that the Platonic stage must soon come to an end, and I was sorry, but my sorrow was virtue *in extremis*. The fine things we read together interested us so strongly that we did not think of love, nor of the pleasure we took in each other's company; but as the saying goes, the devil lost nothing by us. When intellect enters on the field, the heart has to yield; virtue triumphs, but the battle must not last for long. Our conquests made us too sure, but this feeling of security was a Colossus whose feet were of clay; we knew that we loved but were not sure that we were beloved. But when this became manifest the Colossus must fall to the ground.

This dangerous trust made me go to her room to tell her something about our journey to Lodi, the carriages were already waiting. She was still asleep, but my step on the floor made her awake with a start. I did not even think it necessary to apologize. She told me that Tasso's *Aminta* had interested her to such an extent that she had read it till she fell asleep.

"The *Pastor Fido* will please you still more."

"Is it more beautiful?"

"Not exactly."

"Then why do you say it will please me more?"

"Because it charms the heart. It appeals to our softest feelings, and seduces us—and we love seduction."

"It is a seducer, then?"

"No, not a seducer; but seductive, like you."

"That's a good distinction. I will read it this evening. Now I am going to dress."

She put on her clothes in seeming oblivion that I was a man, but without shewing any sights that could be called indecent. Nevertheless it struck me that if she had thought I was in love with her, she would have been more reserved, for as she put on her chemise, laced her corset, fastened her garters above her knee, and drew on her boots, I saw glimpses of beauty which affected me so strongly that I was obliged to go out before she was ready to quench the flames she had kindled in my senses.

I took the countess and Clementine in my carriage, and sat on the bracket seat holding the baby on my knee. My two fair companions laughed merrily, for I held the child as if to the manner born. When we had traversed half the distance the baby demanded nourishment, and the charming mother hastened to uncover a sphere over which my eyes roved with delight, not at all to her displeasure. The child left its mother's bosom satisfied, and at the sight of the liquor which flowed so abundantly I exclaimed,——

"It must not be lost, madam; allow me to sip nectar which will elevate me to the rank of the gods. Do not be afraid of my teeth." I had some teeth in those days.

The smiling countess made no opposition, and I proceeded to carry out my design, while the ladies laughed that magic laugh which not painter can portray. The divine Homer is the only poet who has succeeded in delineating it in those lines in which he describes Andromache with the young Astyanax in her arms, when Hector is leaving her to return to the battle.

I asked Clementine if she had the courage to grant me a similar favour.

"Certainly," said she, "if I had any milk."

"You have the source of the milk; I will see to the rest."

At this the girl's face suffused with such a violent blush that I was sorry I had spoken; however, I changed the conversation, and it soon passed away. Our spirits were so high that when the time came for us to get down at the inn at Lodi, we could scarcely believe it possible, so swiftly had the time gone by.

The countess sent a message to a lady friend of hers, begging her to dine with us, and to bring her sister; while I dispatched Clairmont to a stationer's, where he bought me a beautiful morocco case with lock and key, containing paper, pens, sealing-wax, ink-well, paper knife, seal, and in fact, everything necessary for writing. It was a present I meant to give Clementine before dinner. It was delightful to watch her surprise and pleasure, and to read gratitude so legibly written in her beautiful eyes. There is not a woman in the world who cannot be overcome by being made grateful. It is the best and surest way to get on, but it must be skilfully used. The countess's friend came and brought her sister, a girl who was dazzlingly beautiful. I was greatly struck with her, but just then Venus herself could not have dethroned Clementine from her place in my affections. After the friends had kissed each other, and expressed their joy at meeting, I was introduced, and in so complimentary a manner that I felt obliged to turn it off with a jest.

The dinner was sumptuous and delicious. At dessert two self-invited guests came in, the lady's husband and the sister's lover, but they were welcome, for it was a case of the more the merrier. After the meal, in accordance with the request of the company, I made a bank at faro, and after three hours' play I was delighted to find myself a loser to the extent of forty sequins. It was these little losses at the right time which gave me the reputation of being the finest gamester in Europe.

The lady's lover was named Vigi, and I asked him if he was descended from the author of the thirteenth book of the "Æneid." He said he was, and that in honour of his ancestor he had translated the poem into Italian verse. I expressed myself curious as to his version, and he promised to bring it me in two days' time. I complimented him on belonging to such a noble and ancient family; Maffeo Vigi flourished at the beginning of the fifteenth century.

We started in the evening, and less than two hours we got home. The moon which shone brightly upon us prevented me making any attempts on Clementine, who had put up her feet in order that she might be able to hold her little nephew with more ease. The pretty mother could not help thanking me warmly for the pleasure I had given them; I was a universal favourite with them all.

We did not feel inclined to eat any supper, and therefore retired to our apartments; and I accompanied Clementine, who told me that she was ashamed at not knowing anything about the "Æneid."

"Vigi will bring his translation of the thirteenth book, and I shall not know a word about it."

I comforted her by telling her that we would read the fine translation by Annibale Caro that very night. It was amongst her books, as also the version by Anguilara, Ovid's Metamorphoses, and Marchetti's *Lucreece*.

"But I wanted to read the *Pastor Fido*."

"We are in a hurry; we must read that another time."

"I will follow your advice in all things, my dear Iolas."

"That will make me happy, dearest Hebe."

We spent the night in reading that magnificent translation in Italian blank verse, but the reading was often interrupted by my pupil's laughter when we came to some rather ticklish passage. She was highly amused by the account of the chance which gave Æneas an opportunity of proving his love for Dido in a very incon-

venient place, and still more, when Dido, complaining
of the son of Priam's treachery, says,——

"I might still pardon you if, before abandoning me,
you had left me a little Æneas to play about these halls."

Clementine had cause to be amused, for the reproach
has something laughable in it; but how is it that one
does not feel inclined to smile in reading the Latin—*Si
quis mihi parvulus aula luderet Æneas?*. The reason
must be sought for in the grave and dignified nature of
the Latin tongue.

We did not finish our reading till day-break.

"What a night!" exclaimed Clementine, with a sigh.

"It has been one of great pleasure to me, has it not to
you?"

"I have enjoyed it because you have."

"And if you had been reading by yourself?"

"It would have still been a pleasure, but a much
smaller one. I love your intellect to distraction, Clementine, but tell me, do you think it possible to love the
intellect without loving that which contains it?"

"No, for without the body the spirit would vanish
away."

"I conclude from that that I am deeply in love with
you, and that I cannot pass six or seven hours in your
company without longing to kiss you."

"Certainly, but we resist these desires because we have
duties to perform, which would rise up against us if we
left them undone."

"True again, but if your disposition at all resembles
mine this constraint must be very painful to you."

"Perhaps I feel it as much as you do, but it is my
belief that it is only hard to withstand temptation at first.
By degrees one gets accustomed to loving without run-
ing any risk and without effort. Our senses, at first so

sharp set, end by becoming blunted, and when this is the case we may spend hours and days in safety, untroubled by desire."

"I have my doubts as far as I am concerned, but we shall see. Good night, fair Hebe."

"Good night, my good Iolas, may you sleep well!"

"My sleep will be haunted by visions of you."

CHAPTER XXII

*Our Excursion—Parting From Clementine—I Leave
Milan With Croce's Mistress—My Arrival At Genoa*

THE ancients, whose fancy was so fertile in allegory,
used to figure Innocence as playing with a serpent or
with a sharp arrow. These old sages had made a deep
study of the human heart; and whatever discoveries
modern science may have made, the old symbols may still
be profitably studied by those who wish to gain a deep
insight into the working of man's mind.

I went to bed, and after having dismissed Clairmont
I began to reflect on my relations with Clementine, who
seemed to have been made to shine in a sphere from
which, in spite of her high birth, her intelligence, and
her rare beauty, her want of fortune kept her apart. I
smiled to myself at her doctrines, which were as much as
to say that the best way of curing appetite was to place a
series of appetising dishes before a hungry man, forbidding him to touch them. Nevertheless I could but
approve the words which she had uttered with such an
air of innocence—that if one resists desires, there is no
danger of one being humiliated by giving way to them.

This humiliation would arise from a feeling of duty,
and she honoured me by supposing that I had as high
principles as herself. But at the same time the motive
of self-esteem was also present, and I determined not to
do anything which would deprive me of her confidence.

As may be imagined, I did not awake till very late the
next morning, and when I rang my bell Clementine came

in, looking very pleased, and holding a copy of the *Pastor Fido* in her hand. She wished me good day, and said she had read the first act, and that she thought it very beautiful, and told me to get up that we might read the second together before dinner.

"May I rise in your presence?"

"Why not? A man has need of very little care to observe the laws of decency."

"Then please give me that shirt."

She proceeded to unfold it, and then put it over my head, smiling all the time.

"I will do the same for you at the first opportunity," said I.

She blushed and answered, "It's not nearly so far from you to me as it is from me to you."

"Divine Hebe, that is beyond my understanding. You speak like the Cumæan sibyls, or as if you were rendering oracles at your temple in Corinth."

"Had Hebe a temple at Corinth? Sardini never said so."

"But Apollodorus says so. It was an asylum as well as a temple. But come back to the point, and pray do not elude it. What you said is opposed to all the laws of geometry. The distance from you to me ought to be precisely the same as from me to you."

"Perhaps, then, I have said a stupid thing."

"Not at all, Hebe, you have an idea which may be right or wrong, but I want to bring it out. Come, tell me."

"Well, then, the two distances differ from each other with respect to the ascent and descent, or fall, if you like. Are not all bodies inclined to obey the laws of gravitation unless they are held back by a superior force?"

"Certainly."

"And is it not the case that no bodies move in an upward direction unless they are impelled?"

"Quite true."

"Then you must confess that since I am shorter than you I should have to ascend to attain you, and ascension is always an effort; while if you wish to attain me, you have only to let yourself go, which is no effort whatever. Thus it is no risk at all for you to let me put on your shirt, but it would be a great risk for me if I allowed you to do the same service for me. I might be overwhelmed by your too rapid descent on me. Are you persuaded?"

" 'Persuaded is not the word, fair Hebe. I am ravished in an ecstacy of admiration. Never was paradox so finely maintained. I might cavil and contest it, but I prefer to keep silence to admire and adore."

"Thank you, dear Iolas, but I want no favour. Tell me how you could disprove my argument?"

"I should attack it on the point of height. You know you would not let me change your chemise even if I were a dwarf."

"Ah, dear Iolas! we cannot deceive each other. Would that Heaven had destined me to be married to a man like you!"

"Alas! why am I not worthy of aspiring to such a position?"

I do not know where the conversation would have landed us, but just then the countess came to tell us that dinner was waiting, adding that she was glad to see we loved one another.

"Madly," said Clementine, "but we are discreet."

"If you are discreet, you cannot love madly."

"True, countess," said I, "for the madness of love and wisdom cannot dwell together. I should rather say we are reasonable, for the mind may be grave while the heart's gay."

We dined merrily together, then we played at cards, and in the evening we finished reading the *Pastor Fido*. When we were discussing the beauties of this delightful work Clementine asked me if the thirteenth book of the "Æneid" was fine.

"My dear countess, it is quite worthless; and I only praised it to flatter the descendant of the author. However, the same writer made a poem on the tricks of countryfolk, which is by no means devoid of merit. But you are sleepy, and I am preventing you from undressing."

"Not at all."

She took off her clothes in a moment with the greatest coolness, and did not indulge my licentious gaze in the least. She got into bed, and I sat beside her; whereupon she sat up again, and her sister turned her back upon us. The *Pastor Fido* was on her night-table, and opening the book I proceeded to read the passage where Mirtillo describes the sweetness of the kiss Amaryllis had given him, attuning my voice to the sentiment of the lines. Clementine seemed as much affected as I was, and I fastened my lips on hers. What happiness! She drew in the balm of my lips with delight, and appeared to be free from alarm, so I was about to clasp her in my arms when she pushed me away with the utmost gentleness, begging me to spare her.

This was modesty at bay. I begged her pardon, and taking her hand breathed out upon it all the ecstasy of my lips.

"You are trembling," said she, in a voice that did but increase the amorous tumult of my heart.

"Yes, dearest countess, and I assure you I tremble

for fear of you. Good night, I am going; and my prayer must be that I may love you less."

"Why so? To love less is to begin to hate. Do as I do, and pray that your love may grow and likewise the strength to resist it."

I went to bed ill pleased with myself. I did not know whether I had gone too far or not far enough; but what did it matter? One thing was certain, I was sorry for what I had done, and that was always a thought which pained me.

In Clementine I saw a woman worthy of the deepest love and the greatest respect, and I knew not how I could cease to love her, nor yet how I could continue loving her without the reward which every faithful lover hopes to win.

"If she loves me," I said to myself, "she cannot refuse me, but it is my part to beg and pray, and even to push her to an extremity, that she may find an excuse for her defeat. A lover's duty is to oblige the woman he loves to surrender at discretion, and love always absolves him for so doing."

According to this argument, which I coloured to suit my passions, Clementine could not refuse me unless she did not love me, and I determined to put her to the proof. I was strengthened in this resolve by the wish to free myself from the state of excitement I was in, and I was sure that if she continued obdurate I should soon get cured. But at the same time I shuddered at the thought; the idea of my no longer loving Clementine seemed to me an impossibility and a cruelty.

After a troubled night I rose early and went to wish her good morning. She was still asleep, but her sister Eleanore was dressing.

"My sister," said she, "read till three o'clock this

morning. Now that she has so many books, she is getting quite mad over them. Let us play a trick on her; get into the bed beside her; it will be amusing to see her surprise when she wakes up."

"But do you think she will take it as a joke?"

"She won't be able to help laughing; besides, you are dressed."

The opportunity was too tempting, and taking off my dressing-gown, I gently crept into the bed, and Eleanore covered me up to my neck. She laughed, but my heart was beating rapidly. I could not give the affair the appearance of a joke, and I hoped Clementine would be some time before she awoke that I might have time to compose myself.

I had been in this position for about five minutes, when Clementine, half asleep and half awake, turned over, and stretching out her arm, gave me a hasty kiss, thinking I was her sister. She then fell asleep again in the same position. I should have stayed still long enough, for her warm breath played on my face, and gave me a foretaste of ambrosia; but Eleanore could restrain herself no longer, and, bursting into a peal of laughter, forced Clementine to open her eyes. Nevertheless, she did not discover that she held me in her arms till she saw her sister standing laughing beside the bed.

"This is a fine trick," said she, "you are two charmers indeed!"

This quiet reception gave me back my self-composure, and I was able to play my part properly.

"You see," said I, "I have had a kiss from my sweet Hebe."

"I thought I was giving it to my sister. 'Tis the kiss that Amaryllis gave to Mistillo."

"It comes to the same thing. The kiss has produced its effects, and Iolas is young again."

"Dear Eleanore, you have gone too far, for we love each other, and I was dreaming of him."

"No, no," said her sister, "Iolas is dressed. Look!"

So saying, the little wanton with a swift movement uncovered me, but at the same time she uncovered her sister, and Clementine with a little scream veiled the charms which my eyes had devoured for a moment. I had seen all, but as one sees lightning. I had seen the cornice and the frieze of the altar of love.

Eleanore then went out, and I remained gazing at the treasure I desired but did not dare to seize. At last I broke the silence.

"Dearest Hebe," said I, "you are certainly fairer than the cupbearer of the gods. I have just seen what must have been seen when Hebe was falling, and if I had been Jupiter I should have changed my mind."

"Sardini told me that Jupiter drove Hebe away, and now I ought to drive Jupiter away out of revenge."

"Yes; but, my angel, I am Iolas, and not Jupiter. I adore you, and I seek to quench the desires which torture me."

"This is a trick between you and Eleanore."

"My dearest, it was all pure chance. I thought I should find you dressed, and I went in to wish you good day. You were asleep and your sister was dressing. I gazed at you, and Eleanore suggested that I should lie down beside you to enjoy your astonishment when you awoke. I ought to be grateful to her for a pleasure which has turned out so pleasantly. But the beauties she discovered to me surpass all the ideas I had formed on the subject. My charming Hebe will not refuse to pardon me."

"No, since all is the effect of chance. But it is curious that when one loves passionately one always feels inquisitive concerning the person of the beloved object."

"It is a very natural feeling, dearest. Love itself is a kind of curiosity, if it be lawful to put curiosity in the rank of the passions; but you have not that feeling about me?"

"No, for fear you might disappoint me, for I love you, and I want everything to speak in your favour."

"I know you might be disappointed, and consequently I must do everything in my power to preserve your good opinion."

"Then you are satisfied with me?"

"Surely. I am a good architect, and I think you are grandly built."

"Stay, Iolas, do not touch me; it is enough that you have seen me."

"Alas! it is by touching that one rectifies the mistakes of the eyes; one judges thus of smoothness and solidity. Let me kiss these two fair sources of life. I prefer them to the hundred breasts of Cybele, and I am not jealous of Athys."

"You are wrong there; Sardini told me that it was Diana of Ephesus who had the hundred breasts."

How could I help laughing to hear mythology issuing from Clementine's mouth at such a moment! Could any lover foresee such an incident? I pressed with my hand her alabaster breast, and yet the desire of knowledge subdued love in the heart of Clementine. But far from mistaking her condition I thougtht it a good omen. I told her that she was perfectly right, and that I was wrong, and a feeling of literary vanity prevented her opposing my pressing with my lips a rosy bud, which stood out in relief against the alabaster sphere.

"You apply your lips in vain, my dear Iolas, the land is barren. But what are you swallowing?"

"The quintessence of a kiss."

"I think you must have swallowed something of me, since you have given me a pleasurable sensation I have never before experienced."

"Dear Hebe, you make me happy."

"I am glad to hear it, but I think the kiss on the lips is much better."

"Certainly, because the pleasure is reciprocal, and consequently greater."

"You teach by precept and example too. Cruel teacher! Enough, this pleasure is too sweet. Love must be looking at us and laughing."

"Why should we not let him enjoy a victory which would make us both happier?"

"Because such happiness is not built on a sure foundation. No, no! put your arms down. If we can kill each other with kisses, let us kiss on; but let us use no other arms."

After our lips had clung to each other cruelly but sweetly, she paused, and gazing at me with eyes full of passion she begged me to leave her alone.

The situation in which I found myself is impossible to describe. I deplored the prejudice which had constrained me, and I wept with rage. I cooled myself by making a toilette which was extremely necessary, and returned to her room.

She was writing.

"I am delighted to see you back," said she, "I am full of the poetic frenzy and propose to tell the story of the victory we have gained in verse."

"A sad victory, abhorred by love, hateful to nature."

"That will do nicely. Will each write a poem; I to

celebrate the victory and you to deplore it. But you look sad."

"I am in pain; but as the masculine anatomy is unknown to you, I cannot explain matters."

Clementine did not reply, but I could see that she was affected. I suffered a dull pain in that part which prejudice had made me hold a prisoner while love and nature bade me give it perfect freedom. Sleep was the only thing which would restore the balance of my constitution.

We went down to dinner, but I could not eat. I could not attend to the reading of the translation which M. Vigi had brought with him, and I even forgot to compliment him upon it. I begged the count to hold the bank for me, and asked the company to allow me to lie down; nobody could tell what was the matter with me, though Clementine might have her suspicions.

At supper-time Clementine, accompanied by a servant, brought me a delicate cold collation, and told me that the bank had won. It was the first time it had done so, for I had always taken care to play a losing game. I made a good supper, but remained still melancholy and silent. When I had finished Clementine bade me good night, saying that she was going to write her poem.

I, too, was in the vein: I finished my poem, and made a fair copy of it before I went to bed. In the morning Clementine came to see me, and gave me her piece, which I read with pleasure; though I suspect that the delight my praises gave was equal to mine.

Then came the turn of my composition, and before long I noticed that the picture of my sufferings was making a profound impression on her. Big tears rolled down her cheeks, and from her eyes shot forth tender glances. When I had finished, I had the happiness of hearing her say that if she had known that part of physiology better, she would not have behaved so.

We took a cup of chocolate together, and I then begged her to lie down beside me in bed without undressing, and to treat me as I had treated her the day before, that she might have some experience of the martyrdom I had sung in my verses. She smiled and agreed, on the condition that I should do nothing to her.

It was a cruel condition, but it was the beginning of victory, and I had to submit. I had no reason to repent of my submission, for I enjoyed the despotism she exercised on me, and the pain she must be in that I did nothing to her, whilst I would not let her see the charms which she held in her hands. In vain I excited her to satisfy herself, to refuse her desires nothing, but she persisted in maintaining that she did not wish to go any further.

"Your enjoyment cannot be so great as mine," said I. But her subtle wit never left her without a reply.

"Then," said she, "you have no right to ask me to pity you."

The test, however, was too sharp for her. She left me in a state of great excitement, giving me a kiss which took all doubts away, and saying that in love we must be all or nothing.

We spent the day in reading, eating, and walking, and in converse grave and gay. I could not see, however, that my suit had progressed, as far as the events of the morning seemed to indicate. She wanted to reverse the medal of Aristippus, who said, in speaking of Lois, "I possess her, but she does not possess me." She wanted to be my mistress, without my being her master. I ventured to bewail my fate a little, but that did not seem to advance my cause.

Three or four days after, I asked Clementine in the presence of her sister to let me lie in bed beside her. This is the test proposed to a nun, a widow, a girl afraid of consequences, and it nearly always succeeds. I took a packet of fine English letters and explained their use to her. She took them examined them attentively, and after a burst of laughter declared them to be scandalous, disgusting, horrible in which anathema her sister joined. In vain I tried to plead their utility in defence, but Clementine maintained that there was no trusting them, and pushed her finger into one so strongly that it burst with a loud crack. I had to give way, and put my specialties in my pocket, and her final declaration was that such things made her shudder.

I wished them good night, and retired in some confusion. I pondered over Clementine's strange resistance, which could only mean that I had not inspired her with sufficient love. I resolved on overcoming her by an almost infallible method. I would procure her pleasures that were new to her without sparing expense. I could think of nothing better than to take the whole family to Milan, and to give them a sumptuous banquet at my pastrycook's. "I will take them there," I said to myself, "without saying a word about our destination till we are on our way, for if I were to name Milan the count might feel bound to tell his Spanish countess, that she might have an opportunity of making the acquaintance of her sisters-in-law, and this would vex me to the last degree." The party would be a great treat to the sisters, who had never been in Milan, and I resolved to make the expedition as splendid as I possibly could.

When I awoke the next morning I wrote to Zenobia to buy three dresses of the finest Lyons silk for three young ladies of rank. I sent the necessary measurements, and instructions as to the trimming. The Countess Ambrose's dress was to be white satin with a rich border of Valenciennes lace. I also wrote to M. Greppi, asking him to pay for Zenobia's purchases. I told her to take the three dresses to my private lodgings, and lay them upon the bed, and give the landlord a note I enclosed. This note ordered him to provide a banquet for eight persons, without sparing expense. On the day and hour appointed, Zenobia was to be at the pastrycook's ready to wait on the three ladies. I sent the letter by Clairmont, who returned before dinner, bearing a note from Zenobia assuring me that all my wishes should be carried out. After dessert I broached my plan to the countess, telling her that I wanted to give a party like the one at Lodi, but on two conditions: the first, that no one was to know our destination till we were in the carriages, and the second, that after dinner we should return to St. Angelo.

Out of politeness the countess looked at her husband before accepting the invitation, but he cried out, without ceremony, that he was ready to go if I took the whole family.

"Very good," said I, "we will start at eight o'clock to-morrow, and nobody need be at any trouble, the carriages are ordered."

I felt obliged to include the canon, because he was a great courtier of the countess, and also because he lost money to me every day, and thus it was he, in fact, who was going to pay for the expedition. That evening he lost three hundred sequins, and was obliged to ask me to give him three day's grace to pay the money. I replied by assuring him that all I had was at his service.

When the company broke up I offered my hand to Hebe, and escorted her and her sister to their room. We had begun to read Fontenelle's "Plurality of Worlds," and I had thought we should finish it that night; but Clementine said that as she had to get up early, she would want to get to sleep early also.

"You are right, dearest Hebe, do you go to bed, and I will read to you."

She made no objection, so I took the Ariosto, and began to read the history of the Spanish princess who fell in love with Bradamante. I thought that by the time I had finished Clementine would be ardent, but I was mistaken; both she and her sister seemed pensive.

"What is the matter with you, dearest? Has Ricciardetto displeased you?"

"Not at all, he has pleased me, and in the princess's place I should have done the same; but we shall not sleep all night, and it is your fault."

"What have I done, pray?"

"Nothing, but you can make us happy, and give us a great proof of your friendship."

"Speak, then. What is it you want of me? I would do anything to please you. My life is yours. You shall sleep soundly."

"Well, then, tell us where we are going to-morrow."

"Have I not already said that I would tell you just as we are going?"

"Yes, but that won't do. We want to know now, and if you won't tell us we shan't sleep, all night, and we shall look frightful to-morrow."

"I should be so sorry, but I don't think that you could look frightful."

"You don't think we can keep a secret. It is nothing very important, is it?"

"No, it is not very important, but all the same it is a secret."

"It would be dreadful if you refused me."

"Dearest Hebe! how can I refuse you anything? I confess freely that I have been wrong in keeping you waiting so long. Here is my secret: you are to dine with me to-morrow."

"With you? Where?"

"Milan."

In their immoderate joy they got out of bed, and without caring for their state of undress, threw their arms round my neck, covered me with kisses, clasped me to their breasts, and finally sat down on my knees.

"We have never seen Milan," they cried, "and it has been the dream of our lives to see that splendid town. How often I have been put to the blush when I have been forced to confess that I have never been to Milan."

"It makes me very happy," said Hebe, "but my happiness is troubled by the idea that we shall see nothing of the town, for we shall have to return after dinner. It is cruel! Are we to go fifteen miles to Milan only to dine and come back again? At least we must see our sister-in-law."

"I have foreseen all your objections, and that was the reason I made a mystery of it, but it has been arranged. You don't like it? Speak and tell me your pleasure."

"Of course we like it, dear Iolas. The party will be charming, and perhaps, if we knew all, the very conditions are all for the best."

"It may be so, but I may not tell you any more now."

"And we will not press you."

In an ecstasy of joy she began to embrace me again, and Eleanore said that she would go to sleep so as to be more on the alert for the morrow. This was the best thing she could have done. I knew the fortunate hour was at hand, and exciting Clementine by my fiery kisses, and drawing nearer and nearer, at last I was in full possession of the temple I had so long desired to attain. Hebe's pleasure and delight kept her silent; she shared my ecstasies, and mingled her happy tears with mine.

I spent two hours in this manner, and then went to bed, impatient to renew the combat on the following day more at my ease and with greater comfort.

At eight o'clock we were all assembled round the breakfast-table, but in spite of my high spirits I could not make the rest of the company share them. All were silent and pensive; curiosity shewed itself on every face. Clementine and her sister pretended to partake the general feeling, and were silent like the rest while I looked on and enjoyed their expectancy.

Clairmont, who had fulfilled my instructions to the letter, came in and told us that the carriages were at the door. I asked my guests to follow me, and they did so in silence. I put the countess and Clementine in my carriage, the latter holding the baby on her lap, her sister and the three gentlemen being seated in the other carriage. I called out, with a laugh,——

"Drive to Milan."

"Milan! Milan!" they exclaimed with one voice. "Capital! capital!"

Clairmont galloped in front of us and went off. Clementine pretended to be astonished, but her sister looked as if she had known something of our destination before. All care, however, had disappeared, and the highest spirits prevailed. We stopped at a village half-way between St. Angelo and Milan to blow the horses, and everybody got down.

"What will my wife say?" asked the count.

"Nothing, for she will not know anything about it, and if she does I am the only guilty party. You are to dine with me in a suite of rooms which I have occupied incognito since I have been at Milan; for you will understand that I could not have my wants attended to at your house, where the place is already taken."

"And how about Zenobia?"

"Zenobia was a lucky chance, and is a very nice girl, but she would not suffice for my daily fare."

"You are a lucky fellow!"

"I try to make myself comfortable."

"My dear husband," said the Countess Ambrose, "you proposed a visit to Milan two years ago, and the chevalier proposed it a few hours ago, and now we are on our way."

"Yes, sweetheart, but my idea was that we should spend a month there."

"If you want to do that," said I, "I will see to everything."

"Thank you, my dear sir; you are really a wonderful man."

"You do me too much honour, count, there is nothing wonderful about me, except that I execute easily an easy task."

"Yes; but you will confess that a thing may be difficult from the way in which we regard it, or from the position in which we find ourselves."

"You are quite right."

When we were again on our way the countess said——

"You must confess, sir, that you are a very fortunate man."

"I do not deny it, my dear countess, but my happiness is due to the company I find myself in; if you were to expel me from yours, I should be miserable."

"You are not the kind of man to be expelled from any society."

"That is a very kindly compliment."

"Say, rather, a very true one."

"I am happy to hear you say so, but it would be both foolish and presumptuous for me to say so myself."

Thus we made merry on our way, above all at the expense of the canon, who had been begging the countess to intercede with me to give him leave to absent himself half an hour.

"I want to call on a lady," said he; "I should lose her favour forever if she came to know that I had been in Milan without paying her a visit."

"You must submit to the conditions," replied the amiable countess, "so don't count on my intercession."

We got to Milan exactly at noon, and stepped out at the pastrycook's door. The landlady begged the countess to confide her child to her care, and shewed her a bosom which proved her fruitfulness. This offer was made at the foot of the stairs, and the countess accepted it with charming grace and dignity. It was a delightful episode, which chance had willed should adorn the entertainment I had invented. Everybody seemed happy, but I was the happiest of all. Happiness is purely a creature of the imagination. If you wish to be happy fancy that you are so, though I confess that circumstances favourable to this state are often beyond our control. On the other hand, unfavourable circumstances are mostly the result of our own mistakes.

The countess took my arm, and we led the way into my room which I found exquisitely neat and clean. As I had expected, Zenobia was there, but I was surprised to see Croce's mistress, looking very pretty; however, I pretended not to know her. She was well dressed, and her face, free from the sadness it had borne before, was so seductive in its beauty, that I felt vexed at her appearance at that particular moment.

"Here are two pretty girls," said the countess. "Who are you, pray?"

"We are the chevalier's humble servants," said Zenobia, "and we are here only to wait on you."

Zenobia had taken it on herself to bring her lodger, who began to speak Italian, and looked at me in doubt, fearing that I was displeased at her presence. I had to reassure her by saying I was very glad she had come with Zenobia. These words were as balm to her heart; she smiled again, and became more beautiful than ever. I felt certain that she would not remain unhappy long; it was impossible to behold her without one's interest being excited in her favour. A bill signed by the Graces can never be protested; anyone with eyes and a heart honours it at sight.

My humble servants took the ladies' cloaks and followed them into the bedroom, where the three dresses were laid out on a table. I only knew the white satin and lace, for that was the only one I had designed. The countess, who walked before her sisters, was the first to notice it, and exclaimed——

"What a lovely dress! To whom does it belong, M. de Seingalt? You ought to know."

"Certainly. It belongs to your husband who can do what he likes with it, and I hope, if he gives it you, you will take it. Take it, count; it is yours; and if you refuse I will positively kill myself."

"We love you too well to drive you to an act of despair. The idea is worthy of your nobility of heart. I take your beautiful present with one hand, and with the other I deliver it to her to whom it really belongs."

"What, dear husband! is this beautiful dress really

mine? Whom am I to thank? I thank you both, and
I must put it on for dinner."

The two others were not made of such rich materials,
but they were more showy, and I was delighted to see
Clementine's longing gaze fixed upon the one I had intended for her. Eleanore in her turn admired the dress
that had been made for her. The first was in shot satin,
and ornamented with lovely wreaths of flowers; the second was sky-blue satin, with a thousand flowers scat-
tered all over it. Zenobia took upon herself to say that
the first was for Clementine.

"How do you know?"

"It is the longer, and you are taller than your sister."

"That is true. It is really mine, then?" said she,
turning to me.

"If I may hope that you will deign to accept it."

"Surely, dear Iolas, and I will put it on directly."

Eleanore maintained that her dress was the prettier,
and said she was dying to put it on.

"Very good, very good!" I exclaimed, in high glee,
"we will leave you to dress, and here are your maids."

I went out with the two brothers and the canon, and
I remarked that they looked quite confused. No doubt
they were pondering the prodigality of gamesters; light
come, light go. I did not interrupt their thoughts, for I
loved to astonish people. I confess it was a feeling of
vanity which raised me above my fellow-men—at least,
in my own eyes, but that was enough for me. I should
have despised anyone who told me that I was laughed at,
but I daresay it was only the truth.

I was in the highest spirits, and they soon proved in-
fectious. I embraced Count Ambrose affectionately,
begging his pardon for having presumed to make the
family a few small presents, and I thanked his brother

for having introduced me to them. "You have all given me such a warm welcome," I added, "that I felt obliged to give you some small proof of my gratitude."

The fair countesses soon appeared, bedecked with smiles and their gay attire.

"You must have contrived to take our measures," said they; "but we cannot imagine how you did it."

"The funniest thing is," said the eldest, "that you have had my dress made so that it can be let out when necessary without destroying the shape. But what a beautiful piece of trimming! It is worth four times as much as the dress itself."

Clementine could not keep away from the looking-glass. She fancied that in the colours of her dress, rose and green, I had indicated the characteristics of the youthful Hebe. Eleanore still maintained that her dress was the prettiest of all.

I was delighted with the pleasure of my fair guests, and we sat down to table with excellent appetites. The dinner was extremely choice; but the finest dish of all was a dish of oysters, which the landlord had dressed *à la maitre d'hôtel.* We enjoyed them immensely. We finished off three hundred of them, for the ladies relished them extremely, and the canon seemed to have an insatiable appetite; and we washed down the dishes with numerous bottles of champagne. We stayed at table for three hours, drinking, singing, and jesting, while my humble servants, whose beauty almost rivalled that of my guests, waited upon us.

Towards the end of the meal the pastrycook's wife came in with the countess's baby on her breast. This was a dramatic stroke. The mother burst into a cry of joy, and the woman seemed quite proud of having suckled the scion of so illustrious a house for nearly four hours. It is well known that women, even more than men, are wholly under the sway of the imagination. Who can say that this woman, simple and honest like the majority of the lower classes, did not think that her own offspring would be ennobled by being suckled at the breast which had nourished a young count? Such an idea is, no doubt, foolish, but that is the very reason why it is dear to the hearts of the people.

We spent another hour in taking coffee and punch, and then the ladies went to change their clothes again. Zenobia took care that their new ones should be carefully packed in cardboard boxes and placed under the seat of my carriage.

Croce's abandoned mistress found an opportunity of telling me that she was very happy with Zenobia. She asked me when we were to go.

"You will be at Marseilles," said I, pressing her hand, "a fortnight after Easter at latest."

Zenobia had told me that the girl had an excellent heart, behaved very discreetly, and that she should be very sorry to see her go. I gave Zenobia twelve sequins for the trouble she had taken.

I was satisfied with everything and paid the worthy pastrycook's bill. I noticed we had emptied no less than twenty bottles of champagne, though it is true that we drank very little of any other wine, as the ladies preferred it.

I loved and was beloved, my health was good, I had plenty of money, which I spent freely; in fine, I was happy. I loved to say so in defiance of those sour moralists who pretend that there is no true happiness on this earth. It is the expression *on this earth* which makes me laugh; as if it were possible to go anywhere else in search of happiness. *Mors ultima linea rerum est.* Yes, death is the end of all, for after death man has no senses; but I do not say that the soul shares the fate of the body. No one should dogmatise on uncertainties, and after death everything is doubtful.

It was seven o'clock when we began our journey home, which we reached at midnight. The journey was so pleasant that it seemed to us but short. The champagne, the punch, and the pleasure, had warmed my two fair companions, and by favour of the darkness I was able to amuse myself with them, though I loved Clementine too well to carry matters very far with her sister.

When we alighted we wished each other good night, and everybody retired to his or her room, myself excepted, for I spent several happy hours with Clementine, which I can never forget.

"Do you think," said she, "that I shall be happy when you have left me all alone?"

"Dearest Hebe, both of us will be unhappy for the first few days, but then philosophy will step in and soften the bitterness of parting without lessening our love."

"Soften the bitterness! I do not think any philosophy can work such a miracle. I know that you, dear sophist, will soon console yourself with other girls. Don't think me jealous; I should abhor myself if I thought I was capable of so vile a passion, but I should despise myself if I was capable of seeking consolation in your way."

"I shall be in despair if you entertain such ideas of me."

"They are natural, however."

"Possibly. What you call 'other girls' can never expel your image from my breast. The chief of them is the wife of a tailor, and the other is a respectable young woman, whom I am going to take back to Marseilles, whence she has been decoyed by her wretched seducer.

From henceforth to death, you and you alone will reign
in my breast; and if, led astray by my senses, I ever
press another in these arms, I shall soon be punished
for an act of infidelity in which my mind will have no
share."

"I at all events will never need to repent in that fashion. But I cannot understand how, with your love for
me, and holding me in your arms, you can even contemplate the possibility of becoming unfaithful to me."

"I don't contemplate it, dearest, I merely take it as
an hypothesis."

"I don't see much difference."

What reply could I make? There was reason in what
Clementine said, though she was deceived, but her mistakes were due to her love. My love was so ardent as to
be blind to possible—nay, certain, infidelities. The only
circumstance which made me more correct in my esti-
mate of the future than she, was that this was by no
means my first love affair. But if my readers have been
in the same position, as I suppose most of them have,
they will understand how difficult it is to answer such
arguments coming from a woman one wishes to render
happy. The keenest wit has to remain silent and to
take refuge in kisses.

"Would you like to take me away with you?" said
she, "I am ready to follow you, and it would make me
happy. If you love me, you ought to be enchanted for
your own sake. Let us make each other happy, dearest."

"I could not dishonour your family."

"Do you not think me worthy of becoming your
wife?"

"You are worthy of a crown, and it is I who am all
unworthy of possessing such a wife. You must know
that I have nothing in the world except my fortune, and

that may leave me to-morrow. By myself I do not dread the reverses of fortune, but I should be wretched if, after linking your fate with mine, you were forced to undergo any privation."

"I think—I know not why—that you can never be unfortunate, and that you cannot be happy without me. Your love is not so ardent as mine; you have not so great a faith."

"My angel, if my fate is weaker than yours, that is the result of cruel experience which makes me tremble for the future. Affrighted love loses its strength but gains reason."

"Cruel reason! Must we, then, prepare to part?"

"We must indeed, dearest; it is a hard necessity, but my heart will still be thine. I shall go away your fervent adorer, and if fortune favours me in England you will see me again next year. I will buy an estate wherever you like, and it shall be yours on your wedding day, our children and literature will be our delights."

"What a happy prospect!—a golden vision indeed! I would that I might fall asleep dreaming thus, and wake not till that blessed day, or wake only to die if it is not to be. But what shall I do if you have left me with child?"

"Divine Hebe, you need not fear. I have managed that."

"Managed? I did not think of that, but I see what you mean, and I am very much obliged to you. Alas! perhaps after all it would have been better if you had not taken any precautions, for surely you are not born for my misfortune, and you could never have abandoned the mother and the child."

"You are right, sweetheart, and if before two months

have elapsed you find any signs of pregnancy in spite of my precautions, you have only to write to me, and whatever my fortunes may be, I will give you my hand and legitimise our offspring. You would certainly be marrying beneath your station, but you would not be the less happy for that, would you?"

"No, no! to bear your name, and to win your hand would be the crowning of all my hopes. I should never repent of giving myself wholly to you."

"You make me happy."

"All of us love you, all say that you are happy, and that you deserve your happiness. What praise is this! You cannot tell how my heart beats when I hear you lauded when you are away. When they say I love you, I answer that I adore you, and you know that I do not lie."

It was with such dialogues that we passed away the interval between our amorous transports on the last five or six nights of my stay. Her sister slept, or pretended to sleep. When I left Clementine I went to bed and did not rise till late, and then I spent the whole day with her either in private or with the family. It was a happy time. How could I, as free as the air, a perfect master of my movements, of my own free will put my happiness away from me? I cannot understand it now.

My luck had made me win all the worthy canon's money, which in turn I passed on to the family at the castle. Clementine alone would not profit by my inattentive play, but the last two days I insisted on taking her into partnership, and as the canon's bad luck still continued she profited to the extent of a hundred louis. The worthy monk lost a thousand sequins, of which seven hundred remained in the family. This was paying well for the hospitality I had received, and as it was at the expense of the monk, though a worthy one, the merit was all the greater.

The last night, which I spent entirely with the countess, was very sad; we must have died of grief if we had not taken refuge in the transports of love. Never was night better spent. Tears of grief and tears of love followed one another in rapid succession, and nine times did I offer up sacrifice on the altar of the god, who gave me fresh strength to replace that which was exhausted. The sanctuary was full of blood and tears, but the desires of the priest and victim still cried for more. We had at last to make an effort and part. Eleanore had seized the opportunity of our sleeping for a few moments, and had softly risen and left us alone. We felt grateful to her, and agreed that she must either be very insensitive or have suffered torments in listening to our voluptuous combats. I left Clementine to her ablutions, of which she stood in great need, while I went to my room to make my toilette.

When we appeared at the breakfast table we looked as if we had been on the rack, and Clementine's eyes betrayed her feelings, but our grief was respected. I could not be gay in my usual manner, but no one asked me the reason. I promised to write to them, and come and see them again the following year. I did write to them, but I left off doing so at London, because the misfortunes I experienced there made me lose all hope of seeing them again. I never did see any of them again, but I have never forgotten Clementine.

Six years later, when I came back from Spain, I heard to my great delight that she was living happily with Count N——, whom she had married three years after my departure. She had two sons, the younger, who must now be twenty-seven, is in the Austrian army. How delighted I should be to see him! When I heard of Clementine's happiness, it was, as I have said, on my return from Spain, and my fortunes were at a low ebb. I went to see what I could do at Leghorn, and as I went through Lombardy I passed four miles from the estate where she and her husband resided, but I had not the courage to go and see her; perhaps I was right. But I must return to the thread of my story.

I felt grateful to Eleanore for her kindness to us, and I had resolved to leave her some memorial of me. I took her apart for a moment, and drawing a fine cameo, representing the god of Silence, off my finger, I placed it on hers, and then rejoined the company, without giving her an opportunity to thank me.

The carriage was ready to take me away, and everyone was waiting to see me off, but my eyes filled with tears. I sought for Clementine in vain; she had vanished. I pretended to have forgotten something in my room, and going to my Hebe's chamber I found her in a terrible state, choking with sobs. I pressed her to my breast, and mingled my tears with hers; and then laying her gently in her bed, and snatching a last kiss from her trembling lips, I tore myself away from a place full of such sweet and agonizing memories.

I thanked and embraced everyone, the good canon amongst others, and whispering to Eleanore to see to her sister I jumped into the carriage beside the count. We remained perfectly silent, and slept nearly the whole of the way. We found the Marquis Triulzi and the countess together, and the former immediately sent for a dinner for four. I was not much astonished to find that the countess had found out about our being at Milan, and at first she seemed inclined to let us feel the weight of her anger; but the count, always fertile in expedients, told her that it was delicacy on my part not to tell her, as I was afraid she would be put out with such an incursion of visitors.

At dinner I said that I should soon be leaving for Genoa, and for my sorrow the marquis gave me a letter of introduction to the notorious Signora Isola-Bella, while the countess gave me a letter to her kinsman the Bishop of Tortona.

My arrival at Milan was well-timed; Thérèse was on the point of going to Palermo, and I just succeeded in seeing her before she left. I talked to her of the wish of Cesarino to go to sea, and I did all in my power to make her yield to his inclinations.

"I am leaving him at Milan," said she. "I know how he got this idea into his head, but I will never give my consent. I hope I shall find him wiser by the time I come back."

She was mistaken. My son never altered his mind, and in fifteen years my readers will hear more of him.

I settled my accounts with Greppi and took two bills of exchange on Marseilles, and one of ten thousand francs on Genoa, where I did not think I would have to spend much money. In spite of my luck at play, I was poorer by a thousand sequins when I left Milan than when I came there; but my extravagant expenditure must be taken into account.

I spent all my afternoons with the fair Marchioness Q——, sometimes alone and sometimes with her cousin, but with my mind full of grief for Clementine she no longer charmed me as she had done three weeks ago.

I had no need to make any mystery about the young lady I was going to take with me, so I sent Clairmont for her small trunk, and at eight o'clock on the morning of my departure she waited on me at the count's.

I kissed the hand of the woman who had attempted my life, and thanked her for her hospitality, to which I attributed the good reception I had had at Milan. I then thanked the count, who said once more that he should never cease to be grateful to me, and thus I left Milan on the 20th of March, 1763. I never re-visited that splendid capital.

The young lady, whom out of respect for her and her family I called Crosin, was charming. There was an air of nobility and high-bred reserve about her which bore witness to her excellent upbringing. As I sat next to her, I congratulated myself on my immunity from love of her, but the reader will guess that I was mistaken. I told Clairmont that she was to be called my niece, and to be treated with the utmost respect.

I had had no opportunity of conversing with her, so the first thing I did was to test her intelligence, and though I had not the slightest intention of paying my court to her, I felt that it would be well to inspire her with friendship and confidence as far as I was concerned.

The scar which my late amours had left was still bleeding, and I was glad to think that I should be able to restore the young Marseillaise to the paternal hearth without any painful partings or vain regrets. I enjoyed in advance my meritorious action, and I was quite vain to see my self-restraint come to such a pitch that I was able to live in close intimacy with a pretty girl without any other desire than that of rescuing her from the shame into which she might have fallen if she had traveled alone. She felt my kindness to her, and said——

"I am sure M. de la Croix would not have abandoned me if he had not met you at Milan."

"You are very charitable, but I am unable to share in your good opinion. To my mind Croce has behaved in a rascally manner, to say the least of it, for in spite of your many charms he had no right to count on me in the matter. I will not say that he openly scorned you, since he might have acted from despair; but I am sure he must have ceased to love you, or he could never have abandoned you thus."

"I am sure of the contrary. He saw that he had no means of providing for me, and he had to choose between leaving me and killing himself."

"Not at all. He ought to have sold all he had and sent you back to Marseilles. Your journey to Genoa would not have cost much, and thence you could have gone to Marseilles by sea. Croce counted on my having been interested in your pretty face, and he was right; but you must see that he exposed you to a great risk. You must not be offended if I tell you the plain truth. If your face had not inspired me with a lively interest in you, I should have only felt ordinary compassion on reading your appeal, and this would not have been enough to force me to great sacrifices of time and trouble. But I have no business to be blaming Croce. You are hurt; I see you are still in love with him."

"I confess it, and I pity him. As for myself, I only pity my cruel destiny. I shall never see him again, but I shall never love anyone else, for my mind is made up. I shall go into a convent and expiate my sins. My father will pardon me, for he is a man of an excellent heart. I have been the victim of love; my will was not my own. The seductive influence of passion ravished my reason from me, and the only thing that I blame myself for is for not having fortified my mind against it. Otherwise I cannot see that I have sinned deeply, but I confess I have done wrong."

"You would have gone with Croce from Milan if he had asked you, even on foot."

"Of course; it would have been my duty; but he would not expose me to the misery that he saw before us."

"Nay, you were miserable enough already. I am sure that if you meet him at Marseilles you will go with him again."

"Never. I begin to get back my reason. I am free once more, and the day will come when I shall thank God for having forgotten him."

Her sincerity pleased me, and as I knew too well the power of love I pitied her from my heart. For two hours she told me the history of her unfortunate amour, and as she told it well I began to take a liking for her.

We reached Tortona in the evening, and with the intention of sleeping there I told Clairmont to get us a supper to my taste. While we were eating it I was astonished at my false niece's wit, and she made a good match for me at the meal, for she had an excellent appetite, and drank as well as any girl of her age. As we were leaving the table, she made a jest which was so much to the point that I burst out laughing, and her conquest was complete. I embraced her in the joy of my heart, and finding my kiss ardently returned, I asked her without any circumlocution if she was willing that we should content ourselves with one bed.

At this invitation her face fell, and she replied, with an air of submission which kills desire——

"Alas! you can do what you like. If liberty is a precious thing, it is most precious of all in love."

"There is no need for this disobedience. You have in-spired me with a tender passion, but if you don't share my feelings my love for you shall be stifled at its birth. There are two beds here, as you see; you can choose which one you will sleep in."

"Then I will sleep in that one, but I shall be very sorry if you are not so kind to me in the future as you have been in the past."

"Don't be afraid. You shall not find me un worthy of your esteem. Good night; we shall be good friends."

Early the next morning I sent the countess's letter to the bishop, and an hour afterwards, as I was at break-fast, an old priest came to ask me and the lady with me to dine with my lord. The countess's letter did not say anything about a lady, but the prelate, who was a true Spaniard and very polite, felt that as I could not leave my real or false niece alone in the inn I should not have accepted the invitation if she had not been asked as well. Probably my lord had heard of the lady through his footmen, who in Italy are a sort of spies, who enter-tain their masters with the scandalous gossip of the place. A bishop wants something more than his breviary to amuse him now that the apostolic virtues have grown old-fashioned and out of date; in short, I accepted the invitation, charging the priest to present my respects to his lordship.

My niece was delightful, and treated me as if I had no right to feel any resentment for her having preferred her own bed to mine. I was pleased with her behaviour, for now that my head was cool I felt that she would have degraded herself if she had acted otherwise. My vanity was not even wounded, which is so often the case under similar circumstances. Self-love and prejudice prevent a woman yielding till she has been assidiously courted, whereas I had asked her to share my bed in an off-hand manner, as if it were a mere matter of form. However, I should not have done it unless it had been for the fumes of the champagne and the Somard, with which we had washed down the delicious supper mine host had supplied us with. She had been flattered by the bishop's invitation, but she did not know whether I had accepted for her as well as myself; and when I told her that we were going out to dinner together, she was wild with joy. She made a careful toilette, looking very well for a traveller, and at noon my lord's carriage came to fetch us.

The prelate was a tall man, two inches taller than myself; and in spite of the weight of his eighty years, he looked well and seemed quite active, though grave as became a Spanish grandee. He received us with a politeness which was almost French, and when my niece would have kissed his hand, according to custom, he affectionately drew it back, and gave her a magnificent cross of amethysts and brilliants to kiss. She kissed it with devotion, saying——

"This is what I love."

She looked at me as she said it, and the jest (which referred to her lover La Croix or Croce) surprised me.

We sat down to dinner, and I found the bishop to be a pleasant and a learned man. We were nine in all; four priests, and two young gentlemen of the town, who behaved to my niece with great politeness, which she received with all the manner of good society. I noticed that the bishop, though he often spoke to her, never once looked at her face. My lord knew what danger lurked in those bright eyes, and like a prudent grey-beard he took care not to fall into the snare. After coffee had been served, we took leave, and in four hours we left Tortona, intending to lie at Novi.

In the course of the afternoon my fair niece amused me with the wit and wisdom of her conversation. While we were supping I led the conversation up to the bishop, and then to religion, that I might see what her principles were. Finding her to be a good Christian, I asked her how she could allow herself to make a jest when she kissed the prelate's cross.

"It was a mere chance," she said. "The equivocation was innocent because it was not premeditated, for if I had thought it over I should never have said such a thing."

I pretended to believe her; she might possibly be sincere. She was extremely clever, and my love for her was becoming more and more ardent, but my vanity kept my passion in check. When she went to bed I did not kiss her, but as her bed had no screen as at Tortona, she waited until she thought I was asleep to undress herself. We got to Genoa by noon the next day.

Pogomas had got me some rooms and had forwarded me the address. I visited it, and found the apartment to consist of four well-furnished rooms, thoroughly *comfortable,* as the English, who understand how to take their ease, call it. I ordered a good dinner, and sent to tell Pogomas of my arrival.